Eat
YOUR WORDS

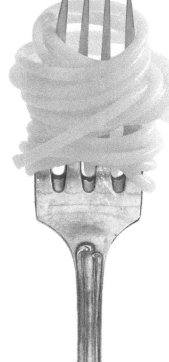

ISABEL CHIARA

ISBN: 978-1-7350726-5-4

10 9 8 7 6 5 4 3 2 1

Wyrd & Wyld Publishing
Spokane, WA

Cover & Layout Design: Heather Dakota
www.heatherdakota.com

Illustrations: Leslie Helpert

www.isabel-chiara.com

*To the power of our stories,
no matter how commonplace or
complex (or both) and how telling
them is a nutriment for the soul.*

Eat

YOUR WORDS

Table of Contents

"I think about what women in many parts of the world go through, who can't even leave the house without a male relative—who can't leave the house without being completely covered, even if that's not their choice—who can't make decisions about their own lives without being punished, sometimes severely even to the point of stoning...and I think—*What the hell are you afraid of, Marianne?* They're going to throw tomatoes at you or say mean things about you in *People* magazine? Who are you if that will stop you? Who are you if being embarrassed or being humiliated will stop you? I think every woman in a free society—and that's only about 20 percent of the peoples of the world—we should think of ourselves as speaking not only for ourselves, but for every woman out there who cannot speak for herself."

– Marianne Williamson on *Under the Skin* podcast, November 16, 2018

Introduction

*L*ook, let's get real. I'm way too scattered to write with the kind of depth and consistency that's required to create a book able to move from beginning to end. But around the time I began to build what I call my "healing home," as I planted lobelia and bougainvillea, I felt a seed germinate. I planted the story of Giana in my garden: a woman whose battle with food, with her internal dialogue and self-image was like my own. I tucked the idea into the landscaping, but by my third summer tending to the burgeoning bougainvillea in my garden, I knew the time had arrived for Giana's lyrical harvest. To scribe her tale, I hired a support team—typical of my managerial personality. Within weeks, I'd manifested a ghostwriter, writing coaches, female-body coaches and eating coaches, neural therapists, hypnotists, and nutritionists. They flocked to me instinctually, coalescing in support of finding Giana. To confront Giana's story, I had no choice other than to confront my own and, subsequently, reclaim a part of myself. In a way, I'd purposefully painted myself into a corner by hiring what felt, at times, like a squad of Ghostbusters to extract, wake up, and reintroduce me to a central aspect of my own body, burrowing underground for far longer than any bougainvillea seed. For this opportunity, for my "Ghostbusters," I am duly thankful. I know I am extraordinarily fortunate to have the opportunity to invest in myself on this level of self-healing, particularly as a woman in the world today.

The story of Giana Giovanni—or "GG," as she's often called—isn't exactly mine, but it's one I know well. GG's is the self-portrait of a *first-generation American-Italian woman, the daughter of immigrants who arrived at New York's Ellis Island after World War II. She is a woman who is outwardly strong and accomplished in significant ways, but her entire life is usurped by obsessive-compulsive thinking about her diet, about when, if, and what she'll eat. It's the story of a woman's internal war waged against self-allowance, of resisting receptivity, of her physical disassociation, of hiding impenetrably somewhere outside of herself, out of touch. Giana is among the many of us who work professionally as a "healer" yet overlook an enormous need to heal our own relationships with our bodies. She is a woman at the end of her fifty-ninth year, one who inspires us to see how it's never too late to untangle patterns that have plagued us for decades.*

Throughout my years of coaching women, I became familiar with my own response to writing a book: the typical "Who am I to do X, Y, and Z?" I only became comfortable with the notion of authoring a story when I came to recognize this story as one that didn't belong to just me. I finally realized I didn't need to search for some unique spin or hot selling point to write about Giana. In fact, it's the universality of Giana's story that makes it so uniquely relatable within the context of the epidemic of self-objectified thinking that has touched nearly every woman's life.

Women have been considered second-class citizens of the world for centuries upon centuries. Within that secondary status, we've lived within a precept, conditioned as to how we should experience our own bodies. Along with each bite of our allotted nourishment, we women have long ingested a collective shame around simply feeding ourselves. We've preoccupied our genius minds in games of restricting or rebelling against prescribed diets, marking our worth through achieving an idealized waist size. This way, we can both successfully waste our power on trite matters while also being sure to never appear as at-large as we truly are—a win-win for the patriarchy. To keep the suppressive game rolling along, we've inherited hand mirrors from our mothers, and our mothers' mothers, mandating and reaffirming

10

our limited self-esteem. However, this secondary status is no longer able to sustain and contain us. We all know it has become irrelevant—and even contrary—to our future. Now, women run companies, operate businesses, build new political platforms and new economies. Like never before, we intimately mother and encourage our babies to love themselves, and we women are recognizing more and more the importance of owning our embodiment! We bring to the table the seat of our own sacral floor, our pelvic floor, a seat of integrity, sacredness—the insightful roundness of that. And thus, this character, Giana, is an amalgamation of me and many others, and that is why I brought in a team to help me tell her story. It's yours, and it's mine, and it's hers.

This is not a how-to manual. This isn't a weight-loss book. This isn't a happily-ever-after size 2, 4, 6, or 8 fairy tale. This is about daring to look at what healing actually is, to brave the discomfort of it, to find sensation in the places we've shunned and numbed. And what kept me writing it, what kept me believing that I should tell Giana's story, was the hope that in sharing it, your courage to lovingly embrace the glorious fullness of all you are will feel supported and nourished in this world.

♡, Isabel

CHAPTER 1

Driving Under the Influence

I keep an eye on the Gulf brand synthetic blend motor oil at Cumberland Farms. It's my quick cover-up plan in case a coworker or someone I know, God forbid, walks in at the same time I'm rummaging. I used to rummage in the Wawas of New England, which is a bit more crème de la crème when it comes to the world of convenience stores. But now, I'm almost always just a convenient five- or ten-minute drive from a Cumberland Farms, and I've developed a habitual hankering for the specific taste of their double-decker, triangle-cut, plastic-packaged tuna stacker. Anyone who knows me is well aware that I know zero—*zilch*—about changing a car's oil. I would never leave my precious Audi Q7 to the mechanics of my own hands, aside from my automatic ability to keep a firm grip on the wheel no matter how asleep behind it I am. Still, I have the plan. Say, Marty, a busboy at one of my restaurants, walks in after his shift is over to buy sixteen ounces of Pepsi from the fountain, or another sugary beverage I nearly always preach against when I'm overseeing the restaurant floor. Now also say, for some strange reason, I happen to look up in the middle of my zombie mission of collecting forbidden calories like an outlaw of my own body and its appetite. Well, I can then say, *Hey, Marty, what's up? Me? I'm just getting some Gulf brand synthetic blend motor oil and perhaps some of this STP Oil Treatment.* I've even looked online to determine what specific blend my car takes just in case I'm caught red-handed. *Yeah, I'm picking up the 10W-40.*

Fortunately, I've never had to pull off this scenario, but I'm prepared. Also, I'm lucky that there happens to be quite a heavy turnover of staff at both of the Cumberland Farms locations I regularly hit, so I generally feel incognito. No one behind the counter, I think, really makes much of the constancy of my patronage; it's something of a magical collusion. I remain unduly free in the two-thousand-five-hundred-plus square feet of Cumberland Farms. I call it a *binge*, but it may just be the average American diet. I mean, even though I'm careful not to make any person-to-person contact on my hit-and-runs, I've still seen what the people in line in front of me at the store's Checkpoint Charlie have loaded up their guns with: Twix and Snickers bars, frozen cookie dough, strawberry-filled powdered-sugar-covered craziness, king-size chip bags. At least in this sense, I'm not alone.

I have three general gears when cruising Cumberland Farms. The worst gear is my *really bad* eating day. In this case, I've got a mini-bag of Cool Ranch Doritos (which, to my credit is no longer a party-sized version, as I chose in my earlier years, but now the fits-in-the-schoolgirl's-brown-bag size). To this goody, I add a small grab-and-go can of Sour Cream & Onion Pringles (why go with any other flavor), a large chocolate bar (usually Nestlé Crunch), and sometimes Oreo Minis or a Rold Gold Pretzel to boot. These are the accoutrements around the main course, which—on a *really bad* eating day—is a grinder: salami on a long, white-bread bun. And while the salami does show up, eventually, on its sticker's list of ingredients, it is only noted after a heavy lineup of additives in the mononitrate family, plus yeast (which activates the speed of potential spoilage—and likely only adds more gusto to my *gotta eat this right now* consumption craze). There's sugar (but, of course, what's a party without sugar). Next is the palatable cottonseed oil (totally American—in fact, purely patriotic), and L-cysteine (a variety of acid sourced, says Wikipedia, from hog hair or poultry feathers—totally legit). Then, finally, we have the salami slabs, or a version of something that tastes like it, plus a form of "kinda" cheese. I call it "kinda" cheese because it's also kinda filled with a bunch of other stuff with mind-bendingly long-winded names.

Sometimes, I'll downshift to what I consider a slightly better gear of market-foraging behavior, which is still pretty stinky. In this mode, I'll bob through the aisles under the market's fluorescent lights, attempt to maintain whatever mediocre words of self-encouragement I've mustered up like a wobbling mantra. My food choices might be a little less toxic than when I'm indulging in my most blown-out spree. They're still far, though, from what celebrity nutritionists might outline in a *day-in-the-life-of* eating article in a magazine feature, complete with a proper recommendation of vitamins and minerals. I've just gone from *baddest* to bad.

The strangest of all my Cumberland Farms eating styles, however, could likely inspire a national psychology conference on freak behavioral anomalies. Here, while purchased calories might not put me over the top, the pressure of my own inner-angst could surely fry my system's stress gauge. This is my *crazy browsing* mode, when I enter the market with the idea that I'm not really getting anything, *duh*. I'm just here to look around, check out the goods, tease myself. Why not? There must a whole Facebook group's worth of people out there who experience the convenience store like quasi-recovered addicts visiting an operating drug cartel. In this case, even though I believe I've convinced myself to abstain from all go-to junk foods, I still wind up, somehow, at my own 5:00 P.M. happy hour. I imagine my face looks pale, pasty, the dark circles under my eyes at an apparent maximum, like any addict in withdrawal. I eye my first snack love, the now considerably vintage Devil Dogs and the white powdered mini-donuts. I give a nod. I'm caught between an *I-don't-care-just-eat-everything* deluge and a jaw-clenched *I'll-look-but-won't-touch* museum tour of the goods. Why do this to myself?

This *abstinence* gear of my Cumberland Farms MO lasts the briefest, because it's off-the-hook nuts. It feels like I have internal opposing generals who come out to sharply debate, retaliate, and fire. One inner voice rises: *Yep, those are the Doritos,* it shares (as though I don't obviously know their vivid orange bag). As a nearly natural response, I might snap them off the pole where they're mounted like bouquets of flowers or pretty ribbons, like sweet corn fresh for the picking. Then another, nonchalant, inner voice kicks in. *Yeah, you don't really even want Doritos.* These inner voices aren't exactly identifiable as *mine*; but more inaudible *thinking* voices, engaging in what they must consider a friendly joust, which honestly, isn't so enjoyable for me. In the middle of multiple directive inputs, I'll fondle the Doritos. My motor skills might operate for a moment like I have dough hands, listless, weak—but then erratically, aggressively, surge forward with an urge to squash those orange triangles into a bag of crumbles. Returning to my commitment of browsing only, I'll determine I'm not here to buy the Doritos, but just to say *hello*, and instead, I civilly release my grip on the plastic edge and let the drama between us be over. The bag is now misshapen, though; it barely hangs on to its metal vine. Do I feel bad? I've now rendered the chips attractive to nobody, a perfect mirror of myself.

I'll eye a salami grinder but then force myself to recall the lines I'd memorized: *That's so disgusting! I don't want that!* And, at last, after passing the motor oil, I'll reach for just a Clif Bar or something that is actually pretty much like nothing, nothing wrapped in a package. Something that falls in the *doesn't count* food group, something I don't have to retain any memory of having put into my mouth. The Clif Bars at the Cumberland Farms must not sell very quickly, as their collected stock nearly always tastes as if it's on the brink of expiration. The bars have a dominantly stale-all-over taste—milled and blended and smooshed into a solid form lacking satisfying crunch. The flavor, all in all, is indistinguishable, though it simultaneously burns the back of one's throat—you know, one of the three angsty places that need to be shut down by binge endpoint: the throat, the gut, and the racing mind. If you can kill all three by the end of a binge, kudos! Hats off! Clif Bars, however many, almost sate one's hunger, but don't penetrate deeply enough for a professional-level emotional eater. No Clif Bar will put out your fire nor convince your blood sugar that, in fact, you are the elected ringmaster of the discombobulated circus called life.

I can pretend just about anything, though, so for a moment I've convinced myself I like Clif Bars, or at least, their packaging. The package, for one's entertainment, features a guy hanging off the face of a mountain; this seems healthy. I'll buy two, even if I can't tell the difference between the Crunchy Peanut Butter flavor and the Chocolate Brownie flavor. It must be the soybeans, soy flour, and soy protein isolate that make up the common filler language between both.

Frankly, whatever gear I'm operating in while at the market, and the food choices I'll make therein—I don't think I taste much during these episodes. At least, my neurons no longer seem to fire in the direction of registering taste. It may have to do with the fact that I'm not really breathing during my actual bingeing sessions, but rather, *wolfing*. *Wolfing* is something the primal part of us does when taking over the puritanical, learned-woman part of ourselves. *Wolfing* is a winning, retaliating, gnarly, vapid, rapid, rabid bundle of contradictions that crisscrosses all the channels in the brain until the screen is just fuzz, no chance against knockout. Sleep inevitably follows *wolfing*.

Let's say I get that double-decker club I mentioned: tuna, the school-day throwback. Tuna on Wonder Bread with mayo and chopped celery; this feels familiar. It's like an old song. It's all ready to go, prepared in advance. I don't mess with any over-the-counter ordering nonsense. Have a human-to-human connection with a deli person? *No way.* My tuna sandwich is germproof in its airtight seal. It was made not even knowing I'd be its eater; it's like a total one-night stand. It has no idea what my name is, just wants to get down the hatch. My Cumberland Farms tuna club contains three slices of thin bread, the *stacker*. Its edges are cut by industrial knives into perfect isosceles triangles like nobody's business, exceeding the best human efforts of exactitude. Its crusts are like thin eyebrow lines, drawn on just to symbolize actual crust, texturally indistinguishable from the rest of the slice when being inhaled. I feel I have a significant eye for art, even in the middle of one of my riots, and on the many late afternoons where I break from the marathon pace of my mental push-push, the *stacker*, well, I can almost admire it. It's sort of a looker. It's nearly pretty.

On this kind of Cumberland outing, I might get just one side item (which becomes, really, two) to accompany my pretty sandwich—like a bag of pretzels, a single chocolate bar, an iced tea. By this decade of my life, I have become adamantly against soda. I know *that* stuff really triggers adult-onset diabetes. Soda's the hard drug, the *no turning back*. Thank God I dropped (even Diet) Tab and Coca-Cola back in the early nineties, along with sunbathing in tanning oil; now, it's just not hip. Even in my worst state of binge eating, I do have *some* rules.

Then, within five minutes, I've clocked in to the World of Convenience and am now almost *finito*. When my hands are full, I go in for the touchdown. One swipe of the card, keep the eyes down, wham-bam. At the counter, I'm likely more anxious than in my early schoolgirl years, when I was forced to attend Sunday morning confession at St. Sebastian Church. But I summon the pin number, silently race through three Hail Marys and three Our Fathers, and I'm out of there, no niceties, no receipt. The prayer of my pin number is an exodus; I'm off obligingly with Ten Commandments' worth of junk food. I've learned to make this transaction with as little presence as I'd emptily recited the force-fed prayers of my Catholic school days, only now I'm in communion with carbs rather than the holy body of Christ. Out the door of convenience in one void-of-sensation sweep, I'm back in my nest, like a bird. The heaviness of the car door feels safer to me than any other door I close, and—believe me—I've definitely closed many a door, literally and metaphorically.

Before I can even leave the parking lot, before I turn on my blinker to get the hell out of Dodge, I'm ripping into whatever I've culled, say, the tuna stacker. A bag of Cool Ranch Doritos. A bag of pretzels. The chocolate bar. If all of life is a stage, here the opera is wild, the rhythm of my crunch, the rate of my *wolfification*, the food vacuumed into my

"GIANA
Behind The Wheel"

mouth by my own ravenous anxiety, wanting to be struck, sedated, knocked out. My anxiety is in charge now. It's behind the wheel, driving solely with its thigh, hands free, reaching for all the substances at once. And Giana, she is curled up in the very back of my SUV. She is carsick, and in the fetal position. She is wanting people to stop pulling on her pigtails, to quit calling her stupid, to stop telling her she is crazy. But the ravenous anxiety knows how to drive, to stay on the surface, "in charge," to multitask in the symphony; this is *normalcy*. Sometimes it is even raining, and the windshield wipers wash it all down, rock us in a steady quarter note, wrap us in a rhythmic *one, two, three, four* of downpour.

My Audi turns left, then right, getting onto the highway and then switching between lanes. No one can stop me; no one can say, *GG, I see you. Giana Giovanni, is that you?* To top it all off, to make it like a dessert, I check out from the checking out, like a checkout cherry on top. I get on the phone. I call my restaurant and ask them about something that doesn't matter much, something trivial. I get into someone else's business. Or I have a meeting I've previously (conveniently) set up with my web designer or my accountant: *Yeah, yeah, yeah. Yeah? Okay! Sounds good!* I'll even call my sister. When the person on the other line is talking, I'll put the phone on mute. This way, they can't hear me chew, slurp, wolf.

GG are you eating? And that would be my sister.

No, what are you talking about?

I hear you; I know you're eating. She's being a bitch.

So I say, *No, my phone keeps going out!*

So she says, *You can tell me you're eating. Why don't you just admit it?*

Then I just change the subject, GG style: *Okay, whatever, let's talk about how you keep letting cousin Lara walk all over you. How about that?*

Whenever I'm bingeing and talking, I try to disguise my voice so that they can't hear the *wolf*, so that I sound cognizant, but I am already disappearing under the seat, under the wheel alignment. I'm already dissipating into the smoky ether, like electric sparks from car jumper cables. I'm evaporating into the nether regions of outer space because I have two locations of being. One could be aptly called *Hardly in My Body*, where I am gripped with a go-go-go anxiety, pushing compulsively through my day, and the other locale is the place to where my escapist flees and no one can find her. She is a pro, evasive to even the strongest pack of wolves. She hides in constellations and outer space, past lives, crystal balls, and tarot symbols.

Over the years, I've found it better to keep my dietary tendencies to myself rather than get a sore neck from nodding absently in response to others' clichéd insights, suggestions bulleted into easy adages. *It's simple*, professed books, diet gurus, workshop giants, my sister, my mom, and even an occasional girlfriend I'd confided in. *Just eat in moderation. Chew. Just abstain from eating at night. Always stop when you're full. Pause between bites. Put your fork down.* (People, **what** fork?) This is decent instruction for someone who can internalize structure, someone who creates things in ways other than I do, which is sort of (on my best days) like Glinda the Good Witch. Move my hands around wildly, a little this, a little that, and *shazam*!

There *is* a method to the madness. Not to sound pretentious, but my mind must be a little like Einstein's: mathematical operators and intermediate variables, equations that look akin to messy child scrawl to an outsider but are actually a labyrinth of genius. Like Einstein's, these complex problems seem to demand a lifetime of solving for X, the mayhem of *how I eat*. Unlike Einstein, however, I've conveniently carved out my life's work far from a dry lab. The *Advanced Chem* of my research takes place on the Connecticut Turnpike midway through metabolizing artificial flavor and corn syrup.

If whatever tangled-up cues signaling me to feed were as easy to detangle as, say, a bunny-eared, double-knotted Ked, I'd have long untied the shoestring—believe me. My natural tendency is to automatically invite a max capacity of disturbance into my external world. I'll answer a flux of interruptive phone calls at any hour, hold virtual client sessions in Europe beginning at midnight my time, set cascading chimes to ring for all of my app notifications and schedule my housekeeper, gardener, and carpenter to pull up my driveway at the same moment. The outside-world stimulation in my brain has nothing on the racket I've got going on inside the damn thing, though. It's understandable that it took me well into my fifties to cultivate enough mindfulness (thank you, hypnosis, buttload of essential oils, books on tape, and a few good shamans) to notice I've distinct, repetitive, demanding voices in my head provoking me to eat. The voices are a high-spun team, like professional cheerleaders on speed, shrewd acrobats who are anything but saccharin sweet. They reiterate their clever routines in unified aggressive insistence. It's quite nightmarish.

Yes, I have a whole programming language of eating vernacular. My specific slew of available eating cues, I assume, present vastly different than what I imagine to be a healthy eater's inner dialogue. (The healthy eater is my generalized ideal, kind of like Hollywood's *perfect girlfriend*. Likely neither fit into actual reality, yet both fit seamlessly into the size-6 sparkling halter top worn by the mannequin in my closet.) For the healthy eater, there is likely a series of rational, gradual voices. She is normal; her internal cues lead to her simple neurological recognition of actual hunger. Her hunger alerts sound like angel songs, followed by the most demure opening of her mouth in an undaunted allowance of one nourishing, leisurely bite after another. When she eats, she allows herself to reiterate her value, her connection to the earth's sustenance. Food is food; eating is eating. It's a clean and simple function.

I imagine the healthy eater's internal eating prompts go something like this: *Hey, sweetheart, I think you might be getting just a little hungry. Honey, not to distract you, but—say—within the hour, you might want a small, lean meal. Sound good, kiddo?*

The healthy eater hasn't been thinking of food nonstop all day. She's breathing deeply, sitting comfortably inside a picturesque movie set where all of her bills are organized and her counters are clear. There is fresh spring air coming in through the open window. She gets the lunchtime prompt, after at least three hours have *just breezed by* since her tiny-but-entirely-fulfilling breakfast. She rubs her stomach in harmonious receptivity. Her stomach—of course—is fit and bloat-free under her form-fitting top.

An entire hour passes before the healthy eater gets her second cue: *My dear, shall we get up and make a special lunch to celebrate our primal need to replenish? Then, of course, if you'd like, we can get right back to this fantastic work project we're loving!*

The healthy eater complies with herself. Her inner hunger speaks carefully, in a soft, sultry voice she can recognize as her own. Nearly carried in a gossamer light, she bounces in a slo-mo fabric-softener-commercial kind of style, her head swaying gently, like she's smelling a fresh sheet. Her face wears a perpetual smile of sensual embodiment.

Mnnnnn. The healthy eater's brain actually excretes relaxing declaratives. *Ahh—time to relax and eat. I think I'll make that beautiful Jamie Oliver recipe. It's exactly what I want! Hurrah!* The healthy eater is already satisfied. This is why I covet her easeful relationship with food.

My Eating Words are anything but easeful—and definitely not enviable. They arrive curtly, bluntly, front and center. Without question, they are the star of the show, but they are more than just the star. My Eating Words infect the stage, stain the curtain, consume the cast, shred the playbill, and undermine the script.

Bitch, you're going to eat the whole thing anyway, so just eat it. Eat it all fast. You can't stop. You can't put it down. You have to buy it all. I want it all, as much as I can have. I can't do anything else until I get it. And get both kinds because who are you to choose? You don't choose. I don't care. You don't care. There's nothing else. Go to the store, then go home catatonically, watch a Hallmark movie, and pass out. That's what I want to do.

You know what the amazing thing is, though? Even though I couldn't bear to consider actually recognizing, confronting, or talking about my Eating Words until I was in my mid-fifties, I remember being fully hijacked and militantly bullied by them as early as in my twenties. This was when I first became employed full time in the family business, when I joined the ranks of the work that consumed my mother and father, aware it would consume me too. Maybe we'd choose different vices, different outlets of letting off steam. Maybe I'd never see either of my parents walk, lobotomized, through Cumberland Farms, hypnotized by a desire for Cheetos. Regardless, once I submitted to supporting their business, my engine started backfiring, my ambition, my rebellion, my escapism—I'm not sure they knew where to go. My bull-like ambitions, which had been previously set upon new horizons, imploded and burned into me. If somehow I was going to wind up sharing the same area code with my family, I was going to have to find a way to vacate on the quick. I needed a dependable respite, a release. Friends, in fact, all intimacy, felt too difficult; I had enough on my plate—or, should I say, I had enough splayed out on the passenger seat, spilling over to the car floor and teetering on the console. All of my cupholders were full.

Oreo Minis: twenty for twenty, polished off. Tuna stacker: not a crumb in site. Pringles: who can leave a Pringle behind? I have only two squares left of Nestlé Crunch. I'm almost in my fortieth year of this ritual. For two-thirds of my life, I've returned to this ceremony, living out the yin and yang of being cognizant, ambitious, committed to the exercise plan, the workshop, the healing path, the therapist certification and then camouflaging in cookies, checking out in chocolate, turning off with tuna. I know I pushed it to the limit; I learned in the last years of that existence that the time had come. I took it to the very end, like a drag race, right to the edge of the cliff. I'd lived out this body response too long. I had no choice but to attempt to gain real insight, to make actual change. I'd traveled as far as Peru and Bali to find out what was *wrong* with me, to fix my obvious brokenness, to quiet or manipulatively shift my Eating Words. Guess you can't really fix manipulativeness with manipulation though. Trying to find new words to counter my abusive internal dialogue, like telling myself, *Stop it!* or *Shut up!* didn't work so well. It ended up being more of a dim-witted effort, like trying to fight fire with fire. I needed new tools to create new rituals, tools I wouldn't necessarily find on a voyage to any distant location, really, but by traveling inward, learning (ironically, as an adult) how to actually breathe and feel my body.

Little could I have imagined, eyeing the last squares of my Nestlé Crunch bar while simultaneously changing lanes at sixty-five miles an hour, that the key to my relief was not in any of these far-off places, but on the contrary, right in the small spill of crumbs I'd collected on my lap, heading home.

Part One:

The Foundational Ingredients

I have to say, I freaking *love* my house, and I really, *really* love my pool. It's heated, and I designed the whole thing, built right into the middle of my front garden. This is the fourth house I've owned, but to me, it feels like my very first real residence. When I bought it, we got intimate from the start. I knocked down its walls and expanded all of the closets (I need giant closets like a cave bear needs a giant cave). Hired artists constructed special pieces for its interior. I gutted the guest bedrooms, bathrooms, and even the gorgeous custom kitchen (ironically, one of my strong suits is building top-notch kitchens just oozing *hearth* and equipped for culinary mastery). Even before I broke ground, I dubbed this house my "healing home," because I just knew it would host profound chapters for me, some type of *recovery*. This would be the house I'd picture when I'd look back on the best years of my life. So I set it up to robustly reflect my penchant for the holistic, the esoteric, the naturalistic, and even the exotic. And I made rules that I wouldn't bring any of my *bad* behavior into my newest house. For example, my bingeing self isn't allowed entry. I'll leave her *wolfing* out in the cold, excommunicated from her own property. (She doesn't mind; in fact, excommunication feels like normalcy to her.) I've been decently successful in obliging this standard of what is allowed and disallowed in my healing home, discounting late-night, half-asleep bouts of eating. These don't count so much because in these instances, I am so tired I can only, at most, fuzzily recall a trek to the refrigerator. I would be left with little evidence of the midnight mission if it weren't for my finding fingerprints on the fridge door handle in the morning, an empty Tupperware container that didn't make it into the sink. When it comes to allowing any purchased junk food into my home sweet home, I'll mandate I round off a chocolate bar in my driveway, leaving the wrapper on the floor. Better yet, I'll throw the rest out. *Throw it out, and make sure you get it deeply covered in the can. You don't want to see it again.* It only gets as close to my doorway as the bin in the garage. It's too unholy, risky, incongruous to allow my pretty kitchen to be defiled by Nabisco's dessert fare.

Out of all of the decked-out features I manifested as a result of my working drive and dedication, I'm most proud of my garden. Even though I grade myself a D-minus in feeling what well-adjusted people might call *joy*, this is the place I can access something as close to a sense of pleasure as I have ever known. My garden landscape is mostly edible (of course) or else used for herbal remedies, infusions, and decoctions: pineapple sage, fennel, milk thistle, nettles, Saint-John's-wort, lemon balm, and lavender. My yard could be a safe haven in the event of an unexpected prohibition against herbal medicine. I'm never satisfied with the concept of *enough*, and have created a surplus of medicinal plants on my acres to provide for a few families, if need be. More than the reaped harvest itself, I enjoy the actual process of cultivating greens. For decades, I've picked up gardening secrets from agrarians, whether at natural wellness conferences or the local farmers' market. My Italian blood simply understands that the real riches are found in the promising morning dew on purple anise hyssop flowers in July, or the clarifying scent of rosemary wafting through my dark garage as I set out for the office in the morning. Regardless of my work hustle, my gardener and home-maintenance man remain central in my daily communications; I oversee and manage each move they make and am proactive in the weeding, planting, and harvesting.

Since, in my healing home, most of my bad eating behaviors are forbidden, it's extra convenient that I just don't really recognize anything like hunger—as a rule—until around 4:00 P.M. Okay, I'll *sometimes* have a truly non-breakfast-like thing before the afternoon (like asparagus slathered in my family's own olive oil, or a baked hot-pepper shrimp or two from one of my fridge's many storage containers). But it's not really until 4:00 P.M. that I actually consider myself an *eater*. There's no way I could get anything done if I permitted myself to identify with my metabolic function before the deemed *happy hour.*

At 4:00 P.M., I'm ready to sacrifice the rest of my day, allow my mind to check in to submission. Having submitted, I start to plan my escape binge; I allow it to take over. *Yeah, uh-huh, uh-huh.* I'll nod at the girl I've put at the salad bar at the restaurant I'm managing that day. My eyes are already starting to glaze over. *Yeah, olives, Patty. More boiled eggs.* I'll check my phone, text something curt, or stroll the floor, but my real smarts are gone. I've done my best to hire people who I trust can take over once I've started to energetically leave premises, people who would never call me out and who can self-manage in my absence. Patty at the salad bar, she knows what to do. She'll refresh the artichokes, refill the Caesar dressing. My restlessness heightens around 4:00 P.M. I'll move through my employees' paths like a wrecking ball, not breathing until my moment of exit. I'm fully consumed in low-blood-sugar mode, thinking: *In one hour, I'm peeling tire out of this spot like a Devil Dog and heading toward some type of Hostess Twinkie-like filling; what a relief!*

That's my 4:00 P.M. But in the morning, I am a different Giana; I'm sated simply by steeping home-brewed tea infusions. This typically looks something like jamming my giant fifty-ounce Breville electric tea infuser with a plethora of herbs because I want all the blends at once. (As always, choice doth not become me.) I'll combine an anti-inflammatory mix with an immune-boosting formula, plus a combo for hormone health. I'll cross purple sage with spearmint, tulsi, lemon balm, fennel, and linden flower, and throw in some vetiver and red clover too. I love my teas, and stand behind the power of my daily dose. However, each herb's individual pungent flavor is dulled, competing within my complex mixology; so the general taste ends up being, well, my specialty: slightly lost—*defeat by overload*. Too many strong medicines at once keep the mind in a stimulated frenzy of forwardness; that's my style. I fill all my cabinets, from the bedroom to the guestroom bathroom to the kitchen, with herbal concoctions of my own making. Anyone I regularly come into contact with remains inundated with my elixirs, formulas, and effective balms. I've crafted these dominantly from homegrown plants, but also from exotic, high-quality natural medicines I've found on my travels around the world.

The plants, trees, shrubs, and vines with which I've surrounded my piece of paradise are beautiful barricades, walling my mini-fortress—guardian protectors. And the saltwater pool is the queen of my acres of heaven, my main-staple squeeze, and ready go-to between late May and (if I can push it) November. I keep it heated to eighty-eight degrees, therapeutic level—a warm invitation, the one place I dare feeling my near-naked skin being touched, soothed. The pool is where I can actually identify with having a body, or feel, at least, that I have one, without necessarily loathing the fact. In so many cultures and healing modalities, water represents emotion, and the pool is where I can handle mine. I can stay cool while I hold phone meetings; manage my company with apparent fluidity; buoyantly direct orders to my employees; think creatively; and plan spiritual retreats, travels, and family dinners—all from the safety of my aquatic refuge. When night swimming, I'll light the six torches I've poignantly placed within the flowering riot of herbs in bloom and bob up and down in the waters, admiring my lantern's soft citronella-stirring glow as dusk turns dark. It feels primal, my manicured wild. The pool covers all I need from a perfect partnership. It's my date-night-with-self spot, my mid-afternoon pick-me-up or wind-down. It's a marker of my sanity that keeps me from drowning in my own deep end. Plus, swimming is the one form of exercise I do without having to absolutely force myself; it's something healthy I actually crave. Maybe the saline waters somehow fool my rebel brain into thinking I'm getting away, that I'm escaping as I manage a few laps of the butterfly stroke or freestyle from one end to the other.

One of the first things I did when I bought this house, before renovations even began, was plant a row of tall neighbor-blocking trees (in the cypress family—*viva Italia*) on the eastern side of the property, in the direction of the ocean, right along the edge of the pool. Inside the safety of my trees, I'm enclosed, covered, surrounded by friendly allies—the best kind, of the grand oxygenating variety. This is my custom-designed *La Dolce Vita*, the "life of indulgent goodness," or at least on the outside, it looks so; of this I'm sure. I move with the superheroine strength of a master of attention deficit disorder and can't typically sit still for longer than thirty seconds (unless in my car or the pool, or—of course—in the airplane), but my healing home is the compensation. It is my sweet, earthy fortress, one into which I'll settle—a benevolent comfort zone, allowing me, piece by piece, to unfurl into a soft downiness, to eventually find sanctuary at my own core.

Yes, these days, Giovannis sleep wrapped in seven-hundred-thread-count Egyptian sheets, but my family most definitely didn't start off in such lush conditions. The pressure to survive, to push forward, to project all sense of achievement into the future and then vehemently fight each day to create it—this mode began before my own life, the life of Giana Clara Giovanni. It started even before my parents came to Connecticut clinging to nothing but their immigrant status, before they worked their way up the social and economic ladders of life in North America as Italians.

CHAPTER 2

Mozzarella in the Time of Mussolini

L ia Cristina di Carlo, my mother, was born in the township of Melilli, a municipality of Syracuse, Sicily. She descended unto the earth as a newborn in the fall of 1937, just one year before the country's dictator, Benito Mussolini, buddied up with Spain's Fascist Franco and joined Hitler's Nazi Germany, preempting the Second World War. Let's just say this was not the most ideal time for a young girl to learn the softness of the feminine, to pet ponies, or to leisurely seek *quadrifoglio*, the Italian four-leaf clover. For the people of Melilli, life and land became a target for intrusion, and, in the unsafe atmosphere, all hints of what my bohemian soul might refer to as *the Goddess realm* were nearly completely hidden.

During the war, my mother, Lia, was a toddler in the crux of what psychologists call her developmental years of implicit memory, the early cognitive state before one differentiates oneself from the rest of the world. While most babies' suckling is intercepted by the heavy-duty dropping of poop bombs in diapers, my mom's suckling, at least figuratively, was interrupted by the dropping of bombs mid *Operation Husky,* a pinnacle of combat. The United Nations chose Sicily as the primary launchpad for taking down the European Axis powers, namely Germany and Italy, and Sicily was a middleman, in ways, shifting political foothold toward the finale of World War II. After hosting German troops for four-plus years of war, Italy's political pendulum swung as the annihilation of Fascist Europe became imminent. In exchange for opening their doors (and ports) to half a million American soldiers, the Sicilians received the perks of the sudden alliance: one, the granting of American naturalization to any Sicilian born between 1931 and 1937, a reconciliation for the youth who'd endured war's calamities without choice. Both skilled opportunists, my mother and father advantageously took America up on its offer, justifying the darkness of their first years by building a life more directly under their control, and one lit with prosperity, at that.

But in the upheaval of World War II, Sicilians likely didn't have much stance in Italy's 180-degree political shift. While Woody Guthrie's convictional "This Land Is Your Land" was being composed on American soil, Sicilians were clinging to traditions like the *Tarantella*, their customary dance marking the single day where women could publicly bare outlandish wildness front and center in a ritualized spotlight—all in homage to Italy's wolf spider. Her bite, the *Lycosa tarantula's*, at least as far as legend has it, sent women into hysterical delirium. The popular folk dance reinforced the patriarchal view of courtship between men and women; affirmed, yes, women have a crazy nature, and, yes, it must be subdued and diffused by religion and fieldwork. While Sicilian villagers held fast to their social customs, striving to maintain the provision of their daily bread and daily prayer along with their identity, ammunition fired. Eventually, the Nazi party was overthrown. Mussolini was shot by Milanese officials and hanged in a free-for-all. The civilians of Milan then (posthumously) put the *eye-for-an-eye* practice in play, shredding Mussolini's dead body to virtual obliteration: shooting it, beating it, cracking the skull open, and then urinating on his ruination. They also hanged upside-down his shot-and-tortured girlfriend of twelve years, exposing her intimate parts and photographing her destroyed body for the world to see. She must have had a really warped concept of TLC if she agreed to this level of soul-contract with the dictator, as her end of the deal seemed to bottom out in all ways. Portraying the outcome of marred faith adjacent to his corpse, Mussolini's lover bared her massacred private parts on necropsied display. In that Milanese square, the savageness of citizens nearly matched the ravages of their former leader. It was difficult to know who was more spoiled by the end of the Second World War, the now-overthrown and dead-as-a-doornail Mussolini, or the heart of the so-called "liberated" Italian country.

Here's an interesting side note on the digestive stress of extreme warfare: It turns out, if the entire city of Milan hadn't reduced Mussolini to smithereens, he'd have likely died anyway from his own gastritis (speaking of poop-bombs). The ex-prime minister was evidently being driven mad by his own duodenal ulcers! His rancid gut goes to show that even the most sociopathic of men may still bare some semblance of conscience when attempting to metabolize their militantly tyrannous outlook on the world, after all.

I know relatively little about her childhood, but I once overheard my mother, Lia, on the phone with my great aunt. I strained my ears, eager to pick up any info on her secret puzzle pieces. Lia casually recalled the significant number of Italian soldiers her family hid during the years of war, and she did so with about as much emotion as if she were sharing an article she'd read that morning in the *Hartford Courant*. Still, I knew I was hearing something essential about my mother, who she might be on the inside—in the places I couldn't see, where light now barely reached. The young Lia, constantly put to work, stewarded whatever was in season: almonds, pears, figs, olives. She'd carry the harvested wheat to the granary, and then, a diligent farm girl and kitchen hand, Lia would roll the fresh-milled flour into bread loaves and prepare the daily provisions for her eleven family members' supper. With soldiers lodged on her family's farm, Lia would deliver warm loaves and olive oil to them by sundown. Along the way, she'd handpick tangerines or ripe tree fruit, adding this to her bundle. My mother, an expert of containing her emotions, seems to have pocketed only a few memories of her war-filled childhood, or—better described—*lack* of a childhood. If I ask her about her early life, she'll show about as much emotion as she would if she were sharing the fact that her hairstylist had retired or that a new bank had

opened in town. Everything, every emotion, is detached. *Like mother,*
like daughter. I've done my homework though. I knew which aunts to
ask, which cousins in Melilli would still recall the time period. This is
how I've gathered the facts.

In 1945, at the age of eight (about the same age when I was
infatuated with my Suzy Homemaker Oven and obsessing over pie),
Lia absorbed the fall of Mussolini, the dissolution of her country's
economy, and the official ending of World War II, in one year alone.
The country was left with the same pervasive sense of self-loss that,
frankly, I can identify with at times. By the time the war was over, the
Italian people had been turned right, then left, and during this erratic
twist, the country lost close to one hundred fifty thousand people.
Sicily had been designated a newly autonomous region of Italy and
attempted to rebuild its economy while coping with mass trauma
(again, a state I can relate to!). It's a true miracle the di Carlos did not
lose any of their eleven family members; their neighbors were not as
fortunate.

One afternoon near the war's end, Lia's grandfather called out to
her from across the plaza, *Lia! Run for the grotto!* At that moment, a
person standing adjacent to her at the market was hit by an explosive
device. When my mother was a child, she watched her neighbor's
limbs get blown off right in from of her face. She dropped her market
parcels, and then, as her grandfather had commanded, ran for the
grotto alone. While the detonated bomb took eighty people's lives, my
mother spent the night, stunned, to say the least, in the underground
bomb shelter. Lia wondered if her family members were among the
casualties, a bit much to grasp for anyone, much less an eight-year-
old girl alone in the dark. She lasted the night without food, without
warmth, without a sense of whether she'd survive. When I contemplate
where my sense of not wanting to starve might have come from, I
think of my mother in that shelter on that long night, hiding in the
buried bunker built into the edges of her farmland. I think about her
in the height of a manmade war, when not only food was scarce, but

in addition, all forms of security were threatened. I recognize how messed up it is that the inherent human right for security can be both granted and taken away by external powers. Such contemplations have generously provided context for pricey psychodynamic therapy and hours of analysis; how we internalize family heritage!

Ironically, during these years—a time of gruesome patrilineal establishment—the di Carlos worshipped at a church, the *Chiesa Madre*, whose name translates to *The Mother Church*. The ceiling of "The Mother Church" is covered in revered frescoes of curvaceous holy women, painted by rococo artist Olivio Sòzzi. Sòzzi's style emphasized asymmetry and sensual ornateness under the acceptable parameters of holiness in a time of squandered pleasures. Early on, like the rest of the women of the day, the women in my family were branded like cattle with the iron-firm belief that any softness, any calm presence of the nourishing feminine could be received only esoterically, spiritually. The sole example Melillese women would ever encounter of a revered, voluptuous female body would remain beyond their fingertips. Within that male-led place of worship, the single feminine image existed, painted onto the breast-shaped dome ceiling overhead. Paradoxically, she would remain forever dismissed in the flesh. Is it any surprise that I found my own sense of spiritual connection so far above my own body, in my own metaphoric constellation, channeling star people? It seems pretty clear to me when I look at the animal tracks, hunting down the story of my familial past.

Obviously, as an Italian daughter, I've been around Italian culture since I can remember smelling my first *ragù*. And now, nearing my sixth decade, I generally feel semi-entitled to speak in generalizations about the whole darn deal. I'll explain something about the Italian disposition: As gregarious and warm as Italians are portrayed, and as inviting and romantic as Italy is regarded worldwide as a destination spot, there are unbendable, unspoken rules passed down generationally within every typical Italian family. These laws are upheld to preserve the Italian-coiffed, finely tailored concealment of emotion. Reserve, sure, it can make sense sometimes, circumstantially. Like if you're Donatella Versace whipping out an arrow-straight pantsuit (yes, please!), or you're Giorgio Armani designing a perfectly tapered silk dress (insert me, fawning). As someone who loves fashion, I give complete artistic liberty to any rigid lines drawn by no-nonsense, hard-nosed Italian designers, and anyone in their high-quality attire, sharply charging down the runway during fashion week.

But at home, among family, emotion tends to remain rigidly off-limits, even during the warmest of moments, and if you're going to share an actual feeling, there are some definite parameters, my dear, *mia cara*. For example, in my Italian family, here are the first lessons you must subconsciously digest, even before you train your body to digest gluten. The rules of thumb include the following: Recounting the past should be done over pasta, and the length of lunch should outlast any wallowing over the past. Smiles and nods are the sole gesticulations to be used for acknowledging memories, and preferably during the last course—a mascarpone-rich dessert, if there's room. And finally, the only secrets a granddaughter might hope to access are the secret recipes of her grandmother's—specifically, her gnocchi.

While I'll never gauge how deeply either of my parents' *emotional wells* actually run, there are some narratives my mother will repeat. By the time Lia had turned double digits, she'd been swept away by the San Sebastiano Church. The parish likely provided the war-weary Lia with a sense of protection, of warmth and safety. San Sebastiano was on the other side of town from "The Mother Church," her family's hub for worship. She'd made it there on her own, an independent seeker. This is one way my mother and I are alike; I, too, wandered from my family and community to find my spiritual center. However, my pilgrimage involved far fewer church wafers and many more intuitive astrologers. My mother, on her sacred path, decided she would become a nun. I might say I've taken a bit of a similar path toward some kind of renunciation. Like Lia, I've doled out my own fair share of vows to abstain from intimacy, for better or for worse.

Lia never made it to the cloistered life, and I'm actually not sure if she would have been able to tolerate the veil of the religious habit. I'm also not sure she could have fully devoted herself to a God less demanding than the business that she preoccupied her life with, which was hugely demanding and larger than life itself. Still, in front of my father, my mother loves to reiterate the fact that she *nearly* became a nun. There's a slight quality of both mourning and playfulness when she recounts how profoundly she'd committed to the holy lifestyle until the very day she left for Ellis Island, at age sixteen, in 1953. She acts as though she gave up something of significant worth to travel toward a life of ultimate matrimony, and it's hard to know if she is serious or seeking her family's recognition. *Lia, how thankful we are that you chose to turn from the life of being a chaste sister, and chose instead a heavier burden: dealing with our sins,* might we say.

I'm not sure if Lia dropped the nun vision somewhere during her seasickness, just after shipping out of Palermo to the Italian mainland, or else in Naples, aboard the *Vulcania*. Was it in the Mediterranean Sea that she rescinded her vows, or was it in the Port of Gibraltar, throwing up again and again into the Atlantic Ocean, headed toward Middletown, Connecticut, to make her new home? Maybe Lia was, in ways, vomiting to clear out her memories of war, her family's depreciated wealth, the threat of losing their land, the wobbling of an economy, and people struggling to gather their wits and find their sea legs, so to speak, after years of massive oppression. Contrary to the bad reputation of immigrant-transporting ocean liners in the mid-twentieth century, Lia thought the food aboard the *Vulcania* was very palatable. However, during her five days of travel, she wasn't able to eat a thing; her appetite yielded to the conditions. An appetite yielding to conditions? I empathize there. Oh, how the conditions of GG's internal turbulent ocean yield to her unwavering appetite for all things with a common denominator of creaminess.

My mother was sent to Middletown with a plan created by her family, as she was of the right age in terms of the new naturalization allowance authorized by the American government. Lia's family chose her to come over to work—with arduous vigor in a nonstop fashion. In a way, she was another casualty of war, by edict, sacrificed and shipped out into a different kind of gunfire, crossing the Atlantic toward a booming American economy. Sent off on family duty. It was prearranged. Lia would mail the majority of whatever money she'd make back to her family to save their farmland, to pay for their new olive-soapmaking machine. There was definite promise of financial opportunity in the burgeoning Connecticut city she'd soon call home, a city already filled with an abundance of Italians—and family members, namely, her two aunts. Lia was to initially board with her unmarried aunt, and, in whatever free time she'd muster outside of work, build rapport among the influential associates of her other aunt, who'd married *well*. In only ten years since leaving Melilli, Lia's aunt had successfully wed into prominence, and was now the wife of an important Middletown businessman who owned factories, real estate, and substantial property. My mother, who had survived much worse than faring in a new economic environment, naturally figured she'd create a life far more substantial for herself in Connecticut than she'd ever dreamed of back in Sicily, where there was no opportunity. Single-handedly focused on her contribution, Lia promptly buried all fears, simply for the purpose of survival. She was Sicilian—a survivor of war, famine, and a faltered economy. It wouldn't be hard to confidently remain callous toward any trite feelings of concern or loss; resistance was effortless for the daughter of the Italian Resistance.

When the *Vulcania* hit land, Lia eased her way through customs. She doesn't even remember anyone checking her passport and swears she simply strolled into town. Lia was swept away in her aunt's 1952 Ford Crestline, just two girls in an American car. It was all quite a thrilling transition, as my mother's life in Melilli had generally involved being transported by her own two legs. On that day, Lia and my great aunt stopped for lunch in the city. Biting into her first hot dog, Lia let go of calling Sicily home. Despite how she made a point of describing American food as distinctly inferior to that of the Melillesi, and didn't much care for the American linked-sausage classic, Lia allowed her hot dog to be a symbol of completion. She was done. Out with the last chapters—all pages of her previous life, pockmarked by destitution and economic despair—and in with the new. She'd not conceive of sorrows past. Taste would be the only one of her senses to retain sentimental connection to her former life.

Like nearly all women in the world, my mother would occasionally watch what she ate, but her eating behavior was generally moderate, and didn't seem to take up much of her mental real estate. She was beautiful, confident, and naturally quite fit, and was too strong-willed to squander time obsessing over something as petty as gaining or losing a few pounds. Instead, Lia fixated on work and moneymaking, bravely surviving. She had no time to fixate on something as manageable as food. While the Germans' attack may have forced her to run and hide, carbs would never intimidate her. She'd spent too many years tending to wheat and cultivating barley, and had the upper hand there. But, being Italian, my mother is also, genetically, a foodie, so, like most Italians, it's natural that her life, including her lucrative business, would revolve around *il alimento*, the aliment, the nourishment, of food. Lia instilled within me the sense that *home* is a flavor, eating is how roots are reaffirmed, and food is the only place adjectives of beauty are justifiable or feeling can be found. This meant that affirmations about the body were unfathomable. We'd recognize the senses exclusively in terms of culinary applications, and her girls would be sure to understand that admiration of the naked body is basically inconceivable. It is only the *dressed* body where one can form any real opinion about one's figure, only after it is fashioned. Never mind what your naked waist looks like; in fact, don't regard it at all. It's only important to assess how you've styled your look. One can take certain concerns over the colors and fabrics of their garments, particularly in appropriate regard to what kind of formal dinner or business luncheon he or she may be attending. The body, finely dressed or in uniform, is for working. This is what mattered. There is leeway to choose the best quality, and become a fashionista of shoes, but always with the outcome of building professional value. My mother showed me that, only with perfectly done mascara, was it possible to look life straight in the eye, seal the deals, and sign on the dotted lines.

Lia settled quite seamlessly in Middletown, the renamed *Mattabesset*, as it was originally called by the Wangunk Native Americans living there, along the Connecticut River. Eventually renamed *Middletown* by the Puritans, the waspy town became awash with immigrants by the 1920s: the Irish, Polish, Barbadian, German, and Italian all coming to call New England home. By the time Lia arrived in the city, Middletown had already been governed by three Italian mayors over the previous decades: Santangelo, Cubeta, and Daddario. In ways, the Italian ethic was more unperturbed in this small North American city than Lia felt Italian life had ever been in Melilli. In Melilli, there was little opportunity for economic pursuit, unless, of course, one wanted to prune persimmon trees, throw cast nets out for sardines, or attend clergy school. Middletown promised factory work and a potential path to new financial prosperity.

By 1946, Lia's new religiosity was firmly set. She'd found her *devotion to staying busy,* to which she remains allegiant. During a recent philanthropic luncheon, I overheard the now eighty-two-year-old Lia affirm the virtues of her faith in preoccupation. When asked by the man sharing her table how she retains her youthful looks, she replied without missing a beat, *I stay busy*. Impressed, the man then called her beautiful. Ever the headstrong Italian, Lia negated the comment immediately: *I'm not beautiful.* This was not modesty for Lia; it was straight talk. Lia had little time for either receiving or doling out aesthetic compliments. Rather, she'd focus on being steadfast about how *good* her family could be and ensuring its economic success.

In those first years of living in Middletown, Lia proved she had incredible skill and endurance, and, as she'd intended, she earned enough American dollars to send a significant amount of money back home. Lia tells me that everything she made in Middletown was to keep her family's Sicilian farmland alive. We still have the farmland in Melilli, thanks to my mother's work. Interestingly, however much she gave her entire destiny for its preservation, the farm is now untended, overgrown, along with dozens of other farming communities that once filled the area. Maybe we can blame this abandon on the difficult economy there, as Melilli never recovered after World War II, not even during the establishment of a new government and budding industrialism. Or maybe Melilli's "Mother Church" and the rococo jeweling the region finally won influence. The feminine mystique outdid the granaries, mills, and farming initiatives—rebelling, going feral, after being abused by an aggressively patriarchal world order. Today, in Melilli, our family's almond tree orchard bears fruit without any fingers to collect, sort, and sell the harvest. Like the wild feminine, the almonds flower and return to seed, recycled into the earth under the twinkling city-light-free, Sicilian sky.

Meanwhile, in the mid-fifties, Lia was immersed in her own fiscal fruit bearing, just one of many Melillesi doing the same in Middletown. In fact, the Connecticut city was nicknamed *Middletown, Sicily* because (at least on the segregated eastern side of Main Street) buildings were filled with Melillesi: the Magnanas, di Marcos, Scamperinos, Saracenos, and Cannamelas. And there, in the midst of the Italians learning to appreciate drive-in-diner hot dogs, was Lia di Carlo, whose first job in America would be at a button factory. Scavenging through my mother's jewelry in my early years, I learned that Lia kept her rosary, which was made of wood and crushed flowers and was gifted to her by her favorite nun, Vicenza Camela, at San Sebastiano Church on the eve of her fifteenth birthday. She'd give up fingering these prayer beads, though, in her first American seasons, exchanging counting prayers for divvying up and cutting button blanks at the Pitkin button mill during the end of her teenage years.

My mother has no opinion to share when I ask her if she liked this job. She shrugs, her perfectly shaped, light-brown eyebrows raise in humor, saying, by this gesture, *Giana, why are you bothering me about these things?* She has long mastered the look: her head leans to one side, and her face falls as though she can't care enough to drum up an answer to my off-topic question. Eventually, I'll receive a short explanation. It feels like an actual triumph to milk any real details about Lia's past from her; I've had to be a real sleuth to put most of it together. The majority of Lia's stories about her early life end pretty immediately with an *Eh, who knows, Giana? You ask too many questions.* If she begins to actually share more, within minutes, there will be a subject change. And if we're on the phone and I ask for details about her inner world or her past, forget it. Lia will always find an abrupt reason to go no more than three minutes into anything intimate. *I've got to go*, she'll say, offering my father as an excuse, *Gino needs something.*

My family is good with abruptness; all transitions happen in such a manner. It's what we know. I've inherited this same quality, of course. We play a game, sort of like poker: who can end the conversation more swiftly. We can be in deep discussion, but if one of us decides we have to hang up midsentence, chances are, we'll say something that would sound terminal or like a state of emergency to the general polite converser: *I'm done here; I've gotta go. Okay, bye.* Whoever hangs up without offering closure wins the hand. Though I'm nearly dysfunctional with closure in terms of, say, rolling up a mostly consumed bag of Doritos, it appears I'm a master at forcefully doling it out in conversation. All of us Giovannis are top ranked not only in closure, but also in the art of remaining defensively guarded. Lia, specifically, is an ace at complaining when I dare ask her a personal question. Once I'd discovered that inquisitiveness is largely considered rude in the Italian family, I learned to stop asking about anyone or anything. This hesitation to ask questions, which I worked hard to achieve in my childhood, has been kind of a communication killer in my adult years. I admit, it's pretty ingrained. For example,

I've been conditioned to never ask you about your wedding, your new job, or your pregnancy, but this is not because I'm one-sided. I truly care about people and want to be there for them, and I am. I once flew across the country to support a best friend when she lost her father. I'm genuinely a *for-better-or-worse* kind of friend. I was just trained to believe that asking someone about their life and getting up in their business is nosy and rude—and even stupidly callous—unless I have a green light to do so. When you risk being attacked when asking a question, you learn quickly to restrain, to keep your thoughts to yourself. When I was little, though, I was sharp with curiosity about people, especially about my family, and now that I think of it, curiosity seems to be synonymous with sense of purpose. How are we supposed to follow our passions if we can't first allow ourselves to feel intrigued, stimulated? It makes sense, like Lia, that I reserved all emotion, including excitement, for my taste buds alone. It was, and still is, easier to stay numbed out rather than deal with the racing beat of my heart, avenge my incessant hunger by extinguishing its fire, starting with a pint of Breyers Natural Vanilla. Yep, it's far easier to concern myself with how my steak hits the pan than deal with the *you know what* hitting the fan.

It makes sense to me, being a first-rate jumble of contradictory characteristics, that both my mother and father come from the region of the Adriatic Sea. The whimsical, dreamy landscape of Italy's southeastern coast has somehow yielded a people known for their stubbornly strong and unrelenting determination. In fact, all the way back in 1414, the Melillesi founded their San Sebastiano Church after saving a shipwrecked statue of Saint Sebastian from the port. The statue, says the legend, was carried away by the men of Melilli, the sole Italian males of the region with enough moxie and *oomph* to save the washed-up statue. And the legend, like most around the globe, has been one of many within the dominantly masculine culture, with its ever-affirming self-importance and virility. Meanwhile, it's comparatively hard to find many legends of Sicilian female martyrs, as per the universal norm. The women who are mythically famed (like Saint Agatha, the patron saint of Melilli's neighbor, Catania, Sicily) are remembered mostly for things like taking a vow of virginity and remaining pious, pure, and devoted, *like a good woman should.*

For the Melillesi, the rescued statue of Saint Sebastian is not only a symbol of unwavering faith and religious martyrdom, but also the story of a young Italian boy who was revived after having been declared dead. I might have slightly changed some of the logistics of the story for my own personal bias, but it goes something like this: The youthful and fervent Sebastian is dragged out into the woods for his love of Christ, perceived as dead, and left to rot. Shortly thereafter, he is saved by a local woman, Woman X (note that she doesn't get a saintly title). Woman X, as conditioned (of course), bestows young Sebastian with the entirety of her nursing nourishment. After reviving him, it is not her beneficent generosity that becomes glorified and fabled, but rather the resuscitated little Sebastian, who is considered the saint in the story, of course, *ma certo.* Sebastian goes right back to where he left off, status quo: on the square, pitching his opinions for all the king's men to hear. The healing woman is left unrecognized back in the woods, likely trying to make up for her depleted reserves, maybe emotionally bingeing on maraschino cherries in the forest, doubling her blood sugar level.

For the last one hundred years or so, Middletown has celebrated Saint Sebastian—like Dublin does Saint Patrick—for about a week of partying in May. I'm not the biggest fan of giant crowds these days, aside from joining spiritual-seeking, workshop-attending kinds of crowds, but I did my due diligence in attending Saint Sebastian festivities as a child. The city center becomes filled with white robes and red sashes, as well as waving Sicilian and Italian flags. With pretty much every color associated with Italian restaurant tablecloths and menus, it's like a giant pizzeria. Indulgent feasts, food-eating contests, and Italian bake-offs are punctuated by parades. A group of die-hard Saint Sebastian devotees run in their socks across town while holding overhead miniature statues of his likeliness and chanting in religious devotion. It's like Max Cardio Conditioning after a week of gourmet extravaganza. Evidently, the Middletown residents celebrate the festival of Saint Sebastian harder than the people of Melilli these days, complete with their own century-old San Sebastiano Church, with its own force of nature, *la forza della natura*. As once did its Sicilian sister church, Middletown's center of faith has, at least metaphorically, also called in lost relics from the sea. Lia, it could be said, is a vigilant Saint Sebastian in her own right. My mother, however, unlike the revered statue of Melilli, arrived onshore more than willing to carry her weight on her own as a so-called *immigrant*.

My father, Eugenio Umberto Giovanni—*Gino*, as everyone calls him—made his way to Middletown from the farmlands of Abruzzo, Italy, a coastal region famous for being the greenest in all of Europe, stretching from the Apennine Mountains to the Adriatic coast. My father, like his homeland, is made of equal parts enduring mountain and driven sea. Whether in a mood of even-keeled, calm sea or on-edge rock cliff, Gino maintains one dominant mode. He operates from the historical quintessence of the Abruzzese people, full steam ahead— all tenacity and self-command. For thousands of years, Abruzzo's people, like Melilli's, have been defined by their agrarian lives and a Christianity steeped in reverent symbols of earth, water, and fire. In my eyes, the Abruzzese style of worship and ceremony seems more like paganism than it does modern-day Catholicism. In my early twenties, when I was the first devotee of woo-woo in my extended social circles, I made no parallel that I was only playing a mishmash style of jump rope, like the holy people of Abruzzo. What I mean is that I avoided delineated lines and mixed up my styles of worship, sprinkling a little Jesus Christ here, and a few water spirits and magic animals there. Like my ancestors, I'll mash up who did what, give saints multiple hats to wear, shake up the roles; it's all sacred story in the end.

In May, for example, there is the *Festa dei Serpari* in Abruzzo. It's an honoring of Saint Domenico, the patron saint of toothaches and snakebites. At the same time, the *Festa* also celebrates the magical healing goddess Angitia, worshipped by my most distant relatives, the ancient Italian tribe of the Marci. Here's something interesting about the Marci and me. In the seventies, my dad's sister, Rosa, and I went on our own, private girls' outing to a museum near Abruzzo. My family was mid-visit on an annual trip we made to Italy from Connecticut to see the extended Giovannis and the farmland. Aunt Rosa happened to be intimidatingly smart, a well-educated historian and professor of economics at the University of Abruzzo. More than her significant on-paper accomplishments, the fact Rosa had maintained any trace of empathy despite enduring a mid-twentieth-century Italian Catholic upbringing in my family, well, this was the *real* testament to her intelligence. In fact, Aunt Rosa remained full of conviction and committed to her point of view despite not being taken seriously, and, in my family, that's a Napoleon-level victory. One might say her feelings were disregarded by the cultural Italian *patriarca* until the end of her life in 2015, when she was literally ignored in the Italian hospital. Aunt Rosa complained of discomfort after an operation because her artery had been negligently cut during the surgery. No one listened to her though, because, in my opinion, simply, she was a woman. That was enough to cause attendants to think that her every expression was exaggerated, unimportant, invaluable. Her voice on her dying day, like throughout the rest of her life, was overlooked. She died without the attendants' support, amid the deaf ears of hospital clinicians, simply dismissed. During her life, however, Rosa remained strong despite the misogynistic climate she endured. Not only was she extremely educated, but also, she had a well-developed sixth sense. I'm assuming it was her heightened intuitive awareness that inspired her to bring me to the museum.

Enjoying our private sojourn inside the museum's quiet splendor, I came upon a collection of the currency traded by my snake-worshiping ancestors, the aforementioned Marci, some three hundred years before Christ was born, long before the Italian lira. The silver coin, called a *denarius*, caught my eye, specifically for the profile of a woman whose face resembled my own, carved with precision on its surface. Now, to be clear, I don't often recognize myself in things or people. I generally can't see myself at all. The etching of the coin, therefore, struck me. I felt something like *connection*. This was a new sensation. The woman carved into the denarius was laureled in a leaf crown. Her gaze was regal and fixed—and her expression, simultaneously rich and stalwart. Already chock-full of shoddy self-image, I had never had a sense of my own physical reflection as anything close to being worthy of immortalizing on a coin, but I think the image of this early-era southern Italian woman influenced my first sense of how I should carry myself.

Most of the denarii within the glass encasement were etched with the bodices of powerful women of the times, women with undeniably in-charge countenances, but even the denarii depictions of men, including knights and kings, looked feminine to me. In fact, the Italian horses etched in midjump on the metal coins seemed wildly female, alive with magic. There was obviously something going on before the dawn of the androcentric *lordship* I'd been born into, something that deemed all things female as being worthy of reverence. In the tiny museum in Campli, I felt resolute looking at these coins, filled, even back then, with the sense that anything I wanted should be mine, especially anything that was deemed off-limits. I made a vow that I would own all the coins under the glass one day, in my own house. I'd trade in for them my Chatty Cathy Dolls, which I looked nothing like.

The coins, with their imperfect, pancake-shaped edges and matriarchal images, in retrospect, stirred my Italian roots, shoots, and fragrant senses. Art has always been a means for one generation to communicate to the next, and, like this, I was handed something there. It was my own saving grace. I was struggling on that particular trip for reasons I'd not the emotional vocabulary to articulate. Where my own emotional intelligence failed, Aunt Rosa took up slack. I assume she recognized my suffering because it resembled the same she'd carried, as we'd both been oppressively belittled by male leaders in our family. During that farm visit to Italy, I'd vacated myself, whether by shrinking within or spiritually ejecting into the great etheric unknown. This was my typical response when in the vicinity of my grandfather or his land. I'd watched all the women in my family do the same, even my grandmother, Vicenza, who was *tough as nails.*

If Lia was a steamroller, Vicenza was a nuclear land mine. But even fierce old Vicenza retracted under my grandfather's regime. We became deflated beings inside bodies that while they still functioned, feared to feel anything outside of our family's accepted anger-infused dialect. This was the currency of how we powered through and between events, how we protected and defended ourselves, both inside and outside our tribal walls.

The male Giovanni elders, despite appearing no larger than the normal-sized, finely dressed Abruzzese people, somehow pulled off wielding intimidating authority simply by stepping into the room. This intimidation was fierce and, to say the least, not so wonderful for a young girl to be around. By the time I was mature enough, though, I was able to observe my grandfather's life through a lens of compassion. I was able to strip away the scary parts, the confusing parts, and see him as simply an outcome of his era. When it came to nature versus nurture, he didn't stand much of a developmental chance. While the details of his early life are for the most part unknown, it's certain my grandfather was at the center of Abruzzo's political and environmental upheaval, including World War I, bloodshed, and POW camps, and (in case that wasn't enough) a devastating earthquake that swallowed around one hundred thousand civilians. This drama was a bit more obviously life-or-death than my own, more than half a world away and over half a century later, but it was sweetly handed down to me through inherited neurological impulses. It's amazing how long the effects of war actually last, if they ever go away at all, right? Interestingly, my grandfather's name actually translates to the word for *being constant* (Constanza), appropriate to his character as he survived the erratic climate of Italy in the first half of the 1900s without collapse. And by the time Constanza was ten, he'd secured his principles, an unwritten rulebook more essential than the Bible itself. His unwritten rules went something like: Life was about winning, no matter what. One should assume and maintain an unwavering opinion until death, and firmly hold one's head high. One should never accept losing, shed no tears, and emit no terms of endearment. Ever. In early twentieth-century Italy, Mother Earth swallowed men via two main monstrosities: battleground (which claimed more than six hundred thousand Italian lives in World War I alone) or the 1915 earthquake (which dissolved thirty thousand Abruzzese people into dust). That 6.7 Richter scale catastrophe struck the very day of my grandfather's tenth birthday, January 13, 1915. Perhaps the quake was the earth's way of protesting men's misuse of her power; however, my grandfather responded only by imitation, eye for an eye, fire for fire. He'd acquire his own tremulous skills of shattering others' foundations and shaking his family to their core.

To be honest, I have a hard time referring to my grandfather either by his given name, Constanza, or just at all, in general. Usually when his name is brought up, I give a kind of GG-style *uh-huh* and then gaze somewhere else, compose to-do lists, sort out a various pile of accumulating things in my kitchen, etcetera. I suppressed most of my memories of him for longer than Italy endured Mussolini's Fascism. You know what they say in spiritual self-help programs though, *What you resist persists.* If I consider my grandfather a major obstacle in my early emotional life, I can also recognize how trial leads to opportunity for triumph, and how blocks can hold the very key to recovery. I'll give Constanza this, at least. He has been a constant catalyst in my own healing journey, and through healing mine, perhaps this somehow helps heal the greater wounds of war and patriarchy. Perhaps one woman's healing path of self-nourishment helps to mend the places where men have fallen out of sync with Mother Earth herself.

Where I may have had it rough, Aunt Rosa endured being my

grandfather's only daughter, which is something I can't even imagine surviving. Rosa was the sole girl within a quartet of siblings steered by the riddled, aggressive atmosphere of wartime Italy. Coming into the world during the years between World War I and World War II in Europe was like being born between a rock and hard place. It wasn't exactly the luckiest time to incarnate, and it sure didn't cater to the faint of heart. If one was going to be born at that time on the Adriatic coast, well, she'd pretty much need to be made out of rock and hard places herself. Rosa acquired significant distinguished titles in her attempt for independence in those days, and the more learned she became, the more she was labeled *crazy, troubled*, or *unstable*. My aunt, however, was actually the most established intellect of her entire family, ultimately with the most degrees and prestige. Who knows, maybe the denarii had once inspired her as well, with her eagerness to find a female role model wherever she could.

As much as I'd found a likeness to myself in the Marci's denarii, if my own profile resembled one side of Abruzzo's ancient coins, my father's likeness would likely be on the flip side, because we are two sides of the same coin. Like Italy's notorious shepherds command their flocks of sheep, Gino excels in the business of organizing his team and building structures for profit. My Abruzzo flavor, however, is a little less strategized. In my business, I prefer to manage things intuitively, like a sage farmer. I'll feel it out—sow a seed here, hoe a weed there. Where I may fail in discerning true hunger pangs, work is the area in which my instincts allow me to thrive. On the Atlantic coast, here in Connecticut, my father and I have both applied our inherited Abruzzese tenacity to figuring out how to make something from nothing. Instead of collecting tree fruit from the land, Gino taught his children how to collect real estate ventures, to be unafraid of the rise and fall of the economic terrain and tide.

My father was the oldest of four siblings, and like most Italian young men—particularly in the years of Mussolini—he learned to never question the patriarch of the family. If my mom is emotionally hard to read, my father is like the Houdini of concealing feelings. Gino is the very spirit of strong Italian caliber: impeccable taste, unreadable face, and strategies that are always more effective than anyone's. He is a master of smiling during difficult business conversations and of appearing unaltered by his environment. Gino engrained within us his sacred principles the first time we dared to appear timid in front of him. *Don't be afraid of them! Make them afraid of you!* Forget about encouraging any kind of mindful communication style; Gino's ethical perspective lacked the capacity for nonviolent language. He knew how to one-up someone in any situation, and that was enough interpersonal dialogue for him to succeed, *capisce.*

For two years, German forces took over my grandfather's farmhouse in Abruzzo as a base of operations, the single instance government trumped patriarch in our family's history. Imaginably, this forceful acquisition of my family's home and land was a period of extreme emasculation for the Giovanni men, one that likely affected my grandfather's psyche well beyond the duration of the war. As much as Gino was taught never to question his father, the head of the family, watching German officials invasively wield their authority over the family's land and lives would've had to have been confounding for Gino. There he was, in his early teens witnessing his father, whose authority he'd assumed was unshakeable, relinquish his position as head of the table to the proclaimed Axis Powers. The Giovannis, without choice, made room for the uniformed German officers at their dining room table. During these years, the family members, reduced to servants within their own home, fed an army of men who reaped the provisions of their seasonal labor. With assumed entitlement, the soldiers pulled up their chairs for supper, reached into the bread basket, ate like hungry dogs, and left the dishwashing for the "kitchen maid." No one digested the situation verbally. The discomfort of mealtime remained unspoken, though it was subliminally imprinted on Gino's mind and thus subtly passed down to mine. Like this, I pull up to the drive-through, charge powerfully through the checkout window, and ignore the whole situation, bullied all the same by forces I can't control. The wartime situation, for my father, also beyond his control, significantly threatened his sense of foundational security, however unable he was (both at age thirteen and afterward) to emotionally comprehend. Home would forever thereafter be a place Gino perceived as high risk, a zone to ardently defend. Somehow, his business sense must have then awakened. My father would be cunning and careful to always remain an Axis Power in his own world, an army of one. Aside from his father, to whom he'd remain forever empathic and always defend by basic Italian law, Gino would never fold to another's mandate. He'd be the maker of his own mandates.

Maybe in a way, after the war, after arriving in America at age twenty-four, Gino had already pledged to be an unstoppable character, one who'd never hand over the head of his table. In fact, he'd never have just one table, no way. Somewhere in his secret inner world, maybe between the Mediterranean and the Atlantic while heading to America aboard the *Christopher Columbus*, he vowed to prosper. While my mother had tossed her cookies into the Port of Gibraltar, Gino gathered an appetite of unstoppable stamina. He would build table after table, in restaurant after restaurant. He would never go hungry, and he'd always be entitled to more. Furthermore, he'd preside over his business, always retaining the position of primary capitalizer of the harvest. Unlike his father, who was forced to hand over the family's provisions since he'd lost rank in his own home, Gino would lucratively gain in sharing the fruits of his labor. He'd employ those who, like himself, had recently arrived in Connecticut from their own war-torn countries. He'd model wealth. He'd invest in multiple properties, ensure his security, and always remain one step ahead with an eye for any enemies, near or afar. He had cleverly become a king in his own hard-earned dynasty, never folding in fear to anyone or anything—not the bank, not the stock market, no one in uniform, and definitely not his wife or daughters. Aboard the *Christopher Columbus*, Gino used the ocean waves as a kind of hypnosis. Peering into the future, he removed all fallible language from his vocabulary.

My mother and father rarely speak of their childhood years in Italy in terms of literal history, outside of referencing the food at the epicenter of our heritage. It's not surprising then that I'd grasp, in self-lost moments, for food when attempting to locate some central part of myself. My mother can bring you into the inner kitchen of her Italian soul, provide you with an intoxicating description of how to thinly slice blood oranges. She'll make you long for real marmalade and ache for custard gelato, forcing you to forever believe it far outranks ice cream and destroying your ability to look forward to a trip to Baskin-Robbins. These missing Italian food staples became our sole acknowledged tender emotions, the only way to gauge how we're doing.

I do my one-second self-inquiry, the GG-style of checking in:

GG, how do you feel today? Are you longing for sweet, creamy things? No? Then, I determine, *you're good.*

I've dealt with my inherited repercussions of expatriation through consumptive obsession, my most recent being whole milk by the gallon. I've found myself drinking a plethora of glasses daily, refilling my fridge multiple times a week, and in so doing, determining which market promised the best, thickest, milk-moustache-y satisfaction. True to Giana-style analysis, I initially assumed I was reliving a past life as a milkmaid. Then I figured I might be experiencing latent outrage for having never healthily latched, for having gone unfortified by my mother's own milk. Now that I've put the pieces together here, however, it's more likely that I have taken on my Sicilian mother's craving for gelato. Simply put, the creamy, sugary stuff tastes fricking good! It tastes like safety, like *forever*, like *love*, like *home*. As an empath and a good daughter, I've done my mother a favor, she'll never have to deal with any future cravings; I'll keep them alive myself.

Yes, Lia can make even a non-Italian nostalgic for the eastern coast of Sicily, giving precise directions for preparing seafood antipasto, seeped in heavenly *agrodolce,* the regal Italian sweet-and-sour sauce of perfection that reaches all the right parts of the tongue. Raw shrimp, raw oysters, her Sicily is all unquestionably sea-and-farm-to-table, so different than American living—and how she's earned her American fortune. In fact, life in early twentieth-century agricultural Italy revolved entirely around the cultivation of food—whether it was growing the food, selling the food, preparing, cooking, conversing about the food, or—when times became hard—rationing the food. Food was the beginning and the endpoint of all endeavors, the expression of wealth. You took your time with food, making it *right.* Any and all socializing, without exception, was to be done around a large and consumable display. Friendships between farmers were based on an exchange of generosities, one often outdoing the other. *The Furcis will bring their fresh slaughter over for Christmas this year, so we'll gift them with enough olive oil to last until spring!* It was like this. For hundreds of years, farmers' markets marked the place where lovers first swooned, where wedding dates were decided upon, concessions were made in local politics. At the market, the seeds of hot *peperoncini* coexisted alongside the seeds of revolution. Seemingly everything grew out of agriculture: social customs, cultural celebrations, education, industry. The quality of crops determined celebratory, or else, sorrowful seasons. Even if you were a hardworking farming man, an expert of the field, you knew how to cut fresh pasta because you were put in the kitchen with your grandmother when you were able to crawl, and she was the real queen of the land. You were trained to work from the start. She cultivated your dexterity, with a rolling pin as your first play toy, rounding and flattening dough in your high chair. Grandmother preoccupied you with work when you'd cry or complain. Keeping the hands occupied was the Italian answer, the salvation. On the farm, there were no toys; there were tools. It's a cliché, but it's true. A baby's first words in rural Italian farmland were *mama, acqua, pasta.* Even *my* first word was *pasta,* but the following two were probably more like *cookie* and *bread.* I probably got around to saying *mom* and *dad* only after I'd managed *sugar, coco, cake, chips,* and a dozen or so

GIANA "FIRST WORDS"

words falling under the umbrella of carbohydrates.

America, in those early days, opened its gates as promised, permitting naturalization for all Italians (and regional Sicilians) born between 1931 and 1937, and this included Gino and Lia. My mother lived with her aunt until she could send for her mother and father, my *nonna* and *nonno* (Italian for *grandmother* and *grandfather*). The fruit of Lia's hard work in both the button factory and later, the Goodyear company, where she made rubber-soled tennis shoes, afforded Nonna and Nonno's travel fare from Melilli. For the next year, after hustling to manifest her parents' relocation, Lia fixed her attention on financing her teenage brothers and sisters' move to Middletown. I'm not sure about the green card logistics at that time, but somehow all the di Carlos squeezed into a home together, like many other Melillese families in the row houses of Middletown. Nonna joined her daughter in the Connecticut workforce, laboring for her new life and the lives of her children, who, aside from the eldest, Lia, were all under the age of fifteen.

Did the family miss their farmland? Did they speak of the absence of blood oranges in the spring, the impossibility of finding pine nuts akin to the ones in real pesto? Did they collectively bring up the strangeness of buying premade mayonnaise filled with handfuls of additional preservatives? Or did they find new pleasures to overtake old affinities, shoving down the past in fixatives like television— trading in their love of *scacciata siciliana* for episodes of *The Ed Sullivan Show?*

When Lia was twenty-one, she met Gino at the wedding-reception dinner of a Melillese friend. He was intrigued by her, as were Lia's numerous suitors. Pipe-shaped curls framed my mother's face, her skin flawless from years of washing with farmland olive soap. However, Lia had something more than physical beauty; she had the backbone of a woman who'd survived, who'd made it on her own, and who—as a sixteen-year-old—was capable of rescuing an entire farm and its people from destitution. My mother didn't need to try to impress any man because she had *grit*.

She emitted a kind of integrity only endurance affords, and her confidence attracted men. Through pheromones, Gino connected to the perfume of Lia's vigilance, which he recognized as familiar. Lia was perhaps less seduced by any perceptible scent of Gino, and was led, rather, by her street smarts. Gino fit Lia's standards: he was hardworking and college-educated, and his family owned farmland in southern Italy. To find an industrious mate was enough. Magic, chemistry—the promise of these factors had been vanquished around the time she'd tucked Vicenza Camela's rosary beads into the corner of her Middletown bedroom's bureau drawer. Lia understood the transactional nature of working relationships and considered each of her male suitors more in the way one might assess a possible business deal. My mother sized up my father's potential long-term durability, determining the likelihood of their collective success in growing a family. Gino, it appeared, was a significant contender.

CHAPTER 3

Il Bocconcino, La Bambina

Within three months, Gino had secured Lia's hand in the traditional way: he'd asked her parents for their permission, and then, more or less, let her know the plan. Before taking the plunge and saying *I do*, she called on her girlfriend, the wife of Gino's doctor. As a measure of practicality, my mother wanted to first confirm my father's "plumbing" was equipped to make a family, which was her Italian Catholic priority. To her delight, all signs pointed to yes; the partnership promised to yield a strong crop of children.

Lia took seriously the job of making a family, because just two years later, in 1960, I was born. Giana Clara Giovanni; the first of the di Carlo–Giovanni offspring. Amazingly, I wasn't born even a bit overweight, evidently having been able to pull off a successful diet in utero. Straight out of the womb, naked as I came, I didn't seem to have any issues of feeling awkward, fat, or in the way. I even risked a wailing announcement of my arrival, born with a naturally brave sense of self-expression like most babies. It was 1960 though, and—like many newborns in the hospital protocols of the day—I was taken immediately from my mother's breast and carted off to another room by my lonesome, where I would be *less of an encumbrance*. I was actually delivered by my mother's cousin Antonino, part of the Melillese brood of Sicilians who'd made their way to Connecticut, and a doctor to boot. True to the controlling patriarchy of the family, my first moves were determined by a male. He properly sorted out the affair: snip, wrap, and package. All new life, whether calf or lamb or child, was manhandled through the traditional system of Italian farmland politics; affairs were to be spearheaded by the maestros of agribusiness. Usher the newborn foal out to pasture from the start, letting her know who is in charge.

Lia and Gino's offspring was less like their baby and more like a symbol of their new life on the American frontier. I was a *zuppa minestrone*, the genetic cross-pollination of my parents' heirloom Italian gardens. But instead of becoming a flower child of the sixties, I would become the expression of the upheaval both my mother and father had repressed over the last years—for when in survival mode in a new country, one must apply all zeal toward securing a new life. I would also be my parents' scapegoat. I'd take on their fear of failure so that they could remain shamelessly on track. I'd exemplify unruliness so they could fit in. Apparently, I signed up to be the recipient of Lia's and Gino's discarded feelings and process all of them *like a mofo*. And for my family, I'd contain all of the refused emotions. Heck, I'd hold all of Italy's refused emotions.

I acclimated to life on earth, and less than two years later, my sister, Francesca Livia, was born. My sister was somehow a gentler expression of my parents' merged DNA, or, at least, it always seemed to me she somehow had it easier, lived with less inner tumult. I think my early personality even formed, somehow, around making sure this would be so. She'd be safe. I elected to be the fussy child, to get in trouble; this way, no one would take their aggression out on my sister. Quite immediately, the two of us became GG (me) and Frankie (her), and often times, a hyphenate: *GG-Frankie, go downstairs*! The monikers made sense, since my father probably would have preferred two boys off the bat. Our shortened nicknames securely neutered all sense of our girlhood from the start.

Our first years of life in Middletown were spent living like a pack of Italian sardines, a Mediterranean full-bodied menagerie, nested in a two-floor home my parents purchased for the entirety of my mother's extended family. Downstairs, to me, was the safe-haven half of the house. This was where Nonna and Nonno lived, plus all of my "elder" aunts and uncles (who felt classifiably *adult* to young Frankie and I, but who were, in reflection, between the wise, old ages of ten and fifteen). My mother's siblings were still youthful enough to be our downstairs playmates and were willing to entertain our not-yet-squelched imaginations. Their attention outweighed whatever meager amount we received from our ever-busy parents since Lia and Gino's sense of play was, at most, pressing go on their own survival-mode buttons before jumping off to conquer Connecticut.

My sister and I have almost no memory of spending any time with either of our parents in our earliest days. Our grandmother, Nonna, cooked our meals before she jetted off to her factory job, dutifully preparing one of three options: chicken soup, pizza, or a basic pasta dish. There was no homemade *agliata* (garlic sauce), no ricotta and marjoram *conchiglie* with a regional fig-infused balsamic reduction, no lime-and-parsley-buttered fresh fish, or any of the dishes I would later identify as the taste of Italy. Still, Nonno fed us what Nonna made because he was home. There was some reason, never really disclosed to us, that Nonno wasn't able to work, and, typical of all our female Italian ancestors, Nonna would handle everybody's needs while remaining behind her man. She'd cook, clean, earn the family's keep, and repeat. This was the way of the early years: Frankie and I making sure to never disturb my mother and father, and remain entertained by the aunts and uncles flying around. On a good day, something might make us laugh. Nonna, Lia, and Gino would come home after a hard day's labor, and if we hadn't been tucked into bed yet, our parents would *yell* us to sleep, demanding our repose. Then the sun would again rise, and we'd go through the same routine the next day.

My mother likes to remind me that, in stark contrast to my obsession with food as an adult, I refused to eat virtually anything in my first years. To this, I'll just say, during a particularly powerful therapeutic-energy session, I went into a deep childhood regression and recalled one of my very first memories. There I was, baby Giana, brand spanking new and genuinely innocent, ready for joy. But I was confined to my highchair, bullied with a wooden spoon, threatened to be hit if I refused a bite of the Gerber baby food, or whatever edible concoction sat before me. More than fifty years later, I can still remember how overwhelmed and invisible I felt in the energy of my environment. I could not arouse an appetite at someone's command. Plus, how is a child supposed to locate her physical hunger if she has vacated her body?

When I later began to decode my own internal eating dialogue, I was mesmerized to discover a type of inner wooden-spoon-striker still there, stalking my psyche. I'd been the perfect Pavlovian child, responding to a command even if the punitive threat no longer actually existed. On the onset of my binges, the wooden-spoon voice in my brain demands, *Eat it! Eat it now! Eat it or else*, controlling me as it barks its caustic orders. The auditory playback ensures my wrongness, its tone the automated sum of all stern authority combined. *How hard*, the voice insists, *I've worked so that you can have the option to eat as much as you can, and so you should*. I've no choice then; I have to eat it all, consume everything, even eat these words.

Some people's first memory is the literal sensation of feeling grass under their feet, excitedly boarding the kindergarten school bus, or freely dancing in their living room, but mine is not a feeling. It's a visual, though not through my own eyes. I'm hovering outside myself, watching. I can see my body freeze, my brain shut out input, my senses plug in a response to my mother's forceful demand. The spoon becomes a conduit, informing my nervous system to adopt the same physiological response Lia had to turbulence, forced into a new life, sans appetite, aboard the ocean liner *Vulcania*. We are more alike than I'd considered: in times of unpredictable stress, Lia and I could switch off our hunger gauge, shutting down all desire for food. In my infanthood, my refusal of food was the only proactive stance to take toward peaceful revolution, like Gandhi. Just as my mother's first years were laden with warfare and aggression, I, too, set off to battle from the start, heading into my own private war with food.

However, even the most cunning of growing girls cannot forever keep up self-starvation as a tactical strategy. As the story goes— around the age of five, on a family vacation, I laid down my arms. Submitting to hunger, I became ravenous, crying over what I insisted was *starvation*. Somewhere near Toronto, says Lia, I consented to the customs of my heritage, first waking a desire for pasta—and with a ferocious demand. After that, the food tug-of-war was on. I existed solely between the state of forcibly putting food out of my mind and the state of fixating on delivering food to my mouth. Like Sicily's politics in the forties, life became a swinging pendulum for me, aligning to polar states. Rather than listening to the dizzying voices of my inner turmoil, I survived by checking out. *Hi, I'm Giana Giovanni, and I only know about extremes. Piacere di conoscerti—nice to meet you.*

Honestly, I've done enough spiritual work to have nearly branded into my frontal lobe *Be here now* and have repeated the mantra *The past is gone* more times than any Italian Giuseppe has answered his mobile with the declarative *Pronto*. So, believe me, by now, nearly in my sixth decade, I'd prefer to feel more oriented to my current, comfortable address than the coordinates of an awkward adolescence. But, in even beginning to mindfully observe the mechanics of my own eating mentality, I have seen, despite how *present moment* I aspire to be, that some part of my brain–body system does not differentiate this moment of now from what occurred years ago (despite how I blur together segments of these first decades, and surely have my own biased, even thwarted, memory). For better or for worse, in my mind, the childhood chapters in my life feel as recent as my recollection of seeing myself awaken this morning as Giana, age fifty-nine, dreading/ anticipating her personal trainer—always the observer.

In the early years, Lia and Gino set the Giovanni pace. Together, they maximized high-adrenaline output, living in an operational state of survival, exemplary immigrants. After we'd made the most of our Middletown double-decker, *stacker* of a home, living elbow-to-elbow with all the Melillese relatives on my mother's side, we made our big move to Bridgewood. Frankie was three, and I was five. Gino was in the early launch phase of his real estate career while working in restaurants, and my mother was a *key puncher*, the term used back then for one who enters data from paper into machines, a form of factory labor in the 1960s. The move to Bridgewood was justified by my parents' practical need to be closer to work, but really, Lia was ready for some breathing room in order to whittle down her obligations of servitude—fewer mouths to finance. Though we maintained a weekly overnight visit to Nonna's, just north on the Merritt Parkway, moving to Bridgewood was like moving to another planet. Somehow, I remember our new house as perpetually dark, isolated. There were no extended buffers of guardian grandparents, aunts, or uncles at home to fortify us with any inkling of playful glee. And while my sister and I felt immediately deflated by the change in our home's atmosphere, my mother gloated. Finally, her life had begun. She may have left Melilli by ship when she was sixteen, but now she was twenty-eight years old and aboard a new vessel, claiming her flag-waving American independence, setting sail from our extended family. She'd done enough to provide for them, to economically support their emancipation for more than five years. Just as she'd prepared to take the vows of cloistered life in Melilli, young Lia had been forced by her family to take a different vow of economic responsibility, which had now been made complete. She'd left her homeland, her farm had been viably saved, and her family had been sent over and set up in America. Plus, Lia had sacrificed most of her childhood and teenage years taking care of others within a harsh political climate. She could wash her hands of her past working responsibilities and look forward to a fresh future.

The now-married, fully adult Lia had her own immediate family to consider, and by American standards, she wanted to thrive, not just *survive*. My mother tacitly made up her own *new rules of family*. Hosting large meals at our house was to be avoided if possible, and keeping visitors astray, preferable. Even Gino's father, my grandfather, who visited a few times in my elementary school years, was eventually turned away from long stays at the Giovanni home. This was an early point of contention between my parents, as Gino was an authentic Abruzzesi, trained to treat his father with unwavering respect and servitude. However, Lia must have made a strong case, because after I turned eight, my grandfather stopped coming to Connecticut for long visits. We mostly saw him after that only on his own farmland, in Abruzzo. I knew Lia's choice had something to do with me, but I couldn't really comprehend what—at least, not for another half century. No biggie, just fifty years of inexplicable underlying tension and feeling a kind of haunted sense of being hated, questioned, troublesome, shamed. But the important thing was to oblige the family rule, and this included never digging backward or processing. Life's passageways were to be forged in one direction only: straight ahead.

But about Lia, don't get me wrong. My mother is a genuinely loved woman in her community, and even in our extended family, she is considered by many to be charismatic, generous, even funny. She is more than precious; she is a whole mountain of preciousness, unmined with a bejeweled, gemmy center. I'm not trying to be two-faced or exploitive here; I'm really attempting to fairly reflect on the pieces that informed the mechanisms of my behavior, particularly how the heck I deal with eating, in the hopes of adopting some new healthy habits. Just to clarify here, I wouldn't trade in Lia for any other kind of mother. I was incredibly fortunate to have been instilled with such a strong business sense, especially as a woman—and this came from Lia as well as Gino. I would be an incredibly ungrateful bitch to fail to recognize the sacrifice both of my parents made in the name of our prosperity, the opportunities they provided for their children. Still, during the years we were growing up, my mother channeled some serious Mussolini-like authority in our house (second only to my father's skillful domination, which we were encouraged to fear). Lia demanded we keep all of our playthings tucked away—*no messes, or else*. In general, we were allowed to leave zero trace of our existence, in terms of our stuff being left out on display. This might totally sound like fair, even effective child-rearing, but I'm not talking about your typical run-of-the-mill parental call to order when it comes to how my mother operated. Her commands were gunfire. Both Frankie and I remember her tone as severe, threatening. Through extreme intimidation, she engrained in us the importance of pushing hard, of making a beeline for adulthood. Since my mother had been starved of her own childhood, her daughters would also be deprived of theirs. There was no time to be a child; there was only time to *get ready, be responsible, do it all*. By Lia's standards, we should've been able to make our own dinner by the first grade because she had cut pasta from flour before she was seven years old, had even carried the wheat to the granary. Because Lia's childhood was really just one long work shift in dutiful family service, her girls would, at the very least, figure out how to warm up their own stove-top frozen dinners and get food into their own mouths. Anyway, Lia resolved, this was the land of independence; she certainly was not going to pick up after us.

One Saturday afternoon, the summer before I started kindergarten, I was in the garage, directed by Lia to carry out some random chore I'd inevitably be scolded for doing insufficiently, a chore probably too mature for the small hands of a five-year-old. The details are fuzzy, but what remains clear to me, however, was seeing my father pull up in his Pontiac. Typical of his heavy-handed style, Gino floored it up the driveway as though he were taking off for a race. Somehow, he managed to smoothly arrive at a standstill by the time he'd reached the garage door entrance, always with mechanical grace. Usually, I'd do everything I could to get out of the way as soon as possible if I was in eyesight since I believed I was the object of his disdain. But he did the thing my father does when he singles out someone. Just one slight half lift of his index finger in an arched type of pointing and, like anyone under his attack, I was trapped, fly on paper. I figured I was about to be scolded, so I braced myself with an anesthetizing brain-freeze, having already mastered that reaction. I prepped for an emotional blow. However, the following shock, while significant, was the opposite of what I'd expected. Instead of being shunned and shot down, Gino went to the back of his Pontiac. He popped the trunk and lifted out a twenty-inch Schwinn Junior, cobalt blue with a white basket and colored flags dripping off of the handlebars. This was a bike made for a kid at least a few heads taller than me, and at least twice my age. But Gino, still pointing his knobby Abruzzese finger, gave me a long look. This was a Gino look I'd never personally received, but which I'd seen him give other men in the family. It read like, *Uncle Sam wants you for his army*, and I was recruited. In my handful of years on the planet, this was the first moment I'd experienced something like fatherly care, and at once, I was fortified, headstrong, and determined to make him proud of me. Even though to this day I struggle to discern between one sensation from another in my body, I still clearly remember the feeling in my stomach back then. It was like suddenly having a floor installed in a house that had been built without one.

In the garage, looking right at me, Gino's face was as hard to read as always, combining something resembling a grin with a rather serious expression, yielding a forever-uninterpretable look. Was my father irritated or jovial as he parked the bike at my side? Steel green, close-set eyes countered the unreadable smile my father permanently wore, even while conducting business. That smile rendered his face charismatic, even handsome. While some curmudgeonly men have naturally down-turned lips, giving them *resting jerk face*, Gino's lips relaxed naturally upward, effusing a kind of glow, a kind of *I've got this* air, giving him *resting champ face*. I think my dad's seemingly amused facial expression allowed him to play all cards to his advantage. He came off as friendly, even infectiously so, and yet he was a fearless rider of life's most rogue waves. This is what thrilled him. In ways, his drive was rebellious. He'd edge toward making his fortune from the most unexpected investments rather than from safe moves. As much as he monitored my every move, he simultaneously modeled rebellion to me through the success of his *I'll do it my own way* attitude. Meanwhile, Frankie and I tiptoed around Gino while unquestionably following the laws he'd laid down. We might've rolled our eyes behind our mother's back, flared our nostrils, but when Gino roared, we'd gather together to make sense of our next steps. *What does Dad want us to do? How can we perform perfectly?* We walked in his footsteps, as expected. In so many ways, for better or for worse, Gino's children have built their own mini-empires from the giant business plan he designed. Our father did pave our paths.

We learned early on to fear Gino. Our mom taught us to do so through her own body language. While every married couple must endure their moments of disagreement, Lia and Gino argued with a kind of Italian ferocity, and ultimately, Lia would always fold to Gino. We were conditioned to do the same. It was something of an order of command typical of 1967. Gino would take out his disdain on Lia, she'd give it to us, and we'd give it to ourselves—dominoes. Life in an Italian family in mid-twentieth-century New England retained the inarguable patriarchy that is popular worldwide. For this reason, all of Gino's girls, my mother included, subtly acted out to either rebuke his reign, win his attention, or beg his pardon. As stern and demanding as my mother was as a female role model, never allowing her children to be spoiled, overly praised, or treated with kid gloves, my father entirely steered her mood. However strong of a point to prove Lia brought to the table, my father possessed the winning hand. For someone as much of a survivor and champion fighter as Lia, whose soul and spirit was, in fact, equally strong as Gino's (if not stronger), this was an unspoken torture for her. Strangely though, my parents' twisted dynamic was the very energy that fed the core of their relationship, as per the norm of the *match-made-in-heaven* marriage model of the 1960s. Because an equal weigh-in of voice and value was simply not possible in the era's husband–wife prescribed relationship, the flame of their passion had no choice other than to agitate as it seduced. Love, commitment, and passion, in our family, had to be laced with fury. This way, we were all free to channel the exhaust from our overly gassed-up Italian drive with cutting remarks, curt directions, and bold honesty teetering on the edge of verbal abuse.

Understandably, with such a daunting leader at our helm, I felt a real thrill when Gino wheeled the Schwinn Junior to my side, presenting me with my first vehicle. I awkwardly bounced from one foot to another, breathlessly letting out an *Oh my gosh!* and *I love it!*—a rare utterance of glee for little Giana. As though on cue, Lia walked into the garage. She must have smelled my happiness as my dad lowered the kickstand at my side while I admired the handsome, shiny-blue machine between us, deeply immersed in the moment.

What in God's name is that?! Lia demanded. *Whose is that? You didn't get that for Giana, did you?*

Lia glared at Gino, their typical foreplay, making a face that read like a curse word.

Gino gave Lia a slow-motion nod, like a Tarantino villain playing out his seductive power just before killing someone.

GG should know how to ride a bike, Lia. It's good exercise. I didn't have a bike, and now Giana is going to be able to get herself around.

The impetus for Gino's gift was the same as any other instance in which he flexed his wealth: everything with which he materially provided his children was compensation for how he'd been deprived.

After their seductive slights, Lia and Gino went at it, yelling at each other at top volume. Their love-hate could make anyone want to scream, *Get a room!* I lived in the next room though, and I knew that even if they made it to their bedroom, the house would still shake with aggressive firings. My parents didn't dare bring up any real issues, including their wavering trust in one another and fears they had about their growing family, or the lack of deep communication between them. It was easier to let surface the little pieces of rubbish symbolizing the larger debris. In our family, processing relationships for the sake of improvement or resolve didn't exist. *Things are fine, actually they're great—and no one here will change because no one here will ever admit they need to, ever, because no one here is up for making a real effort to show up differently.* If we had peace, then what would be left to hold us together? Volatility was all my Italian parents had known as the instigator of life's circumstances.

As per the norm, as soon as I felt I was in the line of my parents' fire, I ran straight to the safe harbor of my room. A few hours later, once the sun had gone down, it became apparent that no one realized my feelings had been hurt, and no one had noticed I'd disappeared. No one was coming to get me to apologize or, at least, invite me to do something. This typical routine of finding myself left alone to sort out my entire reality is probably why, these days, I hire all the help I can. For all the years in which I was isolated, attempting to tend to my own discomfort and unsuccessfully self-soothing, I've compensated by employing fitness trainers, massage therapists, personal organizers, handymen, and hairstylists. But then, back in Bridgewood, held captive in childhood, no one came for me. While trying to figure out how to deal with my childhood needs, I made a decision—one that felt like a solid plan to me. No matter what, if anyone ever told me *You can't do it*, if anyone ever told me *No way*, I would prove them wrong. Inadvertently, left alone in my room, I made dismissal and rejection the fuel for my ambitious achievements. I signed up, Ladies and Gents, to require rejection as ammo for my purpose and to fight pleasure and acceptance as the enemies of my drive. I'd get on that bike and I'd ride my way to another place, some space where I didn't have to deal with anyone yelling, a place where people did things differently, said nice things to one another.

After enough hours of plotting my bike-riding strategy for the days ahead, I grew hungry and went downstairs to find a cold patty of Saturday night's flavor of Hamburger Helper on the counter. "Ready-made" was on tap in my house during my adolescent days (I'll give Lia this culinary credit). After eating two tepid patties, I went out to the garage. The sun was setting and Lia and Gino were nowhere in sight. With the kickstand still down, I rolled the big-kid bike to one side of the garage and leaned it securely against the concrete wall. With my little Giana-sized bare feet, I climbed up the side of the bike frame until I could straddle it. Once I'd accomplished this, I stretched my toes down to the pedals; they barely touched. *Tomorrow, I decided, I'll make my way to the street, practicing when my mother isn't around.* It was the 1960s, a time when helmets made people think of World War II or football players. They weren't necessary for ambitious third graders; let a girl skin her chin! So I worked, day after obsessive day, without a helmet or training wheels, pedaling and falling until I was gliding—a tiny, grinning Giana on a Schwinn Junior. Lia finally consented (of course) to Gino's present, and by the time autumn hit and I turned six, I'd acquired significant scars, but I'd also mastered my first wheels. Cruising my new bike up the street, I'd proven my own method of freedom; Lia's *no*, or any *no* from there on, for that matter, would be my ticket to *Yes-ville*. From that day on, I'd always have my escape plan, be in charge of my destination; vehicles would come to symbolize security. Even to this day, I drive myself to all events. I remain self-assured that my own wheels can take me away at any moment I deem it necessary. My personal principles were formed around my unwavering rule: "I won't ever be held back by anyone's *No*." This mindset worked perfectly then, rendering me triumphant in being a proud five-year-old, free of training wheels. Years later, at Cumberland Farms, the same inability to hear any kind of *no*, including my own, had taken over my whole system. I had refused *no* so fiercely,

I couldn't even abide my own set limits. When I'd attempt a healthy-eating mindset, reciting, *I don't need it; I shouldn't have it,* retaliation would soon set in. *You can't forbid me,* I'd surely argue, *I'll take two, plus extra hot sauce; just watch me.* I'd fight with my inner voice, bullying myself internally, if Lia wasn't there to prove me wrong.

Eventually, my fierce bicycling would lead me to additional rebellious adventures. Theoretically, I was only allowed to ride my bike to the end of the street, but I somehow ventured to the variety store, the ice-cream parlor, and then wherever the kids were getting in trouble. Pedals underfoot, I was like Jacques Anquetil, the guy who'd won the Tour de France five times, unrivaled. Frankie and I had seen him on television, somewhere between a PBS telethon and *The Electric Company* episode. I could have felt like Beryl Burton, the famous female cyclist of the sixties, but no one on PBS or elsewhere much publicized the greatness of women in those days, especially women athletes who kicked butt and would leave any man in the dust. At best, a *woman could do what a man could do.* That was the day's assbackwards standard of achievement. *Don't worry, girls, the women's movement might eventually push you up the ladder of social esteem, but for now, hide those maxi pads and keep up. One day, you might be able to do whatever a man can do!* Only later, much later, would humanity just barely begin to reverse the orientation of that statement. We'd take note, conceive of how we might reframe things, and come together to revolt. Wait a minute; there were many things, after all, a woman naturally did that no man could ever replicate, even in his smartest inventions. These miracles of nature, at last, did not make us wrong or gross; they could (gasp!) possibly be harmless attributes, even biologically outstanding ones! Perhaps, then, we women were not subpar, as much as culture had historically attempted to convince us we were, as much as all of our wide-spectrum, emotionally rich expression had been silenced and shunned.

When Frankie and I were respectively five and seven years old, our brother, Gino Jr., was born. He was an unexpected third child, but he was the boy my father wanted from the start, so we forgave him for the additional responsibilities he presented. My father was eager to mold a boy after his own practical, sharpshooting, single-focused self. As proud as my parents were to advertise the family's new member, the actual weight of taking care of our baby brother seemed to fall on Frankie and me, as my mother and father were fully absorbed in growing the family business.

Frankie's memories of our childhood, and in particular, my role in the family, are usually the opposite of mine. She dubs me a bully, a troublemaker, the family disrupter, while I remember myself as the one always under attack, singled out, dismissed as a nuisance. I tell Frankie she is *judgy*, mean, that her words feel hostile, but she feels I am the one who casts judgments and can't listen. Frankie speaks critically about me, at least that's how my ears interpret the sound of her words. She'll say I make things *all about me*, that I'm selfishly never there for her when she needs me. Strangely, I feel the same about her. I love Frankie in a no-matter-what kind of way, despite any tension between us, because we have an understanding that's bigger than we are. Per this agreement, we can pull on opposite ends of the rope when it comes to our opinions about nearly anything. This is how we grow closer, since we learned that intimacy is created through one means only: a good fight. We landed in the same boat as kids and realized that if we both paddled, we could, together, stick it out, so we established a type of lifelong closeness as well as a lifelong contention. To this day, Frankie and I have never lived more than one hour apart. We travel together, even work together alongside Gino Jr., steering all of our family businesses. When it comes down to it, we hold much of the same moral ethos; we are on the same team. Frankie and I call on each other to bounce our experiences back and forth, probably trying to together figure out what actual reality is, both grappling in our own ways after the rigmarole of growing up as the children of Lia and Gino Sr. At the same time, I feel certain that Frankie has never truly known who I actually am or acknowledged the real me, in some loving, all-guards-down kind of way. Frankie and I weren't the type of sisters to touch, no way. We didn't braid each other's hair or hold hands. The only hand gesture we've successfully mastered in terms of expressing closeness has been to keep our fists raised in fight mode (mainly metaphorically, although we did have a few decent physical brawls in our prepubescence, for sure). Despite our opposite views on practically all matters within the universe, Frankie and I can at least confirm one thing—and one thing alone—as true. Together, we'll agree we largely raised ourselves and we raised our little brother, a quasi-functional unit of two teamed sisters. Left to our own self-care, basically homesteading in New England, we fed ourselves total trash, the fruit of suburban vines. Even when our mom was at home with us, we covered the bases of our basic self-care, figuring it out for ourselves. While Lia is certainly more active in our daily lives now than she was during our childhood and no longer intimidating to us, Frankie and I agree that we lived through a different Lia in our earliest decades—one who was either entirely absent or hyper-controlling us.

While most children our age were playing house, Frankie and I did the real deal. *GG-Frankie Giovanni*, each other's *ol' ball and chain*. We became experts in changing Gino Jr.'s diapers and making sure the house was crumb-free and in top condition when Lia checked on us (or else). We became biorhythm experts, nearly psychically sensing when to move baby Gino from one buckled seat into the next. He'd endure twenty minutes in whichever one (baby swing, bouncy chair, highchair, car seat) before crying, and we'd pace our evenings around him like so, learning how to functionally multitask. Operating as such set me up for, in general, how I get stuff done until this day;

I'm most functional in the eye of a storm, in my own custom-designed chaos. In Bridgewood, we plugged a bottle of formula into Gino Jr.'s mouth while we heated up our only real sense of caring warmth, all of us compensating for the lack of a healthy dose of vitamin M, as in *mother*. We'd nurse on our eighty-five-cent Swanson fried chicken TV dinners, while Gino sucked and chomped on the sweet rubber of bottle nipples. Frankie and I somehow knew our dinners were junky, but we'd never bring it up. We were kids. We were satisfied by the excitement of consuming hydrogenated-oil chicken grease, because we didn't know how to voice a desire for something bigger than the food itself.

Within a few years, we moved again within the town of Bridge-wood, this time, closer to the ocean. My parents had accrued capital, and the growth of our economic status awarded us the luxury of a new abode, twice the size of our previous one. While our new house was now plenty spacious, our home life became more stifled. My parents were absent throughout the week, if not physically, then mentally. Frankie and I, accustomed to providing for ourselves, packed our own lunches, cleaned the house, tucked ourselves into bed, and got ourselves up for school. Raising both ourselves and Gino Jr. was beyond exhausting. It was the late sixties, and there weren't books back then on *where on the spectrum* of ADHD your child falls, and parents didn't have time for getting involved with that kind of stuff anyway. Kids were kids; maybe they weren't able to pay attention in class, but they'd figure it out. In those years, one headed toward puberty on her own. A girl was lucky to find out what menstruation was only after her hips had widened or she'd bled through her pants. As my own body began to change, my patterns of hunger response formed further, nested within my subconscious in animalistic self-preservation. Food represented my sole sense of fulfilling nourishment, so it made sense I'd tell myself, *Giana, don't starve.* I couldn't see this, of course, but I'd deemed it too risky to yearn for what was deeply lacking: tender nurturance, attentive care, real concern, and love. By nightfall, through heated-up TV dinners, my tongue silenced itself with processed flavors, shutting down the last of my heart's longing for something significant, something bigger than our newest American dream house, with its two-car garage, four bedrooms, three bathrooms, and backyard, but no room for Giana's feelings, not even in the basement.

As we grew older, like all good Italian children, I took my vows of swallowing emotions more seriously. Emotions included any display of vulnerable or self-exposing evocation, anything tender. Anger, however, could still fly—because, in my family, anger isn't an *emotion*, after all; it's expectation, the norm. Try to take that away, and it's like trying to tell an Abruzzesi all of the olive oil in the world is gone; it's just part of the foundation of life. Turns out, I learned how to keep feelings from myself in a chest of undisclosed secrets. There were things in our family that I simply normalized. For example, it was normal to feel frightened to bring people home. I couldn't handle being embarrassed or yelled at in front of friends; it was already hard just showing up at school, where I wasn't like the other Bridgewood girls. I was Italian. I was an eater. I was big. I took up room. My skin wasn't the color of a cloud puff; it more resembled the color of the olive oil we harvested every year in Abruzzo. Schoolkids thought I was weird enough as is. I couldn't risk the chance of my classmates having any new impetus to single me out. Therefore, I don't really remember having friends in my early years other than the neighborhood crew, allied only by proximity—fated to share a street. Most days, I settled for spending time with Frankie and Hostess snack cakes instead of inviting anyone over. As an adult with my own self-protection tactics, I can now understand how my mother's stringent decrees were necessary for her. She had to preserve herself through her early twenties, to streamline her attention, to take charge of her own life, to say *No more! I've had enough.* I commend her ability to lay down her law, to know when she'd reached her capacity. I've had my own serious struggles in learning to do the same, like at 5:30 P.M., post–salami grinder and snack pack of Cool Ranch Doritos, driving in my car while fingering a Nestlé Crunch Bar.

Understandably, Lia was maxed out. *She'd had enough.* She'd endured more than her fair share of post-traumatic stress; why bear another mouth to feed, more people to keep alive? My mom, as much as she'd never admit, wanted more than just to reestablish her Sicilian self upon arriving in Middletown. She'd wanted, through the American hustle, to free herself from her past, to arrive at another status of self altogether. That's the thing about hustling off your traumas though: the experience of life becomes more like one long-held breath until— at least in this form—it's over. But Lia and I, we're Sicilian, and we've inherited the ability to recognize beauty (except for in ourselves, of course). It's the basis of all our traditions. So then, isn't there hope for us, both mother and daughter, to finally realize that life's journey is best led with pleasure and joy, that to be religiously devoted to beauty requires self-love as a foundation? Can Lia and I, then, not turn our stern instincts into something like fearless self-esteem? Even if, as women, we are in our fifties and eighties, it cannot be too late to learn, right? Isn't life for learning explicitly *this*?

While I swallowed my emotions in order to toughen up, my father cut his teeth in business. Gino kept a minimum of three jobs, even in his first years in Connecticut. While he started out flipping burgers, within ten years of residency, he'd flipped two houses into funds for opening five businesses. Soon, my father edged his way to successful large-scale real estate investments, which led to exponential fiscal growth. Gino's businesses were based in the field we Italians inherently knew best: the business of feeding people and tending to the land. While my father acquired real estate, he also created a franchise of restaurants. In all of his work, Gino put an American spin on his inherited areas of expertise, and my mother joined his operation. All gears were focused on growing the Giovanni enterprise. Where my parents sacrificed bringing nourishment to their children in ritually shared suppertimes, they succeeded in providing the masses with the experience of agile family-style dining. Together, Lia and Gino offered Connecticut an affordable, dependably filling cuisine. They named their first restaurant the American Grill, and each one they opened afterward, the same. Within just a few years, American Grills became regionally famous for offering seven-dollar rib eyes and affordable buffet-style fare to the working class, a darn-good deal.

Meanwhile, back at home, the Giovanni kids feasted on food a few steps down in quality from the prepared rib eye plates my parents' servers were dishing up to most of southern Connecticut. My mother insists she tried to enforce healthy eating choices on us, adding, *You kids would only eat the bad food*, as though we'd been born with a proclivity for artificial nacho cheese flavor, and there'd been nothing she could do about it. She was not alone; this was parenting in the time in which fluorescent lighting, synthetic fertilizers, and chemical engineering boomed their way toward digital revolution. The decade began sans mention of food restriction, weight, or caloric regulation, into the birth of the first diet soft drink, Weight Watchers, and an idealized five-foot-seven, ninety-two-pound model named Twiggy, the crowned queen of "Thin is in." Meanwhile, the women in our family largely abstained from health-food education in ignorant bliss. There were days, however, when Lia was in the kitchen, though mostly passing through. She'd also take us on our weekly trip to the grocery store. Her nutritive guidance went only as far as suggesting options as we rolled our cart by the carrots, the frozen veggies, the fresh veggies. Lia might grab something lean, like an iceberg lettuce, which would later rot in the fridge. As she put it in the cart, she'd say, *Susan Martucci swears by eating this lettuce and grapefruit salad. Giana, make it for Frankie and baby Gino.* I'd nod while flipping through an item I'd borrowed from the newsstand as we ambled down the aisles, my body pushed listlessly against her cart. I could wash my love-starved angst in the momentarily borrowed *16* magazine, a torchlight illuminating my hopeful teenage future. I preferred to determine which Cassidy brother was cuter than consider fresh vegetables as a food to desire. The truth was, when Frankie and I had already subconsciously identified our main escape as watching television, and our indoctrinated religion as whatever was commercially enticing, why would we trade the propaganda of ready-made processed food for carrot sticks? Was Lia kidding? Her carrot sticks would go slimy while we ate our freshly defrosted freezer pizza, long drips of palm oil–enriched synthetic cheese dangling off the slice in hand, too hot to eat, but worth sacrificing the roofs of our mouths. Those days, we were quite far removed from *Emily Post's Etiquette* rule book; we ate sans thought or napkins and talked, when necessary, with our mouths full. Grease covered our young faces, and we let it shimmer, content to fold our posture into the arms of whatever was there to hold us, in this case, the couch. In this deranged way we filled our parental void with *Father Knows Best* and *Leave It to Beaver*, waspy shows that enforced the family power dynamic. The entertainment fortified us with the values our absentee parents didn't have time to properly address. Mrs. Cleaver's impactful mantra: *Nothing matters as long as your waist is half the size of your hip width*, Beaver's message: *Whine about every problem you have*, and the motto of Mr. Anderson, a.k.a. the rule-maker of the family in *Father Knows Best*: *Drink. Drink a lot, and—if you are the man of the house—no one can take you down because, well, you'll always know best*. While our father, who "knew best," continued to wrestle his own boulders up a hill, I scraped the fried bits of *insta-meat* from the foil plates that housed my polished-off TV dinner. The aluminum emptiness, bent on my lap, was the shell of evidence of my first bonds to the comforting chemical additives I'd later crave. As an adult, no matter how many natural flavors I'd combine within my self-labeled "holistic" batter of myriad culinary expressions, I would never recreate the zing of Blue No. 2 with Yellow No. 6 Lake chemical flavor. This was, in fact, an inimitable tang of manufactured fakeness I'd mistakenly registered as the taste of pleasure, satiety, and comfort. It would take me some years before feeling, and I mean *really* feeling, that I could fill the anxious pit, the void, with my breath, with a sense that I actually lived inside my body. In all of the containers I sought out to find something like relief, I couldn't dare conceive of my own physical shape as a place I might ground the restlessness of my spirit. Instead of Swanson's aluminum emptiness continuing to haunt my lap, what if I learned to identify with the limbs underneath that foiled container, which were unable to be spoiled, naturally preservative-free?

Turns out, therapy has shown me that containers are a pretty huge deal for me. That safety I found hunkering down with what was warm—a rectangular-shaped disposable tinfoil dish pulled from the oven—set a type of subconscious standard for my measurement of security, like home base. With a container cooled just enough to not burn my own lap-turned-table, which was parked in front of the TV, I secured undisturbed *me* time, couched in solo date-night mode, night after night. When home life consisted of dodging parental bullets, the combination of television and food was my one free pass, where I could not be tagged or punished, where limits, rules, and directions did not apply. This was just the first thing containers had going for them. Later, I'd use them for many other purposes, far beyond the superabundance of my pickling Bell jars, dozens of tubes of lip gloss, dropper bottles of homemade tinctures, or boxes of glass-bottled spring water in the garage. I discovered a use for containers that was greater than just holding my *things* securely. I found containers to contain me, ones that could hold *me* in a kind of safe embrace.

Today, I have intimate relationships with my containers. My car, for example, has the ability to contain me. As soon as I hear the double chirp of the automatic unlock, my Audi Q7 becomes the outline of my body, my sense of where on Earth I begin and end. On the occasion the car still feels too vulnerable, exposed to attack, I'll *double contain*, parking between two narrow buildings in a suburban New England alleyway. I'll work out of there, a strange office. Securing my attention within containers allows my nervous system to feel close to calm, or at least barricaded. I've used many of these so-called containers not only to hold my body, focus, and sense of safety, but also to contain distinct aspects of my personality. In each chapter of my life, my containers have served as the main characters: "Life, starring Giana and the pool." "Giana and her car." "Giana and her closet." It's like a romance series. The pool serves as a perfect partner for Giana the Dancer, the one who glistens and glides, glimmers and waves, loves waterproof mascara. My car is the only entity able to remain up to speed with the likely sudden change of direction of Giana, the Machine at Work. My walk-in closet is for Future Giana. There, I display all my size-6 and size-8 strapless dresses and massive jewels displayed on bodices, where I can be sparkling, infectiously feminine, almost sexy.

My top-notch containers are the improved, roomier, temperature-controlled square-footage substitutes for my actual body, places where I can wrangle in my restless spirit. As much as I may want to take credit for having invented this type of adult security blanket, evidently, the connection I have to containers is rooted in my subconscious. I've trained myself to seek out my own version of Lia's bomb shelter, her *grotto* in Melilli. Entering the world through the body of my mother and inheriting her buried fears, I just accepted the inevitable. As a young girl, I would need a place to run to. I'd fall under siege, even if my attackers came from within my own family. Only years after I developed a proclivity for using containers as a substitute for my own self-abandoned body, did I confront the statistics. For people who have had challenges with creating healthy boundaries in the past, the dissociative behavior of emotional eating is something like six times more likely. For all the years I spent trying to figure out what was wrong with me, searching all around the world, far and wide, what if I had just put these pieces together myself? I might have found a way to just look in the mirror, really, into my own eyes, to recall the buried memories—but denial, well, it can take a lady for an endless mile.

There were moments of collected containment for my family, little rituals of togetherness where we agreed to be a unit. While I really can't drum up a single childhood memory of the Giovannis sitting down for a meal together at home, we had a regular collective eating rite on Sundays, our version of church attendance. This was our family road trip time, taken under the guise of *work research,* of course. Pleasure was out of the picture. It was mandatory that we venture out and taste the competition, and so we'd travel to other regional towns to compare our restaurants' food to theirs, *undercover agents of carne.* The restaurant was a safe place to have family time; thus I could eat. I found my appetite. It was a *container.* Generally, my mother wouldn't intimidate me at volume in public, and my father, however distant he was in general, felt less far away when we were connected by a table. Just two forks and one wine glass apart, my dad and I could find a middle ground while dining on a Sunday. Where I was the center of negative attention at home, getting in trouble left and right anytime my mouth opened or I made a move, I was able to camouflage myself among the other patrons. In restaurants, my family found it more interesting to size up the menu, the decor, and the dinner crowd than evaluate my behavior, which was a great relief to me. To add balance to our fortunate position of having the means to dine out weekly, my father imposed the Giovanni rules for ordering. We were allowed to choose one main course, anything we wanted, but nothing else. While I fully understand how having the opportunity to select a single, warm meal off a menu is clearly a position of great fortune in this world, Gino's set limitations sparked my desire for *more.* Hence, the seeds were planted there for my rebellious fixation years later, during my own so-called *restaurant research.* I've established no ordering parameters. Let me tell you, I've gone through phases: ordering handfuls of finger-food starters (*one for each finger, please*), selecting two-thirds of the appetizer list (*Who can choose?*), dining with friends (*We can order everything and taste it all!*). In addition to these, I make sure not to skip trying the soup of the day. It's like the day's horoscope; *one must indulge.* After the soup, I enjoy a main course or split two or even three with my tablemates. *We must taste it all!* I refuse, just as my father did, to live within the limits set by anyone else. I'll set the rules; I'll break the rules.

When out on our Sunday eating adventures, even if we were limited to one entrée each and no appetizers, I would devour a bread basket (or two) and numerous individual servings of cool butter, delighting in the fact that no one seemed to count how many I'd unwrapped and emptied. I would lace my entrée with a generous shaking of salt, prefacing my fingers' direct dive into the crushed red pepper. They'd emerge with a hefty pinch of sense-slapping heat induction. Then I'd add (as a *rule of tongue*) a fresh dab of condiments to every bite. I needed my food to be flavorfully dominating, maybe because I felt I'd been dominated. I couldn't allow myself to feel my emotions, but could at least compensate with a walloping dollop of extreme intensity. Even though I'd successfully shut down my emotions, I couldn't kick a remaining sensation, something like I imagine a faucet might feel if forced off while the water pressure remained on high. In order to stay semi-anchored at the dinner table, I had to extinguish my own out-of-control squirminess. Hot sauce fueled my fire and simultaneously killed it. It made perfect sense as a form of nutrition since I'd ingested the contradictory dynamics of my family since day one. In restaurant mode, I fell in love with condiments and added extras. They were how I'd handle family outings, arm myself against likely sharp attacks. I'd win in the family's open fire by setting my taste buds aflame mid-war, letting the blood-red hues of peppers and tomato sauce go to battle for me. With fried eggplant or a double bacon burger and mashed potatoes piled high, the plate was my safe haven.

The thing is, in restaurant mode, we were conceivably *doing something* as a family, something beyond consuming heartily. Since mindful eating would require we acknowledge one another, we framed our *restaurant research* mode through the lens of being *strictly business*. Our family unquestionably identified as *eaters*. It was the shameless cultural norm for Italians. An Italian's appetite was generally off-limits to question. It was just assumed that *of course* you had one; why wouldn't you? I was allowed to eat where I wasn't allowed to do a million other things I wanted to do, so eating became the one place where I was able to find some freedom. Still, Gino would make sure to chime in throughout our shared dining experiences, reminding Frankie and me of our inherent low value, making sure we'd never truly feel good about ourselves or actually *enjoy* something. *GG-Frankie, you girls are going to get fat, you know that?* While the Italian appetite was unquestionable, a woman's figure would always be up for scrutiny. During nearly every meal, Gino would make sure to reinforce this conviction: I would never be destined for anything outside of *Blimpville*. The only surefire acquisition my father could conceive I'd successfully gain would be a weight problem. Other than providing us with this sole beacon of prophetic wisdom about our predetermined metabolic challenges, Gino kept mostly to himself on these Sundays, as usual. There were many times, in fact, that his work obligations prevented him from making it to our Sunday meal altogether. When he was there, Gino fixated less on his medium-rare steak's rubbery texture, and more on his ever-growing business vision.

Despite the subtle battles taking place within my family, at the restaurant, eating things was my deserved luxury. After a week of Frankie and I fending for ourselves in strange, defrosted diets, here we'd feast without having to warm up a frozen block of something from a colorful box. We'd get a break from our haphazard dinner-on-the-sofa evenings, relinquish our Stouffer's prefab provisions. Plus, at a restaurant, somebody else was hired to put something like love (or at least professional-level concern) into my meal. I'd finally get to sit back, be remunerated for all the fumbling self-care I'd managed that week, and receive provisions from whatever stranger in the kitchen I'd never have to actually, intimately meet. With chefs, I could forge a healthy attachment. The kitchen's swinging doors peacefully distinguished us as separate. My relationship with cooks was my first taste of easy communication. In fact, I never had to see any of their faces. I think all of the Giovannis found their own way to enjoy the experience of the restaurant, each for him- or herself. Where not one member of our family could functionally provide another member with a sense of well-being on his or her own, we coalesced in *restaurant research* mode. Here, we could mutually agree to pawn off the tiring task of creating family concordance; we yielded to our servers, trusting they'd successfully navigate the rivers running between us. For me, restaurant meals were like being latently bottle-fed after being prematurely weaned from milk, making up for my never having been properly babied. For Frankie, the restaurant was a place she didn't have to feel caught between Lia and Gino cannonading me. For Gino Jr., gosh, did Gino Jr. have needs? If so, we really never recognized them, even to this day (and probably to his detriment). Maybe Sunday's *restaurant research* excursions were Jr.'s time to study his father and to gawk at his mother, as both were typically MIA in his early years. To him, Lia and Gino were less mother and father and more a collective myth or legend. For Gino and Lia, attending others' restaurants in *research mode* was a way to ensure they were *keeping up with the Russos* (the Italian Joneses). Here, my parents made it appear as though they really enjoyed quality family time. Really, however, they were taking inventory for their next business plan, prepping Monday morning's execution. Restaurants were like free babysitters for the Giovanni kids, like extended family. Drop us off at a tablecloth, whether checkered or white, and we'd play with menu possibilities the way other kids would play in sandboxes. And as much as we might leave filled to the brim, we still requested a Carvel ice cream on our way home, one last mouth-plugging vice on a Sunday before again being left to our own devices.

Other than on these *research trips*, the immediate Giovanni family didn't share meals together. We'd get through our mandatory holiday meals with the extended family, birthday feasts, baptism brunches. We'd do our due diligence. It was best, however, to avoid eating together if possible. It's ironic that while both my mother and father came to America to save their farmlands, to raise enough profit to send surplus home to Italy, a country revolving around the importance of family mealtime, in the flux of it all, in the whirl of working ambition and fortitude, the joy of real, slow-food, Italian-style eating was forsaken. I had free reign to eat whatever sugary junk I was able to wrap my fingers around in childhood, but the liberty I likely searched for was the sense of something more than a nullifying placation by food. I wanted the nourishing celebration, the rite of feasting on life my family lost around the time of Mussolini's madness. Meanwhile, the concept of a consistent heartwarming, family-style suppertime meal was as far off as Italy felt to me, planted in front of the TV over my bowl of Cocoa Krispies and the black-and-white world of *Mister Ed*, where I could fix my attention. Yep, an easy, dreamy family supper seemed as distant as Rome's Leonardo da Vinci Airport was from JFK.

CHAPTER 4

School Years: Fair Girls with Cucumber, Crustless Sandwiches

Structured education eluded me. From the get-go, grasping the concept of doing one thing at a time felt impossible (not to mention utterly boring). My first years of living with my overly stimulating, sometimes explosive extended Italian family set my system up for a life of remaining on high alert, dodging one uncle chasing me around Nonna's living room, pit-stopping to play jacks with another. Skirt between Nonna's legs and the kitchen island, jump into Nonno's lap as he's watching TV. Hide when Lia comes home at the end of the day because she'll be angry about something. Come out only if she has still-hot french fries from the Grill for Frankie and me. Stay out of my dad's path always. If accidentally getting in the line of Gino's fire, shield Frankie; be the reprehensible one. To survive in a large Italian family, one must remain on red alert. So when lining up numbers in rudimentary math while sitting still at a desk for hours, I had nothing to hold on to. I needed zest. I needed urgency, commotion. I needed someone with a wooden spoon to make me add.

I was considered *learning challenged* as a result. My mom masterfully skimmed over participating in all quintessential mother–daughter bonding moments, like cuddling with a bedtime story, or sitting by my side if I had a fever, or thrilling over my first lost tooth, or telling me about what to expect during puberty. But she'd magically appear at my side just in the nick of time to scream at me while I butchered elementary school math. *GG! How can you not get that? If you have fourteen, and you take away half of it, you have seven! I knew this when I was half your age, what's wrong with you? Do you know what half your age is? How old are you GG?*

There was no way to move my mouth; I could barely blink. My brain did the same thing I'd learned to do with my early appetite: trigger shutdown. I believe it's called the *freeze response* of the nervous system. The only mathematical division my body could compute was the truncated flow of my breath, stunted, halved in a kind of primal cease and desist. I learned one of my preferred Eating Words mantras then: *I don't care.* I thought it was the best way to spite my parents in the long run: sacrifice my own tangible sensitivity for the sake of being inviolable. I literally vowed I would squelch my own happiness to spite them. I'd pray for rainy days, arrest all possible enthusiasm. I'd show them that there was no *bubble* of Giana's to burst; one can't deflate something already deflated. I have to give myself credit. It was a mastery-level sort of martial arts technique: control the controllers through passive indifference! I didn't think it through enough, perhaps, like, evaluate the possible long-term repercussions, but who worries about long-term effects in adolescence? I was thinking more about how to watch *Gilligan's Island* without being distracted by Lia's scolding, having to dodge the curt words she'd likely throw at me. Sticks, stones, and words *all* would never hurt me, I personally vowed. At least, that is, aside from my own eating words, which evidently have added insult to injury. From the time I found my *I don't care*, not only did I stop crying, but I also pulled the curtain down on my own inner sunshine. In this way, I did call in the rain, it turns out, regardless of the apparent weather. I committed to feeling unhappy even more seriously than Lia had committed to her vision of becoming a nun. *I don't care* served me well as a faith, like a religion. With it, I masterfully tuned out anything I didn't want to hear, because, guess what, *I don't care.* In ways, I'd designed the first cord-free noise-canceling headphones. Come to think of it, I could've made *bank* getting the patent on that science.

In third grade, I was transferred to a private Catholic school in

Dansfield. It was a commute, but, according to my parents, the miles of driving time each weekday were worth the promise of my character reformation. It made sense to me; I had heard my parents say to each other enough times, *Giana needs improvement,* so I'd already accepted the identity of a bad girl and was filled with plenty of shame and guilt to pass any Catholic school entrance test. At age eight, my so-called outlandishness was quite simple: I was bad because I still cried. (It would take me a few more years to successfully shut down the waterworks while I worked on this newfound *I don't care* plan.) Crying was a normal response for anyone my age, but Gino and Lia deemed it punishable. I was a *highly sensitive* child born before such titles were tossed around by *helicopter* parents; the boom of exceedingly attentive parents hadn't yet occurred. Remember, in the 1960s, one was lucky if her parents allowed for tap dancing; the buck kind of stopped there. People didn't take their kids to therapy, unless they were born, basically, evil. Let's get statistical for just a half a blink. In 1965, the average amount of time each day a mom spent with her child was less than sixty minutes (less than the duration of *60 Minutes,* the television show for which moms probably always made themselves available). By 2012, the reported mother–daughter *quality time* had ramped up to more than twice the 1965 amount. In our days, the quality time Frankie and I had with Lia was mostly spent being policed with orders and tasks, at which I always seemed to fail. This was our mother–daughter bonding. Lia would toy with my reality after I'd attended to whatever chore she'd given me, no matter how diligently I'd made an effort. After I had cleaned the kitchen, for example, she'd inspect my work microscopically, calling me to go over shelves a second or even third time because I'd missed a crumb visible to her eyes only. No matter how I tried to please my family, at best, I was rewarded only with their next-level criticism. When I'd achieve their set standards, rather than praise, I'd be prescribed with a new tier to reach and be told how I could *do it better.* As a result, in my formative years, I channeled my feelings of never being enough into retaliating. If they were going to hold me prisoner inside a cell of their criticism, I'd figure out a means of protest.

In the early years, I painted Frankie's favorite doll with the leftover wall stain I'd found in the garage and then tucked the doll into my sister's bed still wet, soggily awaiting Frankie's affections. This is the kind of behavior we start to flex when there is little we can control as small people. It's how the inner saboteur becomes our first response rather than the healthy nourisher. These are the means of communication we choose when aggressive expressions are freely fired in our family and all endearments are repressed. How are we to model upholding kindness in our most intimate relationships when we've watched angry words fly and tender sentiments evaporate before they can be conjured? And so, I, the firstborn, was solidly deemed *the troublemaker* in my formative years (a title active to this day within the family quintet). Regardless of how pleasant and generous I would ever be considered in the outside world, I'd find myself the biggest outsider in the nest of my own family tree, sans coziness, sans acknowledgment, sans welcome.

At just eight, on my first day heading to Catholic school, Gino dropped me off on his way to our newest American Grill. I remember getting in the car, just the two of us, of course riding in our normal, constrained silence (the status quo if there was no yelling). By then, I was pretty convinced that my father considered me a hindrance, capable of fabrication and invention. I was already decently detached from my bodily sensations, but I still couldn't ignore my gut and my whole lower body, flipping and then freezing in a kind of inner paralysis in the silence between us, silence softened slightly only by the car wheels' purr. Around my father, I always felt like I had done something *really terrible*, been a burden on our family in some way, but I wasn't able to recognize what it was. I just sat in the passenger seat, a bad girl, nearly poisoning the air in the Pontiac. I didn't know what I'd done—and Gino would never say; I just accepted that I was wrong in a way that, no matter what, I couldn't amend.

I was released at the curb of a long, rectangular brick building with a chapel at its side, my new school. I entered empty-handed except for my schoolbag, which was filled entirely by my packed lunch. Beyond my myriad edible provisions, I was prepared with my trusty phrase, my best-practiced tool to keep it together, to self-soothe. While my classmates learned the words to "Michael, Row the Boat Ashore" and "Amazing Grace" in the first weeks of school, I sowed my own psalms, repeating to myself, *It doesn't matter. I don't care. I really don't care.* If any authority wanted to yell at or punish me, I successfully negated all impact, escaping in the end by escaping myself. *Do whatever you want. I don't care.* This mantra has proven to uphold as holy in most settings. Eventually, *I don't care. It doesn't matter* morphed into *I don't matter*, and *It's no big deal* became *I'm no big deal.* These phrases continue to haunt me to this day. They are my central Eating Words phrases, my guiding lights, how I recreate pain and suffering every time I go to fill my body with something. They command me, prompting my rebellion, well beyond the comparatively small Catholic school walls. In my global excursions, at the airport, *whoot, there it is.* A grande mochaccino and a double chocolate chip cookie, the size of my face. Won't sleep on the plane, but *I don't care.* In business convos, Gino Jr. and Frankie team up against me as we negotiate a property deal. They're monitoring my every move, so I'll purposefully mess something up. *I don't care.* In running my business, *fool me once?* You're fired, even if I have to take on your workload. Why? Because *I don't care.*

I applied my *real* smarts in secret, in subjects the rest of the Giovannis cared less about. This way, they'd never know I was a wellspring of knowledge, wouldn't take anything more from my already-wobbling esteem. I formed my interests solely in the subjects I felt would be mine alone, preserving whatever I could of my triumphant essence by isolating my attention on vintage history. I started with random epic figures of powerful managerial types (surprise, surprise). By delving into the lives of royal Romanovs and

Russian czars I'd study the ropes of manhandling business. I gained a sense of what power felt like by reading about the epic moguls of the world, disappearing in hardbound, out-of-print editions of Sir Francis Drake, the privateer. These were the available role models in the sixties. There weren't yet books available by female provocateurs championing the workforce, like there are today. There was no way I wanted to *Lean In* like Sheryl Sandberg or do anything physical that might involve sticking out my chest, which would reveal the enormity of my growing bust. Better to learn about how to militantly buck up and bear it all like a war hero. I'd sign *Giana Clara Giovanni* in my practiced script on the school library checkout card, like James Madison signing the United States Constitution. I'd tuck the books in my backpack and take the borrowed treasures to the privacy of my bedroom. Reading was something I could do only by myself; my brain was too stimulated to try to read around others. I needed a safe place for absorbing information without interruption, and so I spent time reading alone in my room.

With my checked-out library books, I might have nearly found coziness on a Saturday—complete with a bowl of sugary cereal, a Kit Kat bar, or a hot mug of instant cocoa with mini-marshmallows floating on top. I'd disappear into my cocoon under the covers, absorbing stories about tough-as-nails men and their indestructible empires, page by page fortifying the walls of my bedroom. Historic conquerors were, decidedly, the best allies to bring home from school (and the only ones I didn't feel embarrassed to host under the same roof as Lia and Gino, thunderously arguing as a means of managing a household). I readily absorbed the influence of Russian czars, so if my door was opened without warning and I came under attack, if I was blamed or disgraced by any family member, I could protect myself by emulating the behavior of those I'd read about. I'd channel Russia's Romanovs and make like Alexander or Nicholas, in a perpetual state of defense.

At school, other than checking out library books, there was little

I felt drawn to aside from lunchtime. Lunch was my one unrestrained hour of the academic day, so I'd make sure not to cut corners. Because school was drab and limiting enough, my packed meal had to offer up the missing spectrum of colorful options the rest of my day lacked. Our kitchen cupboards were packed with to-go options, each in their shelved place, like in a factory. Grab this, that, and the other thing; add a napkin and plastic spoon; seal the bag; and then ship out. I'd choose five things, my *famous five*. It was a rite as religious as the weekly mass and regular confessions all Catholic school students attended. Five foods for my sins, from my five wrathful self-determined core food groups: the Hostess group, the Frito-Lay group, the Wonder Bread and tuna group, the Campbell's tomato soup group, and the cookies group. These species fell within the genus of *Will Immediately Turn to Sugar in My Blood*, sweet relief after a long day at school.

In the school cafeteria, there was little choice other than to share a table with the "Fair Girls," who made up most of the student body—the non-Italians. Once I hit my Catholic school years, it was hard to find a kid in school like me, a first-generation American. I was the odd one out. My parents were MIA from the PTA, hustling for money rather than hosting Tupperware fundraisers for the volleyball team. And my body announced its own square peggedness (or, more specifically, *pear-shaped peggedness*) by standing out remarkably from those of the Fair Girls, the ones whose pegs fit seamlessly. Tall, peach-complexioned, and waifish, Fair Girls brilliantly avoided puberty until the near end of junior high, in the privacy of summer break, which was the appropriate, even pious time for this event to take place. They simply returned in the early fall after having metamorphosed into butterflies. They'd breezily, seamlessly transformed from girls to young women in perfect sorority-style synchronicity. The Fair Girls would never leave one another to stand out alone. Ann Johnson, Dottie Sullivan, Jennifer McMann, Kristy Carter—boom, boom, boom, boom—without much ado, modest mounds appeared flawlessly on each of their chests in time for the very first day of high school. It was nothing that would cause an enormous amount of attention, but just enough curvy evocativeness to claim their status as young women.

For me, the process was far from perfectly timed. Years before, there I was, on my own and abruptly forced out of my childhood esthetic. Barely ten years old, the stuck-out sore thumb, I began to develop. None of my other classmates were going through this, and I had no reference point, no clue what was burgeoning under my areolas. I thought maybe I'd fallen asleep on top of our new Zenith Space Command TV remote control. Or, maybe I'd forgotten about a frontal bruise earned playing kickball at recess, immune to the ball's impact, busy shrugging off the blow of being the last person chosen for anyone's team yet again. Yep, there I was—long before the Fair Girls had to consider the embarrassment of buying a bra—in the adult section of our local Fullman's department store. None of the Fair Girls had to be concerned about their mother chatting with the general manager loud enough for everyone in the store to know. *She already needs a B cup at age ten?*

In the fifth grade—while the Fair Girls still played like kids, dressing their buxom Barbies in evening gowns and developing in normalcy—I was left to come to grips with my own body's *bizzarro* metamorphosis. I felt like I was accruing new curves at every turn, regardless of how exaggeratedly I perceived my own shape. When you stand out in grade school, you may as well be Gumby. I couldn't keep up with my own puberty. It seemed I matured in dog years, developing seven years' worth of cleavage, growing the bustline of a girl nearly twice my age. *(How's that for an exponential math equation, Lia?)*

Of course, I acquired tons of feedback about my evermore voluptuously expanding figure throughout the school semesters. As conservative as Catholic school was, gossip and mean-spirited jabs made their way to me between prayers for our sins and wafers on the tongue. I started to receive unusual attention from boys, none of which I interpreted positively. I could literally say to a male classmate, *Jimmy, can I use your calculator?*—something I'd have said without concern just the year before. Now, I'd apparently told Jimmy I like him. I'd seemingly pushed my chest in his face. I couldn't deal with this new interpretation of my gestures, so I quickly adapted: *There'd be no more being seen by boys, no more needing anything—ever—from them.* If they were to look at me, they'd have to see me as one of them, or, better yet, they'd regard me as their boss, their manager, their master.

I'd already had ample trouble in figuring out how to deal with any masculine attention *before* the onset of puberty. For example, while I also longed for his approval, I would try my best to avoid attack under my father's scrutiny. I was so uncomfortable around him, barely capable of pouring a glass of water without breaking the glass. In constant self-observation mode, I perceived myself through the same lens I believed he viewed me, in the terrible light of failure. I literally learned to watch myself from outside my own body, hovering like a satellite far above when he was in the room. Maybe at first, I'd hang by the ceiling fan, metaphorically speaking, eventually learning to position myself over the neighborhood. At some point, I graduated to a cosmic post. But in my actual three-dimensional position, I was barely able to gauge what was happening, make out my own form. I mastered the art of watching myself as an outsider so well throughout my life, I learned to live in external coordinates. It would require a full-time job just to locate my inner compass. Without it, there is no me experiencing me from the inside.

Call me prodigiously precocious, ahead of my time, but the whole *submit to the man* thing just didn't feel super comfy, or even natural to me. What was I supposed to do, so precariously positioned under the eye of my father? It felt I was framed by the patriarch of my family, set up for failure. Just as unconsciously as I'd inherited the belief that the men of the family are the ones with power, I unconsciously convinced myself that engaging with any man was comparable to stepping on a landmine.

At school, in front of boys, at every curvaceous turn of events during my early-onset puberty, I employed my best coping strategy to avoid being messed with or seen. My hardened words came in handy as a form of self-preservation. *I don't care* and all of its iterations helped me ward off remarks—even in the rare case of loving or positive feedback—especially those from the male members of the species. I'd hide out in misconduct and unbecomingness, which was way better than being perceived as *inviting* and *playful.* I would not let myself be vulnerable to male predators. Soon I figured something out: If I acted like a man myself, men were bound to overlook me. But even if my personality copped the masculine take-charge persona modeled on the cover of *Time* magazine in the 1970s, my body could not express a lie. With my long eyelashes, full lips, and high cheekbones, I was turning into the whole kit and caboodle of femininity, so obviously a young woman. Because my body provided me with nowhere to hide, and was so inherently *wrong* and *solicitous,* I had no choice, really. The sole option was to disassociate completely from its unpredictable freakishness; *I don't know you anymore.* (Come to think of it, I've employed the same sudden estrangement with ex-boyfriends, former employees, fired handymen, dismissed office assistants, and past therapists.) It's easy, in a way; I learned this technique before any *new-agey* esoteric practices. I simply propelled right out of taking ownership of my actual skin, like an emergency helicopter leaving a military base—just a little training and bam: it's remote operation only, *mia cara.*

The Fair Girls, however, seemed to maintain their sense of embodiment, growing healthy self-esteem even amid the social torrents of school life. They each sat like a sweet, perfectly formed spear on Cupid's arrow. Everything they touched was done delicately and with poise. They gracefully unpacked their lunch, revealing only one or two items, and seemingly without much willpower, left each of their meals unfinished. This wasn't because they had painfully mastered a forced abstinence, but because, literally, they were not Italian. They just did not know how to eat. Their parents clearly cared about all persnickety requests that came out of their dainty mouths. From pretty-patterned, in-style insulated lunch bags from Bloomingdale's, their sandwiches emerged with the crusts cut off, starkly contrasting my prepackaged cheese-and-cracker snack packs and brightly wrapped Ho Hos. Their agile hands revealed gourmet-looking cucumber sandwiches, the same kind they'd likely order for all of the predictably picturesque wedding showers they'd host in the future. Just below the crustless cucumber sandwich packed for every Fair Girl would be a second lunchtime provision: a Dannon fruit-on-the-bottom blueberry yogurt, and nothing else, except maybe a love note reading, *Packed by Mom xo, or Good luck on your history test today!* At the lunch table, the blueberry yogurts were never more than half eaten. Spoons whirled around the remaining contents while the Fair Girls' eyes rolled, their blond hair flipped, and meaningless conversation ensued. Meanwhile, I killed off all the provisions I'd shoved into my lunch sack in my own morning rush, my *famous five*. I inhaled my lunch like a 1970s Hoover, along with two milks—one plain, one chocolate. *Who the heck could wash down lunch with only one box of milk?* Not me.

This would amp me up enough for math class, giving me a good forty-five-minute window of sugar high before a carb crash. Amazingly—as much as my math brain froze like a gerbil in the mouth of a canine whenever my mother grilled me—I actually kind of rocked math class. And later, when I took on my own enterprise, I found I could crunch numbers with as much ease as I could crush grinders at a mini-mart. The chocolate milk, the Cheetos, the Devil Dogs—they'd worked as a multifaceted buffer. With food to suffocate sensations, I wouldn't have to deal with my pubescent, uncontrollably developing body or my low self-esteem resulting from any so-called *learning challenges*. With my *famous five* food groups as ammo, I was armed and ready. So there. *I don't care* resounded throughout my own booming body, an Italian Army battle cry of my own.

"GIANA and THE FAIR GIRLS"

CHAPTER 5

The Obsessor and the Escapist

Deciding that my schoolmates simply *did not know how to eat* seemed smarter than dealing with making myself wrong. Being familiar enough with the sensation of feeling innately wrong at home, I used every muscle of my young zeal to fight against the same assessment at school. If all else failed, I would assume popularity by cunning effort. I preferred fake friends to no friends. I was already isolated enough in my home life; I couldn't survive further exclusion.

I balanced out the inherent discrepancies I perceived between my classmates and me by at least donning the dress-code fashion: the Catholic school plaid-skirt uniform decorated with a touch of the day's flair—a macramé bracelet, preppy clogs, and a Farrah Fawcett hairdo. There seemed no way to do anything about our appetite differences though (at least, before I discovered wacked-out forms of dieting in high school). I wasn't able to hide the fact that while the Fair Girls were still able to be pressed like spring flowers between the pages of sacred texts, I was nearly too curvy to fit comfortably into the opening of our classroom desks, or so I felt. These unalterable qualities of my body were easier to ignore than obsess over. I was a Giovanni, after all. I adapted by turning a thick-skinned cheek toward what I couldn't seem to change and focused on realistic tactics, doable strategies for conquering social situations. Therefore, I ignored the snickering of boys when my bra straps were spotted under my white T-shirt in the beginning of fifth grade and learned to stop measuring the vast difference in meal size when I lunched with the Fair Girls. I taught myself to feign interest in conversation, compartmentalizing a private world inside myself, where I could remain fixated on consuming calories while outwardly engaging in conversation about school dances. Pretending to listen, I convinced myself I cared about the Fair Girls' upcoming family trips to Disney World and our latest grammar test. In those lunch hours, Lay's potato chips would come soothingly to my rescue when my palms began to sweat or I felt awkwardly out of place. The Fair Girls did more things with each other outside of school than they did with me, but I wouldn't let myself chew on this; instead, I'd chew on the delicious Tootsie Roll I'd brought from home as a special treat. I rationalized that my social exclusion from their extracurricular fun was due to geographic challenges because I didn't live in Dansfield. It would be inconvenient for them to invite me to things. But it was obvious, however unspoken, that I just didn't fit in. I was not fair. I was olive—like the shrub, short and squat, a mess of shoots emerging widely from a gnarly trunk. At that age, I didn't see the value in being related to this botanical, how much it might yield, how well it produced and sustained the heart of the community. All I knew was that my family and the Fair Girls' families would never socialize because Cucumber parents would literally never understand Gino or Lia with their impossibly thick Italian accents. Our saucy meatball parm oozed far too much for them. While we'd been forced to speak only English in my own house, forced to *waspify*, my Mediterranean heritage wafted uncontrollably from me, like Nonna's garlic sauce, which might not be so becoming to those foreign to our culture.

Setting up camp with my private island-sized lunch bag, nonchalantly extracting contents one at a time throughout the lunch hour, I buried my secret operations even from myself. I chomped, chewed, and swallowed to soften the blow of my social reality, and in so doing, developed a workable facade. Bite by bite, I dedicated myself to a persona, as per norm for the preteen girl. I'd be a *what you see is what you get* type: *a girl next door* mixed with *just one of the guys*. Giana: friendly but tough, approachable but unconcerned about her popularity, street smart but not exactly academic. At school, I figured out how to fit in without seeming like I was trying. My superhero skill was being able to render myself invisible when necessary. I'd already mastered that by age five.

Even though I'd crafted an outer personality to fit in as best as I could, there was no way to pull it off 24/7 or act as seamlessly poised as my classmates. I'm a natural-born limit pusher; it's in the Giovanni blood. So I typically managed to slip up, revealing my inner uncouthness. It wasn't unusual for me to land an awkward delivery and bring conversation to an abrupt halt. Despite how much I tried to fit in, it was a metaphorical brainteaser, like a crossword puzzle.

Imagine this as a scene in a movie: The Fair Girls sit at our lunch table with a fictitious *Connecticut Post*. They're on the Entertainment page, insisting on my answer. *It's just four letters across, GG! Rhymes with "dialed." Here's the word clue: it's how you should behave, the appropriate female nature. GG, this is simple; you know this!* I look down at the three oyster crackers in my Campbell's Tomato Soup. Do I have to really figure this out? I slurp one spoonful of saucy, creamy, pink-red citric-acid flavoring, inhaling the mouthful of its thick warmth like some might take in a deep breath. Then I take a stab at the answer the Fair Girls are seeking. *Dunno*, I say. *Wild?* The camera zooms in on their eye rolls and hair flips. Their slight skunk-like spray in my direction subtly fumigates me, the outsider of the group. I'd gotten it wrong. *Duh, Giana, the answer is "mild,"* the Fair Girls reveal. *It's the acceptable demeanor of a girl. Piece of cake, Giana, should be obvious. Really, though, how could Giana ever be mild?* [Laughter.] End of scene.

Even in the movie version, however hidden through symbolic dialogue, what they said was true. My whole body could barely contain its inner *wild*; I literally lacked the phenotypic expression to demonstrate anything near to *mild*.

Along with the pair of mounds growing on my chest, I was steadily building two more parallel attributes. These parts, rather than being physically apparent to the eyes of the world, were more covert, carefully rooted within my psyche. Let's call them *the Obsessor* and *the Escapist*, a kind of yin-yang danger duo. They're like the Thelma and Louise of my nervous system, tweaking extremes of the fight, flight, and freeze responses. The Obsessor and the Escapist emerged as determined interior guides to fill up the places I'd abandoned. They stood in for my sense of self-trust, my ability to follow through. They compensated for my inability to rest, give myself slack, or react moderately.

If you told me in the early days—while I zoned out on the *boob tube*, inhaling Stove Top stuffing—that my behaviors would eventually lead to *beaucoup* cold cash spent on therapy, naming parts of my inner self, I'd have looked at you like you were *bat-sheet* crazy. I'd have asked you to change the channel back to *Betty Boop* or *The Brady Bunch*. I don't feel bad that it took me a significant investment in therapy and a heck of a long time to sniff out these inner *frenemies*, as it turns out that approximately 95 percent of human brain activity is unconscious. How was I to know I'd given myself over to this pair of internal decision-makers pretty much from the get-go? By evaluation, the Obsessor and the Escapist were perhaps not exactly the healthiest authorities to hire, but honestly, in the case of handing over authority to psychologically developed *parts*, I think we're already in a territory beyond a state of healthy, right? The side effect of giving myself over to this true-blue pair was that in exchange for their control, I'd remain gripped in cycles of self-abuse.

It seems I'd followed the wise adage of Michael Corleone in *The Godfather: Part II*, true to Sicilian stereotype. He advised, "Keep your friends close, but your enemies closer," and that was no problem for me. The Obsessor, therefore, was hired. I'd let her compulsively occupy herself to death to pick up slack for *actual* Giana's lack of discipline. I found her an office in a large wing of my headspace. While she paid rent on one hemisphere of my brain, her polar opposite took up residency in the other. Residing in the plush half of my neurological real estate, the Escapist claimed her reign in a luxe and lofty room filled with fragrant flowers and a lavender bubble bath.

Here's how the Obsessor works:

Just as Lia carved out *right* from *wrong* through her religious covenant, the Obsessor fixates on my logistics, sizing me up along the way, holding me to her high standards. She exerts drive, aims, and fires as she lives to prove—regardless of what anyone thinks—that she'll have whatever she sets her sights on. She loves collecting tubes of lip gloss and has hundreds of shades, ranging from mauve to bubblegum pink. (Yes, believe it or not, she's taught us that there are actually a hundred shades between those two hues.) This go-getter is a globe-trotter; she racks up stamps on her passport. The Obsessor keeps us *up*. She's all about excitement and stimulation. She'll spontaneously book international flights in the middle of the night, just after ordering face-tightening botanical serum online. She's incredible at finding the right people to hire, people who are excellent at carrying out her many instructions. *You—make my website. You—take care of my real estate. You—prepare my garden for winter.* The Obsessor, like my father (not a coincidence), lives by the principle that there is *no room for fear*. In fact, my Obsessor models a toughness like my father's, like that of my whole family, which makes sense. One day, if I no longer have Gino and Lia, or even Frankie and Gino Jr., keeping me on my toes, I'll be able to maintain firmly under the sergeant's commands: *Toughen up and keep your head straight, Giana. Don't even think about breathing.*

Racing through life, the Obsessor speeds into solving all equations of her future, with a firm handle on how everything unfolds. It's my Obsessor who will never take *no* as a suitable answer, who hears *no way* only as *yes, definitely*. She can turn anything around. She learned how to do that by age five, championing a teenage-sized bike although she couldn't even reach the bicycle seat. She'd take over in a total dictatorship if she could. She'd control everything in an Italy-circa-

1940s style, but, as are so many of us, she's entangled in a special codependent kind of relationship. She has to share her world with her housemate, her above-mentioned parallel part, the Escapist.

The Obsessor and the Escapist are two sides of the same ancient Abruzzese coin, really. They ultimately operate back to back, butt to butt. Each is as distinctly different as a cold-pressed olive oil and a sharp, fermented balsamic vinegar, whose flavors combine in a timeless, classic favorite. Strangely, it is for their polarities that they so strongly magnetize, succumbing like the best of us to Plato's supposition, the one about opposites and how they attract.

How do they meet? Well, the Escapist and the Obsessor are not so different than any other contrasting couple. Think Wile E. Coyote and the Road Runner, the Tortoise and the Hare, Bugs Bunny and Elmer Fudd, Tweety and Sylvester, Tom and Jerry. Gosh, there are so many classic examples of strangely paired duos whose overwhelming relationship challenge becomes their full-time gig. Perhaps I could have just analyzed cartoons and gotten as much insight on my path to personal growth and development, with a bowl of cereal to boot. I might even consider whether or not my habit of binge-watching cartoons in childhood—in those early neurologically impressionable years—has anything to do with my having developed my own warring twosome. Maybe if I'd abstained from investing hours and hours into *Looney Tunes* characters, memorizing their patterns of marriage and madness, I'd have spared my own loony development of polar parts. Who knows? Experiments have been done linking television consumption to the formation of children's behavior (see the Bobo doll experiments of the sixties, in which a scientist basically programmed violence into children as a form of research through TV programming). Many of my early less-than-genius interests probably came from commercials and animated shows.

Like the Road Runner, my Obsessor functions in a single, operative *GO mode*. Racing ahead, she inevitably crashes over a cliff once she's maxed her assertive output ad nauseam. When the Obsessor despairingly discovers that there is nowhere else to go and no energy left, she has no choice other than to surrender to her overwhelm. This literally feels like a death to her.

By the way, I have a long-time transpersonal acupuncturist, Bill, who, more than just sticking needles in my various body parts, has impacted my life significantly. Bill's clinic is right up the street from my healing home, and after all of our years together, he really *gets* my collective operating system quite well. Just a heads-up: I frequently reference Bill in a way similar to how some religious zealots might reference Job. His precise understanding of my nervous system, for example, is as meticulous as a Tesla owner's manual, with way more info than the average Jane who just wants to turn the dang thing on cares to know. But when Bill describes my nervous-system function and how different aspects of it relate, I'm pretty sure he is talking about my *parts*. I'm certain Bill scientifically understands exactly how my Obsessor deals with things more than I ever could, but as best as I can describe in GG language, however, the scene unfolds like this: Right as the Obsessor lays down her weapons, which is more dramatic than Geronimo's surrender, a great coin tosses up into the sky and spins. Tails down, my destiny lands in the arms of the Escapist, who declares, *See! I told you that you couldn't make it here. I told you that you should get away, tune out, turn it off. Come now; come with me. We'll find relief in our void-filling paradise. Let's go. You have a free pass to Bingeland. I'll let you eat whatever you want there— everything that has been forbidden!* I have no choice but to go with her. She's the other half of my placebo caregiving duo, who generate a vicious cycle in standing in for my practice of self-care.

Here's how the Escapist works:

As you might imagine, the Escapist is the one who plants those infectious anthems, like, *Powder donuts! Powder donuts! Powder donuts!* that play alluringly in my head. In the beginning, her intentions were pretty dreamy; she held my hand and kept a torch of hope lit inside of my mind's eye. She insisted that there was *something else, someplace else* where people were nice to one another, somewhere I wouldn't be wrong, where I'd feel secure. And she's the one I'd seek out in my childhood Saturday ritual. I'd find her at the bottom of my third bowl of Lucky Charms as I watched back-to-back *Scooby-Doo* episodes, *ahhh, safety*. When not fixating on the screen, the Escapist would zone out on the back of the cereal box, resting her eyes. She'd give me a break, allow all of my cares to float off to some faraway future world—maybe to Orbit City, where the Jetsons live. For the Escapist, a distant location was more appealing than a place like Bridgewood, Connecticut, on a Saturday, especially with imminent homework pressing. She'd whisper, manipulatively posing like a kind of fairy godmother, *GG, we'll not think about that.* The Escapist never considered sating her desire by pausing at the top of a full breath. There were no advertisements for *conscious breathing, finding your center*, or the like between scenes of the sleuthing Scooby gang.

The deal looks like this. At first, it's wonderful to surrender to the Escapist's plan. It's the right idea. She'll console us after we've been whipped around by the Obsessor's voraciousness. The Escapist says, *There, there*, and we'll let ourselves believe in her nurturing ploy. *There, there, GG, go get that salami grinder. It's easy. There, there, it's a chocolate bar kind of afternoon.* The Escapist offers consolation in my first bites. *Yes, yes, exactly. Drake's Devil Dogs. Don't think about it. It's so good; just wolf it down, wolf away. There you go!* She secretly smirks at Giana's catatonic expression as we get close to passing out in caloric overload. The Escapist smirks because as hard as the Obsessor worked, in the end, it's her dreamy, lofty ideals that always have more sway over me. She endures. Regardless of never training for any kind of sportive competition, she's squashed the Obsessor with just a few thousand pounded-down calories.

The most important element of the Obsessor and the Escapist's relationship, however, has been achieved, and that's what matters:

they've kept me firmly under their thumbs—their united mission. In exchange for their tenancy, I get to tune out and do nothing. I get to safely give up on myself, numb out. I get to fixate on them rather than embrace my passion, my joy. Plus, I've ensured this duo extinguishes my bright fire in the place of my ever having to risk getting close to the flames of passion, intimacy, relationship. Why deal with internet dating, ladies, when you can have your socks knocked off without having to screen creeps, swipe right, deal with repetitive heart break, and brave posting a photo of yourself in your most perfect light?

It's perhaps unfair to so harshly pick on these two inner aspects of myself, these two central stars of my behavioral puzzle. I wouldn't have chosen them if they also didn't have some star-like qualities, I'm not *completely* thick. I'm smart enough to know a good bargain when I see one, after all. Truthfully, my Escapist has come in handy, particularly later in life. In ways, she has helped me visualize my professional goals. She contains my intuition, sees the best possibilities. She can locate gold mines and yellow brick roads. Likewise, who would I be without the constant bullwhip of her partner, the Obsessor? Who else could collect spicy pepper from around the globe with me, harvest olive oil by the truckload each autumn in Italy, pull off regular twelve-hour workdays in the restaurant? Like two-pack socks, one white, one black, they come in cahoots, the Obsessor and the Escapist. On most days, they pretty much operate all of my functional systems. They run my stomach's autonomic nervous system response and dictate what address I punch into my Audi's automatic navigation system. There they are working together through me while I'm in my car, directing my apparent requests: *Siri: Map the quickest route through traffic to Dunkin Donuts on Housatonic Avenue.*

Of course, I'm not consciously thinking I'm a bundle of *parts*. Typically, I identify simply as GG. I at least feel *slightly normal* knowing that entire modes of psychology are dedicated to understanding the individual psyche exclusively through its so-called *developed* parts. A personifying lens has proven to be a more doable way to shed light on befuddling psychological makeup, mine included. I've a strong hunch that most of us emotional eaters are asking ourselves on repeat a version of the question, *WTF is wrong with me? Who or what is it inside me that is deciding upon this bingeing behavior?* We'll arrive, exhausted and at the mercy of all interventional therapists on Earth, begging to know answers, which, evidently, are inside of ourselves. We want to hear the professionals' explanations, exhaustively querying, *Why the heck do I keep doing this when I know I don't want to? What's willpower, and how do I get me some?* I've been chasing my tail like a confounded dog for some years, dropping serious coinage to fix or rid myself of my extreme behaviors, attempting as best as I can, whether under hypnosis or strict elimination plans, to form new habits, new rules. In the process, I've ultimately had to get intimate with my own inner parts—my inner turmoil and contradictory qualities. In a way, the interior journey is not so dissimilar to the medical student's path of study, learning to identify the chambers of the heart.

In naming the Obsessor and the Escapist, I've been able to see where these extreme parts of me intersect, and how they rely on each other despite the dysfunctional quality of their relationship. They work together in a way similar to how I learned to operate within my family on a primary, transactional level to get my needs met. In response to Gino or Lia's assertions or demands, I'd flee, meaning I'd check out, and emotionally turn off, regardless of my innate need to be well-parented. Ultimately, I'd end up repeating this pattern, as we humans tend to do. I'd repeat-fire the neurons I'd networked together, retreading familiar paths to create a similar condition again and again in most of my relationships, whether taking a role of assertiveness or passivity. Upon entering my adult years, I suspended a part of myself in a childlike state and continued to operate from that place, creating systemic stress and then reacting to it. This is what happens when one or more of our human fundamental relationship needs go unmet. Evidently, these relational needs are universal (as much as rebellious Giana wants to deny a reality of needing anyone or anything at all).

These basic requirements for an individual's well-being are neatly mapped in Maslow's hierarchy of needs diagram. Even science reveals that, *darn it*, we've got these emotional needs on a level of basic survival. We're wired for attachment and recognition, however insecurely we might experience these needs. And if our needs can't be safely satisfied within our family unit, we'll compensate with particular behaviors we've developed. In our adult years, most self-destructive behaviors emanate from the very place where our inner child resides, still trying to get her primary needs met. All of this information, I've gotta say, sounds great on paper. I sound like I could have a PhD in this stuff by now, but snotty GG is still prone to her thinking. *Great*, she cynically retorts, *but how is being privy to this information going to keep me from wolfifying a tuna fish sandwich from the fridge section of Cumberland Farms despite supposedly knowing better?*

Understanding why I've internalized my extremes has, at the very least, been preoccupying in a useful way. It's better than simply bingeing on a Hallmark Channel movie, and the drama of it is almost as fulfilling. All stubborn playfulness aside, it appears that understanding myself is actually vital and necessary. I'll even admit that it is imperative to my ability to create real health, however bitter a pill to swallow. It is how I've come to learn that my Obsessor and my Escapist have struck a deal. It goes like this: Once the Obsessor exhausts herself, she lands, overtaxed, at the Escapist's feet, like a junkie needing a fix. It's go-go-go for her and then crash. Since addictive intensity is an inherent trait of my Obsessor, this arrangement works. When the Obsessor breaks down at the feet of the Escapist, all three of us, the Escapist, the Obsessor, and me, unconsciously agree to self-anesthetize, *check-out*. We don't look one another in the eye; we simply collectively submit into our agreed-upon alliance, even though independently, each one without the other knows it's not the best personal choice. To keep our alliance alive, we'll *wolf* together, the only shared language between us. It's a sad affair, but at least it's catered. Two jelly-filled donuts and an iced mocha Frappuccino later, each of us leaves the scene practically chanting, *I can't do this again.*

In grade school, however, there was no way I was psychologically informed enough to notice anything like archetypes influencing the function of my brain's frontal lobe. The only thing close to the word "archetype" I'd have cared about was trying to convince Lia to drive us to the golden "arches" of McDonald's, which, at the time, was my "type" of ideal meal. All synthetic-cheesy puns aside, it was bad enough that I had to start wearing a bra and deal with puberty before anyone else at school. I had no remaining resources with which to worry about anything like inner demons. Plus, even though I felt my behaviors developing, they seemed fun, like playmates. They promised me, *All roads lead to Rome, bambina. Push on till you can be free.* These dispositions of character, let's call them, offered me the coping skills that I seemed to lack, and were way more dependable in nature than any of my relatives. Where Giana was prone to burn toast and break kitchen glasses in front of Gino, the Obsessor and the Escapist averted all scolding, for neither one could be stopped, called out, or caught.

CHAPTER 6

You Say Ragazzi; I Say Risotto

O ne of the fundamental beliefs I absorbed in my adolescence was how important external appearance is for a girl. More than acing math or history, I wanted to conquer being beautiful, and that meant being slender, a straight line, like the girls at my lunch table. Despite feeling enormous in my school days—especially when compared to my future pants sizes—I was a pretty *skinny* version of Giana. I mean, I know it's *so* out of fashion to fat shame, and I shouldn't judge myself by contemporary standards. Yet, despite our progressiveness, we still have quite a bit of unpacking to do around body image. In my day, girls were encouraged to enter the workforce and help to grow industry, but, paradoxically, we were considered something of a commodity ourselves. According to the covers of women's magazines, in the top fields for my gender (secretary, teacher, or nurse), the best I could hope for was to be considered sexy and skinny in my uniform. Plus, even before the influence of cover-girl images, we still bore about two thousand years of body hatred on our shoulders, all for carrying the curse of curviness, for being shaped anything like an apple, the original round fruit. With so much condemnation heading her way, it's surprising that Eve wasn't psychically intuitive enough to pick a cucumber from the garden or a zucchini from the vine. She picked a shape representing sweet curvaceousness, and her act was then forever considered the root of all evil. It makes sense that in adolescence I avoided dealing with my own hips, that I couldn't bear the natural shape of my body. Even to this day, I avoid weighing myself, which comes as no big surprise since I'm unable to conceive of having a close relationship, even with a bathroom scale. Regardless of whatever number I am now or have been before, I felt size "too big" from day one. I thought myself fat in third grade, and in the fifth grade, considered myself a *dysmorphic house*. Thereafter, more than my fair share of pasta, I swallowed the notion that I was destined to be forever fat. It was my biggest *poor me*, the one area in which I was allowed self-pity. Where I couldn't feel empathy or compassion, much less encouragement, from Gino or Lia, I could allow myself to wallow in this self-criticism. *Woe is me; I'm a whale.*

Throughout my school years, despite my belief that I was inappropriately gross and strangely asymmetrical, my body was actually the ideal standard, you know, the Playboy Bunny dream shape. It makes me cringe to even admit this. I mean, despite my colossal capability for consumption, I have no appetite for receiving compliments, and a near-anorexic response to feeding myself with praise. *Go figure.* It just seems to be the case that my body happened to be naturally fit, well proportioned, even (gasp) feminine, regardless of how much I lacked awareness of that. I mean, can anyone possess an unbiased sense of his or her own body? Wouldn't it be wonderful if we could develop an interior gauge, like a barometric sensor, to perceive our physicality by measuring how acceptably fit we *feel*? How might it change the world if our first sense of beauty was anchored in our knowledge that it truly *comes from within*. What if this concept was less of a one-liner on magazine covers and, rather, a practice we culturally developed? Imagine what physical education might look like in grade school: kids lined up, mindfully investigating how breath moves inside their bodies at the start of gym class. I know modern education continues to evolve, and the world is culturally different today than it was even last year. I know I'm not alone here in considering the value of cultivating healthy self-esteem and how, especially as women, we can free ourselves from feeling self-objectified or objectified by society. There are many passionate teachers these days who are inspired to teach people to connect with their bodies and treat them less like slaves to our ambitious agendas and more like temples we respectfully inhabit. That being said, I'm not there yet. I'm still sizing myself up on a freakishly amalgamated meter of what is "acceptable," and always, of course, falling short. That's why I had no sense of actually being fit in my early years, and I'll literally tune out when people recall the younger Giana. *Really?* they say, still under the influence of the media-idealized body. *Giana, you had, like, that perfect bikini body; boobs, hips, and a small waist.*

In my adult years, I've done a solid job of hiding my excess pounds under layers of flowing fabrics. I do my best to avoid being sized up, *literally*. However, I can't control the evaluation of those who knew me in my earlier years, when I let myself be susceptible to the eyes of the world while tanning by the public pool, exposed to the sun and everything under it. Honestly, I don't believe anyone's recollections of my "great" body, because, to me, I felt enormous even then, hunting for whatever would take me away from feeling sensation, something to relieve my emotions and dispel my nervous energy; the perfect *physical disassociation* concoction. To imagine I've ever been physically desirable? I only *barely* felt that way when I discovered the great combination of alcohol and diet pills in my late teenage years, basically the equivalent of speed and muscle relaxants. Unmedicated, I was awkward and clumsy. Meanwhile, the truth is that, however swollen I physically felt, I was simply a *Pubescent Adolescent Without a Clue*, like the title of a less sexy James Dean movie. I avoided the call of my hormones as long as possible, since they'd gotten me into all of this tectonic-shifting trouble to begin with and were surely not to be trusted. When the boy down the street, who spent every summer throwing rocks at me, started to pay a different kind of attention to me, I pretended not to notice. I was doing my best to avoid the call of the wild and instead cling to whatever naive youth I could in the face of the incoming juvenile wind.

To deal with my hormones, I took to our neighborhood streets, pulling Frankie along with me, and we found a little team of local rug rats and menaces. We didn't get into significant trouble with our young gang; we just attempted to make something out of the suburban nothingness we'd all been provided with as our mutual romping grounds. Soon enough though, games like Kick the Can turned into Spin the Bottle, and I was sent to explore Seven Seconds in Heaven with Johnny Marconi, who was probably the worst conversationalist I'd ever encountered. On the street, Johnny was mean, sort of a head-of-the-gang type, brusque, in charge—the kind of male I was used to. In the closet, however, Johnny was a different species. He felt smaller than me, warm, a little nervous. But *I* wasn't nervous. Johnny's anxiety allowed me to take control, to fill up our space with a manager's know-how. In ways, I'd learned, through my father's modeling, how to take control of situations (except for, of course, when it came to having control over the bag of Frito Lays on my lap).

In the closet, I assumed a manner similar to the one Gino displayed at home when he denied me the ability to make choices or to navigate my own experience. One perk of having no sense of safe personal boundaries is knowing how to act like someone else. Without thick enough skin one tends to absorb the personalities of those around her. She gains excellent observational skills as a result of her needing to stay on high alert for all potential threats, which later lends itself to becoming an expert in assessing the conditions and then taking charge. She learns to employ a martial arts–like response in her primary relationships just to get her basic needs met. Obviously, Seven Seconds in Heaven (and, furthermore, all intimate experiences) called for stepping up with directorial control. The way Gino iron-handedly dealt with me would largely be my safe way of dealing with men. I'd find the guys who had disappeared into themselves more than I had, those who would let me take charge. I assumed control by projecting my prescribed protocol onto our shared reality; this was my only working definition of a harmonious relationship. My dad, in order to make his way in a new world after being robbed of place and purpose by the war, seemingly did the same. He was a medalist-level manager, an Olympian survivor, and his torch would be passed down to his children, even if two out of three of them were mere girls.

Those seven seconds in heaven *were* heavenly mostly because I'd stumbled upon my own power. However I'd sourced it, it felt sultry and seductive to me. Even though I was a novice in the realm of actual kissing, I knew we couldn't get out of there without accomplishing our seven-second mission. I simply stated matter-of-factly, *Johnny, let's just do it.* He was at a loss for words, but also at a loss for moves, so I initiated, putting my hand on his thigh. He mirrored the action, pressing his hand onto mine and leaning forward. The weight of his hand and arm felt heavy, like a rock—his energy, boyishly bottled up. His face twisted into something of a flirtatious scowl, just mean enough to look attractively tough in the dim light of the closet. I could feel Johnny's frustration or desperation, something like urgency. His aroused energy probably came from the pent-up aggression he carried in his adolescent life, being picked on at home, treated like a worthless fledgling by his older brother. I related. Together, we transformed our young, nervous irritations into a first kiss. Curious about the feeling of the never-been-shaved growing fuzz of dark hair on his upper lip, I planted my lips on his. His were thick, like mine, but even bigger, and of a slightly purplish hue. His breath made me think of maple syrup. It was the weekend, probably a Bisquick-pancake-and-Aunt-Jemima kind of morning. Thanks to the hint of maple syrup, Johnny tasted good to me. I counted on my fingers to make sure our mouths touched for seven entire seconds. Then, I sat back. I remember he looked a little stunned. *Let's get out of here*, I chortled nervously. Maybe this was kind of fun. I'd have to figure out later what to make of the experience. That night, I decided kissing Johnny was definitely better than his hurling rocks at me. If there were two options for contact, I'd go with the soft lips and warm hands over the rocks thrown at my bike spokes and book bag.

I'm ashamed now to admit that liking boys proved a decent measure for enforcing diet. While I didn't dare trust my body in my own hands, or size it up with my own sense of reality, I could gauge my value to some degree by their level of arousal as a result of my provocation. I developed this self-worth appraisal system as the years went on, continuing to draw conclusions. For example, in my twenties, I calculated the following formula: three weeks of weight loss due to a no-bread diet plus freshly blown-out salon hair equals the attention of whatever man I'd chosen as prey. Of course, I couldn't imagine that it was simply my apparent self-value I'd turned on, a glimmer of joyfulness dancing in my eye. No way. I'd determined I was only worth looking at once I'd slimmed down to a size 8 or smaller. To be brutally honest, securing a boy's affection was just another type of container, like my car, my pool, my closet. The boy was the place I could nearly deal with the experience of being in a body, where I'd accept my curves, interpreted by the assessment of his hands. Through his eyes, I might feel worthy, depending on the extent he'd come on to me. While I wasn't capable of feeling self-empowered, I could powerfully command a man, at least through my body. I set up the dynamic from the start: I'd lure him in, and I'd be the tough one. I'd be the one in control. I'd have the money, and I'd call the shots. If need be, I'd change the locks while he was gone and kick his things to the curb (and I have). If I'm going to broach the subject of love, I mean, if we're going to get into the whole entangled fettuccini alfredo of my relationship patterns, kissing Johnny Marconi in the closet was probably a fine place to start.

For a season, Johnny and I played Tom and Jerry. He'd chase me, and I'd pretend I wasn't interested. He'd do his own thing, and I'd create a disturbance, getting his attention. At home, I'd had practically zero education on the subject of how to deal with boys, so cartoons, as influential as they proved to be in all realms of my fundamental psychological construct, also did the job here. More or less, Tom and Jerry's relational behavior provided me with the closest thing I could find to Dr. Ruth, as far as understanding love dynamics. I'm not sure I was authentically sexually piqued about any boy at that point, really, but I *was* interested in the possibility of getting into trouble. Trouble was the only avenue out of Bridgewood, Connecticut. Rebelling seemed the sole means of conjuring any fun, and negative attention was the only type I'd been trained to receive. Of course, my budding Obsessor and Escapist encouragingly agreed; trouble was their favorite and most familiar highway to cruise.

In the summer after I'd turned ten, despite the back-and-forth antics with Johnny, he asked me to be his girlfriend. My girlfriend status lasted about two and a half hours, a perfect length of time for a first go, my inaugural romantic commitment in the foreign territory of establishing a mutual affinity. Here's how it went: We were at the pool and Johnny cornered me in the deep end. I was treading water, trying to make sure my nose wasn't running. *Yeah* was my big answer when he asked if I'd "go steady." I kept treading, kind of awkwardly, while he gave me the obligatory peck on the lips. I was in the pool, one of my places where I could safely sense I had limbs, so I could track the stimulation; the feeling of my stomach free-falling to my toes. Johnny swam off to buy a hot dog, and I emerged from the pool and got my footing. On land, I immediately capped any hint of my own excitement. *No big deal—now I have a boyfriend. I don't care. It doesn't matter that I'm the only fifth grader I know who's actually been asked out by a boy.* Whatever. Johnny and our team of little misfit friends continued to play Marco Polo in the pool for the next few hours and partake in diving board competitions. I laid out on the lounge chair in the sun, opening my eyes and lifting my head every so often to look at Johnny. He was mine now, according to the songs, to the movies, to *Teen* magazine's standards. I watched him dive, serve a semi-deflated beach ball, and dunk his scrawny friend's head. *Why did he hit the ball that way and call out those goofy words to his friends?* Anything he did now held a deeper meaning for me. I felt kind of confused; did I even like him anymore? In retrospect, how could Johnny have seemed enough for me when I hadn't ever considered I was enough. Where I couldn't bear my own pockmarks of inadequacy, I'd engage in speculating about his, now that he was my mirror. Of course, making sense of this new commitment, *Johnny and Giana, Giana plus Johnny, Giana Marconi, Giana Giovanni Marconi*—was far too much. The Obsessor's appetite for sabotage growled, signaling me to pour fuel on the fire. My destructive nature triggered as reflex, conjuring the same kind of behavior that led me to paint my sister's favorite doll. I had *inflammation of the personality*, a type of agitated response to life that I would work hard as an adult to control. Maybe in the future of *mindfulness education* that publicly caught fire around 2010, I may have been able to recognize my triggers, learn how to self-soothe, and calm the reactive reflexes before combusting. Instead, without knowing it, there on my lounge chair, my distress escalated. In just two hours, being Johnny's new girlfriend was already too challenging a role for me to step into. I was untrained in the skill of remaining well-adjusted in transitions—or in general, actually, clueless when it came to softening into the moment and leading with gentle curiosity. I definitely didn't ask myself, *GG, what might it be like to relax into this new arrangement without expectations? To feel my way through this new dynamic as Johnny's girlfriend?* Nope. Instead, I acted in a way I couldn't justify and chalked it up to *I don't know why I did that*, which sometime followed suit to my go-to, *I don't care*. As usual, my behavior was confounding to others, and I sure as heck didn't have the means to comprehend my own outlandish rationale. I guess I needed to feel evidence, darn it, of Johnny's care, wanted to be sure of my value to him. To be honest, Johnny probably was about as fit to be a boyfriend as a slab of mozzarella fits shrimp linguini, and regardless, whatever extent of affection young Johnny was available to offer, I'd never be able to receive it, anyway. When someone suffers from deflated self-esteem, they'll generally find a way to enforce their low self-regard. Johnny could have serenaded me passionately with an entire Verdi opera when I agreed to go steady with him, and I still would have thought he was cruelly teasing me. The fact is, he wasn't going to value me because I didn't value myself. Thus, I assessed, this relationship already seemed fated for *suckiness*. I ascertained that Johnny, just like the assortment of processed snack options at Cumberland Farms, would never be enough. I already wanted more, was already restless; I needed to *do* something.

I dealt with the situation like a pious daughter of strict Italian upbringing. Just as my parents had constantly put me through the ringer of their critical evaluations, I expertly sized up Johnny's *enoughness* in spectator mode, poolside. Poor Johnny fell far short of being enough in my scrutinizing, Gino-like eyes. My sense of his deficiency was not much different than my mindset when dining out decades later. Ordering the entire left side of a menu, I operate from my default setting of *never enoughness*. I attempt to fill this looming void. Assessing that having just one or two things lacks *enoughness*, I must make sure I have the entirety of edible possibilities on my plate. Then I'll compensate all-the-more for the still-persistent lack of *enoughness* by burying each dish under a mountain of condiments. Whether relaxing poolside in a Bridgewood lounge chair circa the early 1970s or comparing Mediterranean salads at an exclusive bistro along the azure Aegean coast (forever in *restaurant research* mode), it's all the same. My *It's not enough* is really pointing at *I'm not enough*. This is the hunger I cannot satisfy, the umami-like-flavor detector that always comes up empty on my tongue. The insatiable *never enoughness* operates voraciously, somewhat like a nerve ending that's longing to arrive at a fully satiated point of awareness, self-fulfilled. This is what happens when we leave our bodies at an early age, when we have no place to calmly anchor the momentum of life. It's an expression of disembodiment. This phrase, *It's not enough*, is among the most prevalent within my Eating Words vernacular. Evidently, I zoned out during grade-school grammar class (surprise, surprise). I've confused the subject and the predicate, been tactless with syntax. If *it* is not enough, then *I* am not enough, and, interchangeably, *you*, *they*, and *everything else* also fall short. Regardless of how many exotic spices and kinds of salts I've brought home from every seaside town on planet Earth, I cannot cancel out the dominant flavor, bite after guilty bite: *I am not enough*, and all of the herbs of Italy cannot console my longing.

Meanwhile, I'm well versed in the importance of gratitude, generosity, and the Law of Attraction. I have spent thousands of dollars on workshops, learning how to say thank you and mean it. I know I appreciate the people in my life, and that I express this with generosity. I have a massive sense of respect for what my parents underwent and how they fought to build security for our family. Still, ultimately, the ravenous emptiness descends upon me like a foreshadowing fog. The *never enoughness* always comes back to signal my inevitable collapse, folding and falling into a bingeing eruption.

There are perks of carrying around untreated trauma, lovely little side effects left behind, like gag gifts for post-party souvenirs. I really won the raffle with this one. My take-home party favor? I seem to undergo moments of lapsed consciousness, after which I have no clue how I got from point A to point B. For example, I'm driving along on the highway, fresh from the office, believing I feel pretty good. I'm convinced I'm heading home to speed-read two hundred pages of a book by someone I'm interviewing the next morning on my webcast. Suddenly, I pass a billboard of Subway's new Ultimate Meatball Marinara, and I'm usurped. To me, the advertisement reads seductively, like fascist propaganda may have to a poor Sicilian farmer circa 1920. I'm sold. Suddenly, my blinker's on, and I'm exiting off I-95. They got me with the promise of "healthier ingredients," plus my gateway-drug word, or shall we call it, my exit-ramp cue. There's the word, nearly scripted in the sky: ***ZESTY***—and it's shining like a diamond on the giant billboard. I've no choice; I'm off to find the Subway Ultimate Meatball Marinara faster than you can say *Ultimate Cheesy Garlic Bread*, which I might get on the side. Just three seconds ago, I was clearly heading home, and now it's like a movie, where we flash forward, skipping the moment when the character makes a conscious choice. It's the next scene, and I'm in my car, unwrapping the steaming factory-prepped, boat-length sandwich. The phrase *It doesn't matter* automatically translates in my mind to *I don't matter*, whether it comes to dealing with digesting intimacy or drive-through carbs. My animal instincts are all twisted up. I want so much to receive, to experience the moment, to stay connected and not check out. My body, though, operates like a field with landmines and security spikes, untouchable, despite any alluring bougainvillea blooms. Lia was right in this case: I suck at simple addition. As far as figuring out what is healthy and nourishing, in realms of love (or even gauging what, exactly, constitutes a normal serving of cheese), I have no clue how to add one plus one. Taking in or receiving anything, be it a young man or aged mozzarella, just seemed like an opportunity to zero out, to shrink, to disappear.

In the same kind of point A to point B blackout behavior that leads me from the highway to the Subway for a meatball grinder, I sort of blanked between scenes during that summer of fifth grade, newly inaugurated as Johnny Marconi's girlfriend. I moved from enjoying a poolside lounge, admiring my freshly mauve-painted preteen toenails to rising, guns blazing. I was Rambo-level good at destroying all chances of affection, even then. In perfect sync with my butchered, switched-up behavioral patterns, I celebrated the anniversary of the second hour of our new relationship when Johnny's cousin Joe entered the pool. He'd come to get Johnny for a family lunch or something. Everyone had gotten out of the pool by now and dried off. Joe stood talking with Johnny by the diving board, and I awkwardly positioned myself, standing in my bathing suit a few feet from their conversation, an unacknowledged outsider. It was really Johnny's first opportunity to shine as an awakened male, but he was twelve, and it was 1970. Neither of us had a clue. Rather than call me over, put his arm around me, proudly make an announcement about our new united plan of true romance, Johnny started to leave without saying goodbye to me.

He simply walked away without looking at me, with his cousin Joe following behind. I could make about as much sense of adolescent males as I could of myself, so I responded with nonsensical, disruptive behavior. My rationale was that I was being super funny, even if in the aftermath, along with everyone else, I was sort of left in the dark as to what I'd done and why. Maybe acting out would provide me with the only ample attention I'd known how to secure, punishment for being a *bad girl* who didn't care anyway. Bad-girl behavior was my cry of *Hey! What about me?* It makes sense in terms of how my current form of self-care looks after a kick-ass workday. Rather than going for a luxe day-spa mud-mask facial, I'm more likely to be smearing self-sabotaging bad-girl behavior all over my life.

Because Joe was fully dressed, complete with his Seiko watch—which I guess was not waterproof—my grand gesture of tossing him into the deep end was not to my advantage, or, at least, to the advantage of the romantic rapport between Johnny and me. Quite immediately, before we could reach the magic third hour of our newly formed commitment, Johnny broke up with me. Just minutes later, right after we'd closed the pool gate, standing on the sidewalk, in front of everyone, he kicked me to the curb. Basically, from that point on, Johnny hardly looked at me again. And I promptly decided, *It doesn't matter. He's stupid.* I buffered myself from any further vulnerabilities involving boys, inching closer to *never enoughness*, which seemed to be becoming my constant tried-and-true.

CHAPTER 7

The Hustle and the Hamburgers

By middle school, I looked like a full-fledged adult. Evidently, I'd pulled off the appearance of having a mature body to the point that Lia deemed I was of solid-enough stature to send me out to pasture. For my twelfth birthday, I was given the gift of being *just the right age to start contributing to the family like an adult*. My schoolmates spent their birthdays blowing out candles, receiving gifts of Sassoon jeans, laughing with extended family over shared Disneyland memories. I, meanwhile, trained to haul out garbage and wipe down sticky tables at the Bridgewood branch of my parents' budding American Grill dynasty. At that time, my dad and his uncle shared twelve restaurants—twelve blue-collar havens, where patrons could reward their hard day's labor without breaking the bank, fill up with a flank steak at lunch, and refill their 7UP seven times before getting back to the life of construction work. My parents passed on to me their workaholic zeal; there's no rest for the wicked, like the Bible says. Lia had long left the cloistered life behind. Her confessions were more like mumblings after our holy Sunday *restaurant research* suppers. *Forgive me, Father, for I, again, had Carvel.* By the end of my middle school years, the Giovannis' sense of religiosity was transferred firmly into the faith of working, glorifying the virtue of *professional sacrifice*. In ways—as it had for my father and mother, even early on—work saved my soul and also wore me to the bone, suiting me well, as I'd probably disassociated from my body before learning to walk. *Save my soul? Bingo! Wear down my bones? No prob; I won't take inventory.*

In my first days at the American Grill, I got the gist that employees made something out of the fact I was the owner's daughter. Maybe they'd exaggerated my circumstances, decided that I must be rich and, thus, didn't have a clue how to work hard. Or maybe they were guarded, wary I would rat them out. I wasn't immediately allowed access to the gossip. *Jean and Ann inhaled the end of the whipped cream can to get a nitrous high.* Everyone knew, but *Careful, don't let Giana see because, well, who knows if she'll tell.* Just to look at me, at least in those first years, was apparently already an occupational hazard for my coworkers. I felt like an outcast, a pariah, but frankly, I'd felt this way (or worse) in most places, so this was just another gate to break down. Strangely, for about four decades of being part of a family-run business, I continued to feel like the owner's daughter instead of GG Giovanni, but I learned to grapple with it. I made it work for me. Within my first seasons at the American Grill, I was sure to show my fellow restaurant staff members that I was one of them. I'd carry the heavy loads when needed, just as well as they could. I slid into the Grill's social scene with my chameleon-like skills. A daughter of immigrants knows innately how to adapt.

Before long, work felt more like a social club than a place to perfect how to run a Hobart dishwashing system. Back at school, I'd become tougher than my classmates. I'd graduated into a different stratum of peers. Lia had intended to halt any potential solicitous behavior by sending me off to the Grill, saving me from turning into a *fast girl*. Once I'd proven I could work hard, I felt socially accepted at the Grill, and my shifts felt exciting for a twelve-year-old, like going to a candy store. While the boys in Catholic school were practically still holding their mother's hands to cross the street, the guys working at the restaurant were virile and experienced at age sixteen. They washed dishes to save money for their gas tanks and six-packs while the boys at school were still weaning, comparatively speaking. Why should I care about some waspy girl's recount of *American Graffiti* and her impossible crush on Ron Howard, when I was busy talking to Bobby Johnson in the cooler at work about his new car tires. I'd no more time for eighth-grade girls' antics. I'd already developed advanced hand gestures with Ken in the kitchen, signaling him for a smoke break in the alley. Of course, I hid all of this from Gino and Lia, but by the time I hit thirteen, *conversations in the cooler* had turned into straight-up *make-out sessions in the cooler*, and I was getting a hands-on sense of my body...but not by my own hands. I discovered that guys might take my hips in their hands if I let them, shove their tongue messily into my mouth, rub their hands over my back pockets. These were the available compliments, a way to gauge my worth. I set my boundaries and limits in the fashion of most girls growing up in the early seventies in upper-middle-class Connecticut. These limits and boundaries of mine looked something like this: *We can kiss, but as far as below the neck, for a good season of ball or two, you're not getting off of first base.* There would be no unplanned sex, of course. I'd have to really think about it first, because I planned to stay *decent.* Maybe my lack of remembering to always say grace before my every meal rendered me unable to call myself a *good Catholic girl* per se, but at least I'd stay decent.

My mother and father hoped to instill hard-nosed principles in their eldest daughter by paying her the minimum, $1.85 an hour, forever. While this was the minimum wage in Connecticut in 1973, Lia kept me at this pay as long as possible, insisting that it was still too much. She failed to comprehend I'd want anything in return for my labor. *Giana doesn't need to be paid, to be reciprocated. Giana doesn't have needs.* As was typical, I'd rebel indirectly, refusing to submit to their rule. I found more purpose at the Grill bumming cigarettes off the busboy and flirting with the dishwasher than concerning myself with refilling salad dressings. I decided that if I had to give up my weekends expediting chicken fingers and fries while underpaid, but still be expected to cover my ever-increasing load of homework, I would not sacrifice *fun.* Fun, in young Giana terms, was achieved in one way only: mischievous danger, pushing everything past its limits.

Over summer break, I caught more shifts and graduated from trash hauler to cashier. Before long, Frankie, who was just one grade below me in school, joined me on the job. We'd end each of our shifts with a Super Burger Plate: a hamburger, fries, and free refills of Coca-Cola. After we made it home, Frankie and I would head straight to the couch to catch an *Ed Sullivan Show* rerun or the CBS Sunday Night Movie accompanied by something sweet and prepackaged, like Yodels, those cream-filled cakes coated in a layer of chocolate. I was a Yodels girl, and proud of the alliance. If our Giovanni basecamp supply of Yodels had run out, I'd find refuge in a Ring Ding or a bag of Fritos. While I received an aggressive diatribe in response to even the slightest move I made or criticism of how I did something, there was never any discussion about what I could or couldn't eat. Somehow this was the one place a parental blind eye was turned. However much I was limited in every other way in those days—no talking on the phone, no inviting friends over, no emotional allowance, no forgiveness given—with food, I could practice abundance, I had something I could say *yes* to. Unsurprisingly, given my later work as a self-titled Abundance-Mindset Coach, as a child, I invested my care in the first place I found abundance: inside the kitchen cupboard. I flexed my ability to give my attention to this twenty-cubic-foot area of my world, keeping it securely full. Checking the shelves, I could assess exactly what I had under my command. Hostess Twinkies? Check. Devil Dogs? Check. Ding Dongs? Yep. Ring Dings? All aboard! I'd grab a fistful and join Frankie. Together, we'd drift out into the safe waters of TV land until we carb-crashed like nobody's business into bed, waking up the next summery morn charged with natural Italian gusto.

After my first experience with intimacy, with Johnny and the big swimming pool breakup, I did my best to promise myself that, even if I caught a small thrill from a guy, he would never mean anything *major* to me. As per the day's norm for budding young women, my entry into high school mandated acquiescence. I'd exchange whatever remained of my unfettered raw instinct for an education in the fundamentals of female attractiveness; this was what was deemed important. Like every girl, I was made privy to what caught a boy's attention, and unconsciously ingested the social importance of earning masculine approval. It was drilled into us. I'd learned well enough from my Johnny Marconi experience, however, so I'd keep myself out of the line of fire for as long as possible. Rather than put myself on the front line, I would play it cool, keep my skin thick. In or out of school, no one learned how to have healthy intimacy. The single way to negotiate relationship boundaries was to build walls, blockades, allowing one to remain emotionally and physically buffered. I think it's safe to say that, in general, if we do not develop language to communicate our relationship needs, we just build walls. So I did that.

With my *playing it cool* attitude, I experimented for a few years on and off with Ned, who washed dishes at Bridgewood's American Grill and seemed entirely harmless. *Ned, Ned, Pumpkin Head*, as Frankie and I called him behind his back. It's probably more accurate to describe Ned as resembling the *entire* pumpkin, as he was about two feet tall (at least according to my exaggerated memory). I don't mean to sound rude, but the truth is, I felt safe with Ned *because* he was small. Maybe I instinctually felt more in control with a man who appeared weaker than me. My attraction to Ned was likely less hormonally driven and more steered by my inner six-year-old. However much she'd been silenced, six-year-old GG mustered the volition to call the shots on dealing with the opposite sex, enforcing her clear directive: Boys should be tiny, whether physically, energetically, or both. It was essential that I should always be able to slide right out from underneath them. *Fit that bill? Well, I'll give you my number.*

Ned and I fooled around for a couple of years, nothing too serious. By the time I was fourteen, though, Ned said he wanted my virginity, and I was a good-enough sport in response to his gradually encroaching requests. We didn't actually discuss it, but I knew it was coming; we were *ready* by the day's standards. He'd successfully gotten to some of the bases in the walk-in cooler. We were ready because we'd already made out in at least four different parking lots and on the track behind my school. This was sensual progression; it's what we'd learned in the pathetic mid-seventies version of sex ed. Ned had done his share of the prep work, and I'd done mine. He bought some sort of prophylactic, and I'd shaved my legs. By these protocols, we were ready. My body, however, was not exactly on board, as expected—always the rebel.

As per usual, Ned's mom was home. She was the complete opposite of my conservative mother and actually asked me to call her by her first name, Cindy. She was single, smoked unfiltered cigarettes, was divorced, and for whatever reason, was home more often than not. Cindy was totally fine with Ned and me spending time in his bedroom unsupervised and with the door closed; we could even smoke in his room if we felt like it. While my inner rebel had been well trained to commit devious acts under Lia's rigid rule, I wasn't sure how to let go and feel free in such a liberated household. I kept thinking, while Ned awkwardly tried to stick his hand down the front of my buttoned jeans, of his mother cheering him on. I was kind of *freaking out*. My body, apparently, wasn't in cahoots with Cindy's afforded freedom and couldn't *operatively* consent once Ned and I had shed most of our layers, lying exposed in the stark light of his basic, boyish room. Some part of me wanted to just go home, back to my version of normalcy, back to my control-freak parents who limited my every move. I felt nervous about the sexual proactivity I was attempting to pull off inside Ned's liberally run household. *Something's off* was all I said when I failed to follow through and go all the way with Ned. I assumed I was at fault. I was a slow learner, remember? I also couldn't get all of my messy female parts on board; evidently, they were dumb too. On that day, after the *deflowering* mission derailed, it seemed easier just to ignore Ned for the rest of our lives. I'd done the same with Johnny, my first love interest. I believed it was the only option for self-preservation and certainly better than trying to put my experience into words, to bear communicating. Ned continued to pursue me, for whatever reason remaining optimistic—his ego, obviously less marred by our history. One skill I've inherited from my Adriatic ancestors is the ability to hold firm to my decisions, so basically, at this point, Ned was *dead to me*. Just like that. And I'd turn down my boy radar for a season or two before dialing back in to that current, when I'd crash into an unexpected sensation: a young man who turned around my previously committed *I don't care* mindset. But I'm getting ahead of myself.

$\mathscr{I}$talian Gardening 101:
How to Cultivate a Seed

After eighth grade, our small co-ed Catholic school class of twenty-three boys and girls transitioned to the affiliated high school, and suddenly, I found myself in a swarm of around four hundred students in my class alone. The Fair Girls became yesterday's news, and I spent my time, instead, with the kids who were interested in testing limits and breaking rules. Unruly behavior was the only outlet for my wild nature, for my unrefined feminine expression. Lia and Gino had infused me with low self-esteem when it came to my scholastic capabilities, so I ventured out to find an area where I felt I could thrive: the arena of *troublemaking*, in which I had a pretty supreme ability to excel.

On a particularly favorable late afternoon, ripe for juvenile delinquency, I invited a few classmates over to my house. Lia and Gino were at work, and even Frankie and Gino Jr. weren't home, so we had the whole place to ourselves. I'd not yet had the experience of being *lit*—intoxicated in any way—but my new friends encouraged the exploration of my family's liquor cabinet, even though we collectively possessed little knowledge about most of its contents. Vodka, scotch, rum, whiskey—all of these seemed the same. A dark-colored liquor stored in a rectangular glass bottle with a colorful label looked appealing to our group. Judging it solely on its appearance, we decided this one would do the trick. We each took turns swigging directly from the bottle for a long count of four. Less than a few passing minutes later, most of us were amply intoxicated, with just enough common sense remaining to remember we had to attend the school play within the hour. I didn't bother to refill the nearly drained bottle with water to disguise the fact that we'd emptied the majority of its contents. Instead, I placed it on the counter in an open rebel yell.

The school play was a blur. I recall we loaded up on chewing gum and doused ourselves with drugstore cologne before we sat down to watch a version of *Our Town*, in an attempt to disguise the olfactory evidence of our recent foray into my family's liquor cabinet. It turned out that the level of the high school production aptly called for substantial inebriation in order to seduce the audience members into submission. Thus, appropriately wasted, we sat knee to knee in a back row. I remember being a bit more aware of the physical sensation of the alcohol than the lines being delivered from the stage. With a boy's knee near mine in the darkened auditorium, the muskiness in the air of the unventilated gym-turned-theater magically shape-shifted; my body and my mind were practically in sync. If this was drunkenness, I thought, why had I waited so long to sample from my parents' cabinet? This was almost better than an episode of *Soul Train*.

The actress playing the character of Emily in *Our Town* did her best with the impressive line, *It's not easy for a girl to be as perfect as a man, because, well, we girls are more nervous*, but I was lost within my own star-filled sky, a million miles away when intermission was called. While my reality swirled and stretched into imaginative realms of transcendence, Lia raced the thirteen minutes from Bridgewood to my Dansfield school, arriving in time for *Our Town*'s intermission, fired up and ready to kill me. As we were being ushered out into the hallway, my initial blood-sugar alcohol high settled into what could be better described as a blurred stupor. I wandered around suddenly lost, attempting to locate a bathroom I regularly visited during the school day. It was a perfectly awkward moment, and a prime one for Lia to pounce. With her Italian nose keen for fermentation, my mother called me out like a sommelier can name the vintage, region, and specific vineyard of a wine. The nearly empty bottle I'd left on the counter at home allowed Lia to arrive at a quick conclusion that I was creating a path of trouble. It was obvious that my subconscious mind wanted to make it easy for my punishment-hungry psyche. The sharp pinch of my mother's fingers grabbing my right ear shook me out of my stumbling haze. *My Fast Times at Dansfield Catholic Prep High* were instantly steered in the opposite direction. In a perfectly embarrassing display, Lia belittled me right in front of my friends, who, prior to this moment, had bought into my *tough-girl-in-charge, queen-of-bad* facade. Now, my little Italian mother, eye-to-eye and nose-to-nose equal in size to her firstborn took me down, stripped me of all my toughness. I was infantilized as Lia landed her fiery attacks: *Giana Clara Giovanni, you are in major, major trouble, girl! You are going to really get it bad! You are not going to recover from this one, GG!* Lia's excited fury possessed enough drama to make up for any lack of talent on our high school stage, and for me, the play was promptly over. Of course, more than anticipating my future punishment or conceiving of any potential life changes that might result from this single drunken episode of mine, I was concerned about what my friends thought as my mother took me down. Lia gripped the nape of my neck and marched me to the car, throwing me in the back seat, where my audience members, Frankie and Gino Jr., were seated. She turned on the ignition, breathed heavily a few times, and then promptly laid into me.

This event took place close to the end of my days attending a large high school. I had just a few months remaining until the end of the ninth-grade school year. That night, I'd shown my parents that I couldn't be trusted with the vast number of troublemaking possibilities in a school with over eight hundred students. I was the kind of girl who needed set limits and only bite-size stimuli or else all havoc would break loose. *Wolffiers* could not be trusted to follow their wild gut instincts. I was to live under Lia and Gino's parental allotments.

At age fourteen, empathic Giana lacked the ability to set boundaries, especially so in the middle of a large crowd. Everywhere she turned, she emitted signs of high danger to her parents. And,

"LIA MARCHES GIANA OUT"

while emotionally callous, Gino and Lia managed to be responsible guardians when push came to shove. They responded to my smoke signals with the only language available in our family: anger. After the school-play incident, I was grounded for the remainder of the academic year. I returned to my old social scene of evenings spent with Frankie, involving Stove Top insta-dinners and episodes of *Bonanza, Lost in Space, Green Acres,* and *Petticoat Junction.* After what felt like an infinite stretch of being forbidden to do *anything with anybody* and being cross-checked at every encounter with my mother, I was issued Lia and Gino's latest parental ruling. Frankie and I were now forbidden to attend Dansfield Catholic Prep for the following school year (my sophomore year, and Frankie's freshman). I had proven too troublesome to attend an institute with such a vast, unruly population, and Frankie—as per the usual—would suffer right along with me the effects of my reckless behavior. This was a common theme in our sisterhood, one about which Frankie—understandably—still holds a significant grudge. In the spirit of long-lasting Italian conviction, the ignoring of emotions, and our stubbornness combined, it's understandable we've never had a polite tête-à-tête to process some *doozies* Frankie endured as a result of my behavior. After all, it is the refined *French* who created the whole etymological origin of the tête-à-tête, speaking heart-to-heart and face-to-face—the French, who are known for mild talk and poised sophistication. Italians are better at boldly sharing their opinions, straight to the point and heavy on the gas and brakes. To join in, just pull a chair up to the dinner table and start yelling. In the case of our southern Italian family, this translates well into dropping verbal-attack bombs and maintaining staunch defenses. We communicate as if we are the Mini-Me of Italy, the small, complete replicate, prone to the same historical position. Frankie and I have battled each other and endured strife, but regardless of our agitations, we've stuck together for better or for worse. My sister was a type of witness for me. I needed her to come along when I carried out my shenanigans. Through Frankie, I could affirm my actual being on the planet. If I'd have gone it alone, I'd have been a tree falling in the woods.

As a kid, I never checked in with Frankie to find out what she might need. The exchange was just assumed; I'd create the scene and the havoc. She'd come along, but I'd stomach all the attackers. If I got in trouble, she could hide behind me. I'd take the negative impact for the team and then tuck it deep down into my psyche, use it later to feed my Escapist and Obsessor. Even though I was the troublemaker, the Giovanni girls would be sent off as a pair to reform, to the new terrain of an all-girls school in Bellfield, fifteen minutes in the opposite direction of my former academy. No matter how cleverly we attempted to refuse this parental decision, the ball was in their court, and we were left to obey their command. The only possible chance to escape my parents' decision was to purposely fail the school's entry exam, a plan I'd convinced Frankie to also attempt. I answered the multiple-choice questions as a baker might sprinkle raisins in panettone, at random and to my fancy. Perhaps my early psychic guesswork was more on point than I could have imagined, or the gods were really with my parents, because Frankie and I were admitted. We had no choice; dropping out was not an option. This would be the end of my social life. Having to consent to my parents' punitive limitations felt like a major *biting of the dust* for team Giana. Thanks to the war-zone style of Giovanni parenting, I had been wiped out, and I had no choice but to surrender. I was defeated but unforgiving.

In retrospect, I was quite out of touch with the fact that my parents were spending a significant portion of their hard-earned money on my education. Remaining consumed with my bitter stance was far easier. If I'd had to consciously recognize how much my parents had financially provided for Frankie and me, surely I would've felt consumed by guilt, or else vulnerably exposed and, admittedly, dependent. In fact, to this day, no one in my family can stand to recognize in daylight or bear to speak aloud just how deeply we're financially invested in one another. Economic entanglement is our sole means of securing our bond, the way we've known how to stick together. It's part out of genuine care, and partly the way we disprove each other's fired insults. We'll come back, defensively claiming our further success, regardless of what belittling comment we've endured. *Yeah, don't think I can? I'll hold my own; watch me.* Our business relationship, which is the same as our family relationship, revolves around our collective needs. This means whatever my family needs in the moment, I'll be consumed with it. It makes sense that we thrive together in the working world. Think about it. If there is no safe means to express care or share emotions, we're better off investing heavily in the single currency we do share: working to make money. So this was how the Giovannis expressed family values. In business, we'd built an empire, some version of safety and security, while leaving all family issues unrecognized.

Emotions were out. To share them would be equivalent to modern-day on-the-job harassment. The Giovanni kids weren't able to look Lia or Gino in the eyes in those early years and say *Thank you* with actual emotional sincerity. This would be like, God forbid, saying *I love you*—definitely out of the question until at least 2010. The Giovannis still had to grow up significantly for that to happen, until the youngest of us was well into his forties. The early years were specifically gruff and aggressive. Lia was a completely different person than the woman who looks at me lovingly today, who says *I love you* each time we hang up the phone. We Giovannis have gotten a little better at sharing our emotions and extending loving invitations, but we've not dared to approach unraveling the impact of our early years. Rather, we are calibrated around our collective wound, the sum of all tumult incurred in our ancestral history.

After Frankie and I were enrolled in a new scholastic prison, all of our external freedoms felt wiped out. The only place I had left to successfully flaunt my destructive, rebellious spirit was inside my imagination. Lia insisted I stop working at the American Grill. She said I had to buckle down and study. My parents had emerged victorious in the battle over Dansfield Catholic Prep; I'd have to accept defeat, however irritating. Since my father's mandate reigned, I'd mimic his austerity at school, again assume a facade similar to his in my self-presentation—thick-skinned, unflinching. Even though I ultimately consented, I did a good job holding on to the anger I had toward my parents for their having sent me off into a whole new social climate, with new girls to buffer myself against. It was too much effort; establishing yet more of my *I don't care* irreverence would be my plan of revenge. My grades were hardly impressive. I was (as I'd been from the get-go) uninterested in proving my worth by academic standards. That type of behavior was for the smart kids, the ones who'd developed their self-esteem based on their own diligent focus.

CHAPTER 9

The Father, the Son, and the Holy Chemical Messengers

My self-esteem—or the closest thing to self-esteem that I could muster—required a shorter rewards program, craved an immediate fix. How could I have known then that my neural patterns were being wired and fired to create the quickest route to trigger a dopamine hit in my brain's frontal lobe? I had practically zero interest in any kind of hard biochemistry at that point in my academic career. I should note that Giana-style medical terminology likely falls short and overgeneralizes, so don't exactly quote me on this stuff. But, basically, dopamine is the brain hormone that rewards us for getting what we desire. It's the place in our brain where *yummmm* and *ahhhhh* and *ooooooh* all brew. Dopamine triggers during moments such as when we hear the theme song of our favorite show. It's designed to pull us toward reward, get through a workout to justify french fries, to heed the call of nature, or in today's world, heed the call of our cell phones. The *dope* hit comes on when the game controller is placed into the Nintendo-addict's hand as his turn to play arrives. As soon as the screen refreshes and his ears detect the music prompting the selection of his chosen fighter, that dose of *dope* proclaims, *Okay! It's your turn!* Dopamine desire comes a-callin' for the shopaholic, *You must get what you don't have!* until she slips her freshly pedicured foot into the newest Louboutins and is properly seduced. It arrives with the turn of the ignition switch just in the nick of time to relieve the midlife crisis. During that first drive on the open road, dopamine temporarily lifts all of life's giant questions into the wind off the hood of the BMW

8 Series Convertible. It provides the emotionally numb workaholic with the erroneous conviction that he's discovered the cure for his tedium, however short-lived the fix.

It's not unusual, especially in today's world, to succumb to the *I want it, so I must have it now* withdrawal call of dopamine. I'll go as far as to say that for some of us, like me, our whole day is a process of call and response in the dance of dopamine. Handling my neural chemicals is sort of a full-time job; these effusive transmitters are definitely my main squeeze. The thrill of a chemical messenger's touch can feel comparable to that of all the casino tokens in Las Vegas. It can seduce someone better than even an Hermès Himalayan crocodile Birkin bag. According to researchers, dopamine lives in our sense of future, hope, and imagination. It lives in the possibility of everything outside of what is already in our hands, what we've already got. Dopamine can both help us procrastinate *and* send us on a frantic mission to appease its cry. It's the queen of hearts on a throne in the Codependent Kingdom, and when it shows up on the scene, even the best boss queens are prone to dropping everything for it. I'm no sociologist, but I'd go so far as to say that many of us respond to our addiction-encouraging dopamine neuro cues more readily than we show up for each other. *Baby crying still? Ah, let her cry herself to sleep. Dopamine levels crying for a shot? Better get right out of bed and quell that bitch.* Example: when I'm in Cumberland mode, nobody gets between me and a giant-size Nestlé Crunch bar; I am hijacked by fixation. At least in the case of Cumberland carbs, I'm no anomaly. Those of us who've well honed the same-ol', same-ol' routes of neural firings in quick-fix dopamine-dominant motivational prompts are more likely, according to medical journals, to end up emotional eaters, self-identified *food addicts*. Basically, dopamine-fixed folks are prone to developing some less-than-awesome habits and are equally resistant to breaking them. We get stuck in muddy ruts. *We sound like a charming bunch, huh?*

In ways, it seems like simple math can determine how dopamine-driven brain loops escalate. Take a kid who's disposed to acting out, whose attention is easily disrupted. Maybe the family has failed to provide the basic emotional how-tos; maybe they're on high alert for havoc. Mix in a good dose of direct verbal abuse and the superficial placation of short-lived nourishment, like TV dinners or even a scrimpy Seven Seconds in Heaven with a half-baked boy. *Bam*—you've got a perfect setup for life as a series of short-term fractionalized moments. To be clear, however, dopamine is not our enemy; let's not knock its essentiality to our well-being. Our neural chemistry is a central part of our whole-body system. It is more or less responsible for our evolutionary drive, along with some other genius attributes of our human design. It is not the chemicals themselves that cause problems for us; in fact, dopamine is the chemical messenger of pleasure! Perhaps a useful point to consider is that in repeating dopamine-rewarding activities, we can lead ourselves deep into the thick of chronic mismanaged behaviors that usually become—you guessed it—our best frenemies: *compulsions* and *addictions*.

Dopamine works along with a whole crew of other chemical messengers produced in the brain's kitchen. Just like in any intimately entangled relationship, each can affect the other. In layman's terms (which are definitely *my* terms) the roles of neurotransmitters are conveniently categorized. Noradrenaline helps us concentrate. Serotonin supports mood regulation. GABA helps us calm down. Acetylcholine activates our ability to learn information (*perhaps you can feel yours checking out just about now*). We can see, just by their short bios above, how interconnected this signaling network is. And neurotransmitters aren't limited to the brain, as you may already know. Our gut instinct actually operates our neurotransmitters' communication; it's quite the high-tech infrastructure. We could think of our gut's neurotransmitter production like that of microbes during sourdough fermentation; a type of lactobacillus is actually responsible for both. It's something like a tiny version of healthy Italian farmland in the human stomach; microbes naturally excrete neurotransmitters like fertilizer. I should note, as a small but important disclaimer, that

I'm no expert in this field, and I'm definitely not here to preach about how all of this works. I get that the ever-evolving science of human biology, and especially neuroscience, is, in principle, always changing. I'm not necessarily reaching into textbooks to intellectually justify my personal pathology. Realizing that my decision-making process is definitely *more than meets the eye* has been key to my developing any hint of self-compassion while I attempt to decode my relationship to *diet* and understand why the heck I end up caving in to something as small as a snack pack of Pringles.

It seems I spent most of my formative years strengthening my dopamine-driven brain patterns, especially during my sophomore year, which, frankly, is normal for most teens. Puberty, hormones, and neurotransmitters plus algebra homework—the combo is the perfect setup for sneaking cigarettes or wolfing a Dunkin' Donuts dozen. In some ways, it would make more sense to spend our high school years learning to meditate in a cave, to empower ourselves through extreme cravings and emotions, or, at least, to receive mandatory government-funded therapy. I guess this is why catchphrases such as *Talk to your teenager* exist. Parents are supposed to rise to the occasion during these years and prepare their kids for the internal workings of maturity. It's a steep expectation. Imagining how most adults are gripped by their own brain chemicals—stressing over the cost of living and work responsibilities and finding relief solely in an evening gin and tonic, or the like—can help us to understand the epidemic of inadequately parented children. There I was, the eldest Giovanni daughter in her sophomore year, yet again transplanted into a new environment with no foundational constant. My new uber-conservative, all-girls Catholic prep school was very different from my last school. I'd now successfully been injected into three different academic institutions in the past three years; it was understandable that I felt a little too exhausted to make new friends. Even if I seemed outwardly extroverted (it's just in the Giovanni face), I felt deeply connected to a loner identity that year, something that I've since learned is often a sign of dopamine imbalance.

While the thought of navigating yet another new social circle felt daunting, I managed to maintain the emotional fuel for feeling extreme spite toward Gino and Lia, both of whom had ripped me away from the classmates of my freshman year. Looking back, I'm sure my parents had saved my life multiple times by moving me here or there, but at the time, I took their regulations as a sign that I was uncared for, unworthy. The best response to what felt like their lack of concern for my happiness, I figured, was to reinforce my indifference about pretty much everything. As we know, *I don't care* had already become my safety phrase. Words of detachment were the major players in the stream of my inner dialogue. I believed in them, overlooking the ramifications of their hurtful nature, like how my body became enslaved under their influence, how it collapsed hopelessly around the directives of my own words. My GPA barely chugged along. After listlessly returning home from school, I would spend my free time watching television, drained and disinterested in much else. I had no long-term sense of drive...that is, until the miraculous moment I dedicated myself to controlling my body through diet. Conceiving that I was able to willfully determine my body size was my first conscious awareness that my brain and body were related. I believed I could follow a simple plan that included hardly any labor in order to reap transformative rewards.

I was sold the product directly from my main mentors, the television commercials of the seventies. I'd become seduced by the promise of the diet pill. Take this, and you will be perfect. Take this, and your waist will effortlessly shrink. Take this, and you'll become invincible. To add to my momentum, Frankie also bought into the plan. We'd do it together, and when Frankie and I decided to do something together, we'd do it all the way. Healthy competition was, after all, the best expression of alliance we could muster in our family.

We had encountered a single solicitous commercial a handful of times during our typical after-school TV-a-thon, and—presto—it was as though we'd come up with the idea ourselves. *We should totally get fit, we decided. We should diet. We should take pills that will make our figures acceptable.* We were young and zealous, up for proving wrong our father's prophesy that we were destined for fat-hood. We would be slim and beautiful.

CHAPTER 10

Dexatrim, Tab, and Cigarettes: That's Amore

That summer, my young, dopamine-desirous feet pedaled to the Stop & Shop. I pulled out a pocketful of table-bussing dollars, and went in fifty-fifty with Frankie. We purchased our first box of pretty Dexatrim pills, and the regimen commenced. Dexatrim, Tab, and cigarettes—a magic trifecta to trim our waistlines and slim our thighs. Dexatrim was packed with a formidable amount of the drug phenylpropanolamine, which the FDA has since banned from over-the-counter sales due to its significantly adverse side effects, like its ability to cause brain-chemical imbalances (setting a perfect stage for eating disorders). Phenylpropanolamine raises dopamine levels in the brain and thus convinces the appetite to shut down. That's how it works...at least, at first. Before my neural pathways wore thin of its effects, Dexatrim was a great step in my *dopey* pattern of using external stimulation to regulate my internal system.

At the time, I thought I just wanted to fit into a size 6, but really, my brain had other ambitions. It wanted to quickly downregulate the intensity of my long-term stress patterns, both my own suppressed memories and the post-trauma war narratives I'd genetically chosen to reiterate. I imagine that before its reincarnation my little twinkling soul went out with some other starlit sparks for a stiff drink in a cosmic bar and then decided, once fully inebriated, to jump right into my next life, sans prescreening, sans protection. *Oh? Go down to planet Earth, mop up the remnants of wartime bloodshed, and churn them through a female body? Declare personal liberation, support the universal embodiment of peace, and come right back to my lush personal stargate here in the cosmos just in time for scrambled supernovas and ham for breakfast? Sure! Sounds super fun! I'll go!* On Earth, I'd find Dexatrim, a kind of cosmic speed to hold steady my inherited internalized militancy.

I'd remain dedicated to *I don't care*, with my body following suit. Perfect for part one of the *Giana Liberation* Lifetime series, titled "The I Don't Care Plan," followed by part two: the similarly titled "The I Can't Feel Plan." The mantra *I can't feel* is excellent for keeping hunger and satiety unrecognizable. Part one and part two together made part three an easy follow-up since *I don't care* and *I don't feel* amounted to, simply, *I don't exist*. It was a logical progression. *Tune in to part three of my Lifetime series, "The I Don't Exist Plan," where I shut out everything!* Then, once the effects of dirty Dexatrim wore off, and I had to feed my emptiness with some sort of actual food, I'd nourish myself using the same negligent mindset. *I don't care, so let's take down the whole row of Ho Hos and Cheetos. Let's stuff this pathetic body to death.* I believed that at the end of every one of my binges lay the promise of relief from this sharp escalation of anxiety. Decades later, I'd endeavor to create a final segment: "The Recovery." I got the narrative and wrote the script for the new-millennium release of the *Giana Liberation* Lifetime series.

Even well into adulthood, when I'd professionally mastered putting out fires in all corners of the globe, I'd continue to submit entirely to my own primal response system, *one helluva beast*. I'd freeze, lying on my back like a helpless little animal, paws waving, blacking out under the attack. Just like neural circuits band together, certain to be stronger when working in unison, the various Giana pieces often form into a united alliance. Together, they present as impossible to stop, creating a pretty mean barricade of protection. I still have the parts I manufactured to get through my school years, namely, *The Callous Teen, The Promiscuous Teen,* and *The Shamefully Curvaceous Teen*, along with my lifers, *The Rebel, The Tasmanian*

Devil, The Disassociated Escapist, The Unquenchable Obsessor, The Manager, and *The Renunciate.* Together, they repeat a track of my best Eating Words, my coping skills, and my negative self-talk. As a whole, they vote *YES* on the Continual Funding for Disassociation ballot. They vote *YES* on finding relief in scraps of semiconscious relationships, *YES* on stopping out-of-control emotion by attracting negative attention. They vote *YES* on inviting harsh punishment as a form of love. All of my pieces, together with their complex operational systems, are like a monster virus of compiled trauma. *How do I get nothing?* is its viral motivation, staving off all chances of developing real self-worth. However much I'd eventually work as a healer and rise to become an owner of multiple businesses, however much I would promote abundance and manifestation, my trauma had its own goal, which was to *get nothing,* because I was *nothing.* Dexatrim helped me to reach the next stage of self-limiting control, a touchdown for the monster virus. Pop the pill and starve, and numb it out, *bambina.*

Frankie, who was equally punished for all of my purgatory-worthy acts, was enrolled in the new high school penitentiary right along with me. While she was equally unenthused about the transfer, we both, at least, benefitted from being able to actively compare notes about what worked best in our diet, in accord with the school-day schedule. This was the best protocol, we'd determined, for our newfound plan for perfection: Have nothing until lunch except for one yellow-and-burgundy capsule and maybe some water. After gym, before English class, sneak a cigarette, and then during lunch hour, enjoy the biggest daytime allowance: two or three more cigarettes, a Tab, and another yellow-and-burgundy capsule. I'd wash it down, if need be, with a refill or two of Tab, which contains the artificial sweetener saccharin that allows beverages to remain free of sugar and calories. Little did we know that later, we'd figure out that even noncaloric, "sugar-free" substances could impose substantial effects on us. Saccharin, along with a bunch of other artificial chemicals, such as Butter Yellow and ethylene glycol would later be banned in several countries and linked to cancer, but for now Tab was *all good*. In fact, it was a pillar of my aesthetic health.

I dropped pounds; it was the first time I'd tried anything like that, and I was finding success. In fact, the Dexatrim diet may have been (aside from learning to ride a big-kid bike) the first real, independent success I'd had. Finally, I'd found a way to restrain myself, to regulate whatever trace of emotional vulnerability I had left. Controlling my body with Dexatrim was an artificial way to affirm self-authority. It was the first relationship in which I could model effective self-assertiveness. Never mind that I was significantly under the influence of my three potent daily capsules, or that under their influence, I'd completely forget to eat some days, I was able to focus on my success, lying in bed at night feeling the benefit of my labor, my rib cage nearly bony in my hands. My body dysmorphia subsided. I appeared to be a person, an actual form, a young woman; the fun-house mirrors had been dismounted. Sleep, however, did not come so easily, as I also felt the speedy anxiety (a side effect of Dexatrim) running up and down my legs, arms, and stomach. But this was how I'd learn to define what it meant, to register how it felt, to be *in a body*. Anxiety became my main registered sense, and I'd learn to use it as a general anchor point in order to feel human.

As a result of my hard work, Dexatrim and Lia awarded me with a new wardrobe. Lia was too busy with herself, or with work, or with dealing with my father to take much notice of my sudden decrease in food consumption. Instead, she felt proud she'd made the move to transfer me to a new school, taking notice of my trimmer shape and intense *motivation* (anxiety). My grades may not have improved, but I seemed driven (at Dexatrim speed) and was looking like a healthy young woman. Maybe Lia even became slightly hopeful for my future. Lia's attitude, actually, had changed quite a bit. Once Frankie and I had enrolled in the new school, my mother literally sat us down and said *Girls I'm done raising you. I've disciplined you all I can. Now you're on your own*. I think, in part, she felt safe that we were in a highly secure Catholic environment. It was as though she'd drop us off at her safe haven, the San Sebastiano convent. This set her mind at ease, morally freeing her from certain responsibilities. We were now in institutional lockdown, like cloistered nuns. She was sure we'd have no chance of *breaking bad*, turning to a life of immorality; our uniforms alone were more or less chastity belts. And now that we were looking fit in our plaid skirts, she was nearly proud of us, her little pastinas, growing up. Lia's new motto was the Serenity Prayer: *God, grant me the serenity to accept the things I cannot change, courage to change the things I can, and wisdom to know the difference.* For better or for worse, Lia's prior aggressive conviction that her daughter was a complete lost cause had softened. She couldn't change me now, nor Gino or anyone else. Best to just enjoy the cream of the crop, her top-of-the-line Borghese moisturizer and Chanel lipstick. She'd sown the seeds of her land long and hard enough. Time to roll the windows down and shake out her coiffed, perfectly colored blond hair, allowing her sultriness to stop traffic. Bridgewood's best hairstylist, Juan-Rico, was her new saint. With him, she'd had the courage to change from chestnut layers to a straight, shoulder-length champagne-colored cut. She also changed her nail polish from light pink to blood red, and had her eyebrows sculpted into arcs of perfectly expressed *I won't be messed with* elegance. Juan-Rico stood staunchly by her decree; everything else, they decided, she'd wisely leave alone.

CHAPTER 11

In the Garden of Adam and GG

When Lia backed off, interestingly, my rebel fire cooled slightly. Before long, school became mostly okay. I'd acclimated and made some friends. Everything felt easier once I began receiving attention for my physical transformation; this was a version of esteem. Regardless of how I'd milked my attributes to my best advantage, inside, I remained certain I was not enough to be *actually* accepted. Even though I was invited to parties and asked out by boys in the school adjacent to my small Catholic mini-prison, no part of me really relaxed. I felt restless, but at least my restlessness was motivating me in some way. I used it to my advantage, and each day I affirmed my two best traits of character: toughness and my sense of *never-enoughness*. I was doing a pretty darn-good job of keeping *I don't care* behind the wheel. Then I met Adam, the one who U-turned my *I don't care* mindset.

In the beginning, I didn't think much of him. He was classically handsome, built, tall, funny, and smart, and he asked me out on my first actual date—like, a respectful one, the kind set in advance and with a plan. Since I'd only cultivated an eye for skimpy, shrimpy, scrimpy boys, of course I didn't really register my friendly date with Adam as anything worth remembering. He picked me up in his clean maroon Datsun and we saw *The Return of the Pink Panther*. At the time, I thought our first date just hadn't excited me. In retrospect, I realize I'd just been too nervous, too outside myself to feel the connection between us. It struck me, instead, a handful of months later—typical of me and my suppressed emotional response. Adam was good-looking, nice, and funny. These descriptors definitely did not exist in my vocabulary when I talked about men. Until then, I'd reserved the term *good-looking* for something more safely predictable and typically found in a Hostess package. While, by then, I'd allowed myself to be attracted to the opposite sex, I had few descriptors reserved for guys at that time—all quite derogatory, to be honest. Adam was different. I'm sure I was straight-up stunned by the notion of having a functional relationship. So I told myself that I was still getting over Ned as an excuse for my felt lack of interest. I think that in reality, I just needed a moment to register the kind of comfort I almost immediately felt around Adam. This was freaking *foreign* to me. After our date, I shelved the experience and continued to pursue what I could control: fending for myself, fighting with Frankie, and working on my figure.

By the summer after tenth grade I'd gotten it together on the Giana scale of togetherness—a measurement determined always and only by the size to which I'd been able to shrink myself. I'd whittled all the way down to a size 6, marking what is still my most successful achievement of body mass reduction. In fact, when I consider my nostalgic romanticizing of the Adam era, I sometimes wonder if it was truly Adam or *actually* that tiniest version of GG who was the star of the show in my recollection. I was size 6 and starving, but to the outside world, I effused youthful, vibrant health. The amazing thing about a woman with a medium build is that when she starves herself, and her body mass index drops into whatever is considered to be the danger zone, it can be hard to see. She might look sexy and she might look fit, but for her (in this particular case) typically Italian curvaceous body type, she is emaciated. She is starved. However, I was getting attention and *nearly* had my stuff together. I was developing an attitude of magnitude, and I wasn't going to back down from the diet-mindset marathon now. No way. I was only in it to win it, baby, and the race was on. I was Giana, and it was the seventies; *hear me roar*! Aside from the mandatory Sunday dinners at which I had to join the tribe of *wolfifying* Italians and turn into a momentary *carboholic*, I stuck with my main squeeze, Dexy. We were now on a pet-name basis.

I'd also discovered a real gem of a supplementary plan, one I admit I return to every now and then, for better or for worse. This was the Scarsdale Diet, designed by a man who was actually murdered by a former headmistress of my school. I always felt that strange coincidence stood for something, like a symbol of my own war between dietary sainthood and sinfulness. Their story, anyway, was all the news. I'm not sure why the headmistress killed the Scarsdale guru, but having gone mad following the diet myself, I can only imagine. Give a girl all meat and a few pieces of celery, and be careful if you have a nearby firearm in an unlocked drawer. Anyway, the Scarsdale Diet lured me in with convincing brochures I'd picked up at one drugstore or another. Its gospel was something like an early version of the paleo diet and the primal diet. The reason I chose the health plan was pretty much because, I figured, all the pear-shaped ladies in my family were getting fat on fettuccini. I needed to stay away from anything carb heavy, and everything creamy. Obviously, meals consisting only of meat and a withered piece of celery or two would render me equal in dimension, after all, to those Fair Cucumber Girls. With this diet and my ally, Dexatrim, by my side, I had support, real team spirit. I craved nearly nothing and limited my eating to just a few pieces of roast beef at night before going to sleep.

For most of the summer, I split my time between working and becoming an expert at partying, drinking, and hanging out with new friends. Gino and Lia had allowed me to get a summer job somewhere other than the restaurant. I was hired at Caldors, a discount department store. I'd do the daytime shifts there, making $2.25 an hour folding clothes and paging people on the intercom system. *Jan in housewares, pick up. Pick up, Jan.* It was a steep improvement from my hourly wage and position at the Grill, so I was pleased enough. My friends and I had turned the age of freedom in New England, so we could get behind the wheel and go places. My peers had finally caught up to my adult-sized body, and altogether, we felt we'd come of age. I turned sixteen in August and convinced Gino to give me the car he was trading in, his old BMW 320i. It was a stick shift, which I'd never operated before, but I lied a little and told him I definitely knew how to drive stick so that he'd consent. Without giving myself any extra time for a potential learning curve, my sister and I loaded ourselves into my newly inherited car. Somehow I figured out how to get out of the driveway, but then spent quite a bit of time stalling up hills. In a few weeks, using the actual road as my practice pad, I'd gotten the hang of how to switch gears. We were wild kids behind wheels, but we didn't get far. Mostly, we would end up at the house of whomever's parents weren't home, and drink. Drinking, by the way, was allowed in my diet plan.

At the onset of eleventh grade, my all-girls Catholic prison-school went on a field trip to Ellis Island with the neighboring boys' school, where Adam was enrolled, Adam of the *Pink Panther* date. I didn't know then that Ellis Island was the literal touchdown entry point for both my mother's and father's entrance into *their America*, where they'd join forces. Perhaps that energy itself influenced my senses, tweaked my subconscious in some capacity. That was the day I remember it dawning on me, there on Ellis Island, a handful of months after our movie date: *Oh my God. Adam is amazing.*

After the school trip, I made an effort to spend more time with Adam. Our friendship grew, and he became the first true male friend I'd ever had. We laughed about actual real things that I thought or felt. For the first time ever, I confided aspects of my inner world to someone. Sure, my inner world may have been mostly filled with my takeaways from watching *My Favorite Martian* while talking to Adam on the phone, but yeah, I really did it: I had a genuine friend. The truth is, I realize this now—I loved Adam from the first moment I saw him. He wasn't just cute and nice, he was also funny, often hysterically so, and mature for his age, to boot. He influenced me, and I let him. That was huge for me. But not long after my Ellis Island epiphany, I learned

151

that Adam had a new love interest, a quiet girl at our school. At that moment, I realized there was no way I wanted to lose his attention. I was nervous to attempt confessing my romantic feelings to him, as I'd never really talked to him about actual *feelings*, like on an emotional level. I was pretty much clueless when it came to knowing how to communicate about anything close to matters of the heart, so I needed to wait for the most opportune moment, and that seemed to be once I was significantly drunk, sometime just before Labor Day in eleventh grade.

My friends and I planned to spend Saturday late afternoon playing pool in the basement of someone whose parents were out of town for the weekend—which meant *open bar* for us. By 2:30 in the afternoon, I finished my morning shift at Caldors and was ready to party. I had no interest in playing pool, but it was a good excuse to drink sangria. I was particularly nervous when I got there, not only because of the effects of the Dexatrim, but also because I anticipated seeing Adam, who was eventually making his way to the party, as well. I armed my emotional self efficiently: three sangrias and a heavy dose of *It doesn't matter what he says because I don't care*. The words were not so convincing, in this case.

Yes, my go-to, my *I don't care*, wasn't working as per normal. *So strange.* I noticed there was something else I felt about Adam, like an authentic sense of connection, something like *care*, plus instinct. I knew that Adam and I had to be together; it was one of my first real intuitions, an affirmative voice I heard from within that felt as if it were audible. By the time he came over, I approached him the only way I knew how: I went front and center like a football player on the offence. *Adam can you come here?* I pulled him in the direction of the bathroom before he'd even finished stepping off the end of the basement staircase. He half laughed, seeing I was significantly inebriated, but also because I had no filter. If I wanted something, dopamine took over, and I was gung ho. The great thing about Adam is that he let me be *me*. In the early seventies, this was not such an

152

easy accomplishment. A strong woman operating with command, even if sometimes doing so messily, hasn't always been the strongest sex symbol in the world of men seeking easy-peasy. Adam, who was of Nordic descent and looked like a Viking coming down the stairway, for whatever *bizarre-o* reason wasn't thrown off by my impulsive grab of his hand (already major plus points). *Come here!* I implored again, even though he was fully compliant, curiously smiling as he followed my lead. *Giana! I'm coming!* he exclaimed. I strangely remember every moment, every look he gave me from the bottom of the stairs until the end of that night.

I pushed him into the bathroom and shut the door. The clerestory windows built high into the wall allowed for dusky light to reach us from the ground level. Somehow, the gentle illumination seemed sort of romantic in my friend's basement bathroom (frankly, many things feel romantic after one hits .08 percent blood alcohol concentration). Courtesy of intoxication, I felt confident in my admission, and dove right in. *Adam. So, in the beginning of the summer, when we went to that movie, I didn't know it then, but I know it now: I really like you—as in, more than a friend. I like you a lot. I mean, I want to, you know, I think we get along. I don't want you to go out with Kerry Stradmore. Adam, she's not right for you because I am. I think I'm the one you're supposed to be with. I mean, I want to, you know, be with you.* Amazingly, this worked. Adam lifted my bashful downturned face in his hands, demonstrating more emotional intelligence than most guys I dated in my forties—*go figure*. I bit my lip when he lifted my face to the dusky light, encouraging me to meet his eye. He smiled, almost as if he was going to laugh about something I did that was ridiculous, and rolled his eyes. *Yes, GG. Don't you know? I want that. I want to be with you too. I'm not into Kerry Stradmore. It's you. Forget everyone else. So let's make this happen. I'm ready if you are.* I now understand that most girls don't ever receive a heartfelt confession, like one would see in a romantic movie, but I didn't know that then. To me, Adam had just dreamily delivered the Hollywood-style-courtship lines I'd expected from watching romantic scenes in TV shows. Since research shows that something like 95 percent of our interpretation of reality is bent toward our bias, I might be embellishing a tad based on impressions from a Cary Grant or Harrison Ford movie scene. Still, regardless of how much we tend to skew reality, Adam and I were into each other. We clearly shared the same feelings, and as far as venturing into a relationship, all systems were go. That night, both Adam and I landed the jackpot in the lottery of *first love*. From that moment on, we were inseparable.

We spent the rest of the night making out in the bathroom until we drove off in his car and parked by the Connecticut River. I knew already that I cared for Adam on an emotional level, that I *felt* something. It was like being immersed in a kind of dreaminess that moved through us both or hovered around us. It had its own value. This was the closest I had come to owning any of my feelings other than raging anger. And the whole actualization of us, of *Adam plus GG*, was all made possible by the support of my newfound Dexy-produced self-esteem, plus the Scarsdale Diet. From a little capsule that was managing the entire shape of GG, and a self-determined prescription for what I could and couldn't consume, I'd manufactured a sense of control, stamina, sexiness, and self-worth. The diet-pill commercial had convinced me. The Dexy-dosed GG could have impactful, assertive opinions. People listened to her because she was hot, fit into her school desk, didn't bulge out beyond the seat of her chair. She could be sultry, pout, bat her lashes, be seen. Like most girls, I learned to determine my confidence, my level of attractiveness, and sense of relationship capability in accordance with my body size. The chart looks something like this: Size 14: *F-no. Don't even leave the closet, Giana.* Size 12: *Only poke your head out to bark some orders, manage work like a man, and deal with the family.* Size 10: *Now we're starting to get somewhere! Watch cares and worries slip off the skin.* Size 8: *Ready to date.* Size 6: *I'm fixed! Watch out, closet mannequin, I'm coming to rip that dazzling sequined halter off your plastic chest and enlist in dance class one more time, and if, God willing, I can stay that size, I might even sign up for professional-level tango.* Once under size 8, GG no longer has the word *carb* in her vocabulary. I crave celery, a few pieces of meat, and not much else. But this poses one significant problem: to actually survive in life, I can't be some teensy size. I have to be of inviolable stature and invincible form in order to muscle through my formidable list of daily to-dos, basically the complete opposite of my shapely ideal. I'd have to maintain a colossal girth; I'd have to *manhandle* everything. To protect my world, I'd wear the pants—but not only the pants, the armor too. All revealing and sparkly sequined attire would have to be kept in the closet, joining the rest of my hidden aspects, taboo and unintegrated. Identifying as my feminine self—a smaller, sensual Giana—would allow me no place in the world, not if she was to grab life by the horns. I held these beliefs subconsciously, and they shaped me. However, on that night, next to Adam, I felt safe to take off the armor, come out of hiding, and, as the song says, feel like a *natural woman.*

With Adam, I was in my own personal Eden, the place where it all started. I'd bitten into the fruit of my own messed up self-measurement and, for the first time, believed I'd landed in a kind of eternal garden of the heavenly Father. Here, saints and sinners were all fine sharing property. No one fussed much over pious behavior. Life was beautiful; everyone in Eden agreed. I was *all good*, whether in the hallways of my Catholic school or dancing to a Toto cover band and buying wine coolers with my fake ID on a Friday night. The blooming flowers showed no sign of wilting in this all-inviting Eden; even I had been allowed entrance. Within just a few weeks of our romance, Adam and I were deep in the wild kind of bell-bottomed teenage affair that went down in the seventies. We were full on—free love, reckless partying, wild laughter, and dancing to live music—but also something of greater importance: we were serious about it all. He was more than just my lover; he was truly my best friend. I even braved inviting him to my house. I'd never considered bringing a guy near my father before. It was a high-risk situation, but I intuitively knew my parents would like Adam. It turned out they seemed to take to him even better than they had taken to me. To my fortune, it turned out, they respected Adam so much that they even withheld insulting me in front of him. Effectively, Adam became a kind of armor, and I felt safer with him around, and so I made sure he always came over. As nice of a front as the Giovanni family put up for him, Adam had my back. He knew I struggled at home, and he seemed to care. His family was reserved, with the typical Northern European calm demeanor. He couldn't imagine a dinnertime punctuated by colorful insults and agitated expressions.

At Adam's house, I felt on guard around his mother, Marianne. At the least, I could sense she wasn't a real fan of mine. She probably wanted Adam to date one of her friends' daughters, a more obviously Anglo-Saxon kind of girl. One who might have been more fair, button-nosed, blond, and unobtrusive would have likely suited Marianne. My eyes were too almond-shaped and my hormones, too outrageous. Even when I was silent, the natural curvature of my hips screamed loudly, *Sex, sex, sex*! I tanned too easily. All in all, GG added up to *too much*. As *wrong* as I was deemed to be in Marianne's deuterocanonical book, at the time, Adam didn't seem to care much about his mother's approval. He'd shut the door to his bedroom, even if she was home, and ask me to lie down next to him. As soon as we'd start to kiss, to unbutton something, to break a sweat, she'd come knocking with her conservative-sounding rap on the door, calling out his name with her overly religious, uptight voice: *Adam? Adam? Keep your door open, please!* His mother was trying to instill in us conservative morals, but it was too late. For Marianne, I would always be the slut who took her son's innocence. For Adam and I, although we were each other's first, it didn't feel like it. It felt like we'd forever known each other in an intimate way. Everything just worked between us, including all of our body parts, totally in sync.

Our junior and senior year turned out to be pretty dreamy,

I had my body *dialed in*, under control via spurts of diet pills and breadless meals. Dessert lasted throughout the day in the form of my very handsome boyfriend, who was as kind and fun as he was beautiful. Life seemed like it could continue on like this forever, but metabolisms cannot be permanently controlled. At some point, neither Dexatrim nor Adam would find their way to my lips. By the middle of eleventh grade, Adam announced his future plans, which became unwaveringly fixed. I couldn't figure out what his declared destiny had to do with his heart, his real personality, but he was convinced. He was going to enroll in military school in Virginia, *just like that*, out of the blue. When I asked him how he'd made his choice, he told me something inane. He said his middle name was Samuel and his last name was Grant, so, since he was Adam S. Grant, he should follow the steps of General Ulysses S. Grant, and serve his country. I'd smiled lopsidedly at his straightforward conviction, but I hoped, inwardly, that his decision would change. There was no way I would go with him to military school. First off, it would be another twenty years before his chosen school would permit women, and second, as much as I had disconnected from my sense of self, I knew there was no part of my being that could align with actually *choosing* to be in a militaristic environment. My parents had immigrated to America to escape the climate of war, and here I was, losing my rock, my one anchor of a friend and my beloved to this same stupid thing. Bombs, guns, drills, rigidity—I knew we required self-protection as a people, but I couldn't see taking up arms. Since I struggled in maintaining the preservation of my own boundaries, I couldn't fathom feeling the duty to heed an even greater call to arms. Adam's inclination to serve the military's ambitions felt, to me, like I was being cheated on. How could he desire marching in place versus swimming in the wild ocean of love and dancing all night with me? Adam's plan seemed to follow in the steps of Italy and the whole darn world who proclaimed war on all things innately feminine, sterilizing the wild forces of nature. He would just be a cog in the machine. Perhaps the extremes of his assertive mother's protocols compounded with my reckless penchant for mischief impeded Adam's sense of freedom. His masculinity had a plan of personal revolution: enlist in a place where women were forbidden for the fruit-grappling, vine-twisting apple eaters they are, a place like military school. Through this kind of training, Adam stood to clearly own and operate Eden with take-charge authority. Ultimately, the only kind of girl he'd choose after successful training and *boot-camp brainwashing* would be a wishy-washy type. Not someone like Giana, who is anything other than wishy-washy when she wants something. Adam knew my nature even though my life's path hadn't yet begun to unfold. I was less about a stringent, violence-promoting order of operations, and instead, fixed on cultivating a world filled with opportunity and liberation for all.

Meanwhile, for the rest of our high school years, Adam remained close to me, bingeing on the feast of female nectar before swallowing his own version of a starvation pill: Virginia Military Institute. In the near future, he'd have to shave his head and take a vow of chasteness: no more dancing, no more wild nights, no more passion, no admissions of lust. And there would be no adoring of unrefined feminine nature, just buzz cuts, the rote call and response, battalions prepped for asserting *power over* as a way of life. Outwardly, I believed I couldn't relate, but, in reflection, our imminent life experiences were bound to be more akin than I was able to imagine. Just as Adam would emerge from his college years equipped with the enduring capability of a warlord, I'd graduate from my own higher education with a similar mindset and charge-ahead attitude. Like Adam, but without the *Drop and give me fifty* training, Giana would also condition herself for survival, programmed to think of life as a danger zone.

When Adam got into Virginia Military Institute at the start of our senior year, I pushed aside the thought of our impending separation. I refused to digest it, along with all the nutrients I refused to consume while on Dexatrim. *No big deal* and *It doesn't matter*, my two catchphrases, had made their return. The old words kicked in as protective buffering for me, returning to my inner landscape like thorny vines that had never left at all. They'd only been under the now-melting snow of my winter wonderland, my deluge of dreamy joy I'd accessed by loving Adam. Being safely in a relationship, at least for a few seasons, had abated my familiar patterns, my go-tos: *It doesn't matter* and its rough translation, *I don't matter*.

I hadn't thought much of my future, but now that Adam had a plan, I felt more driven to declare mine. I wanted to look at schools, and there was no way either Gino or Lia was interested in taking time off to drive their daughter hours away from Bridgewood just to investigate possibilities. But I'd decided—with about as much rationalization as one would use in a game of Spin the Globe, landing their finger somewhere, anywhere—that Boston seemed like the right place for me to go to college. Plus, my guidance counselor had told me that Northeastern University *might* grant me admission. According to her, Northeastern didn't have a problem with slightly under-achieving kids whose record of unruly conduct stood out far greater than any evidence of general well-roundedness. Let's just say, I fell short of being an exemplary scholar and had little to show in terms of high achievement in after-school curricula, team leadership, or scholastic prestige. Perfect—a school where I was encouraged to party and could get away with a less-than-stellar GPA sounded good enough to get nearly excited about continuing on the path of structured, authoritarian education. My counselor guessed I had about a 75 percent chance of being granted entry, and suggested that since I was already trying to get into a Boston-based school, I may as well also apply to Boston University. Though, she said, the possibility I'd be accepted there was close to nil. I'm pretty sure the guidance counselor had been enforced by her academic higher-ups to advise all collegiate hopefuls to apply to a minimum of two schools. Judging by the attitude in her voice and her inability to sustain eye contact with me, I'd say she had low expectations for my future. Based on my student records, she likely looked at me as one big *lost cause*.

However academically irresponsible I'd been, I managed to submit my two applications, as directed by my guidance counselor. Assuming I had a fair shot to get into Northeastern, I filled out my application in one weekend, a masterpiece of blue ink with the occasional blot of whiteout to amend grammatical errors. Since I'd supposedly little chance of getting into a school as well-regarded as BU, I treated this secondary application more like a coaster than a ticket to my future. I left it sitting for weeks on my dresser until its edges curled, water stained under an empty can of Tab and a tube of pink lip-gloss. Weeks after I'd managed to shove my Northeastern application into an envelope and out the door, I continued to ignore Boston University's. The truth is, completing a single college application was pretty stupendous for Giana circa twelfth grade. At that time, the only things I'd been able to finish were about seventy-two boxes of Dexatrim between sophomore and junior year and a good twenty cartons of Virginia Slims, a brand I'd chosen based on the second word of the name alone. *Slim.* The television commercial had done a solid job of marketing the brand as sexy. The slim girl *(Ding-ding, I'm already sold)*, looking modern and not Italian *(Ding-ding, sold even more)*, was dressed to kill and embodied the tagline, *You've come a long way, baby (Ding-ding-ding)*. Smoke Virginia Slims, and become slim, stay slim. The solicitous catchiness was infectious, addictive. Plus, I could subliminally manipulate the phrase and turn it right around. Each time I'd pull out a smoke was like going to a twenty-five-cent fortune-teller, paid to ensure my good fortune. Would Adam get into Virginia's top military school and leave me a *lonnnng* way behind? Slim chance. My way, all the way, baby. *Virginia Slims.* Perfect spell-casting. On the weekend before BU's application deadline, I finally mustered enough esteem to complete the paperwork, though at that point I simply assumed the gesture of putting it in the mail was mostly just to clear off my bureau and make room for future debris.

Within a few weeks, I was happily informed that the 75 percent chance of receiving admission to Northeastern worked in my favor, and I was accepted. We went to check it out, *we* being a little trio of Adam, myself, and another friend who was keen to explore Boston. I arrived at the city campus to get a feel for how I could own the premises and rock the city. I went with my best foot forward (which was my most assertive foot, of course) determined to feel Northeastern as my future stomping ground. But as soon as I arrived on campus, I felt *off*, deflated. I sunk inside, thinking, *How am I going to do this?* When I'd imagined attending the school previously, this wasn't the picturesque vision I'd had in mind. Walking around the college campus, I felt a sense of *bleakness*, and there was no way I was going to sign up for *bleak*. I'd already endured Connecticut suburbia with Lia and Gino for nearly eighteen years; I needed something spicy. Spice was, after all, the stuff of life, and both culinarily and experientially speaking, I planned to maintain constant access to all things spicy as soon as I was old enough to leave the house.

Being out of Bridgewood, away from the Gino-Lia state of oppression, my intuition kicked in. Not only did I feel in the first two minutes of strolling the Northeastern campus that this wasn't my school, I had the clear directionality to investigate Boston University, which was only a mere few miles away, closer to the city's center. I'd not heard from the admissions department since I'd sent my application in, so it didn't actually make much sense to head there, but my brain skirted over that detail. I was in Boston, and that was enough of a reason for me; I could veni, vidi, vici my way into anything, especially with Adam by my side. In my own personal Eden, Adam was the closest I'd come to believing I had *God as my witness*. I felt wholly seen by him. Our relationship was perhaps the only clear *yes* I'd ever perceived up until that point. But there, again, in Boston, I distinctly received another *yes*, although this one arrived a bit more mysteriously. I *heard* it; it actually sounded like a discernable voice. Did it come from inside of myself or outside? I couldn't tell, but from wherever it originated, this *yes* was thoroughly encouraging, and served to determine my next step: *I'm heading over to Boston University, pronto. That's my school.* There was no logic to my decision. According to my guidance counselor, my credentials fell far below the BU standard, but I was playing life as if it were a game of Monopoly. Amused, I picked up a Chance card. *Okay, Giana, just roll the dice.*

As soon as we arrived at the campus of Boston University, I noticed a stirring in my body, which for me, was super odd. Outside of the anxious effects of caffeine and over-the-counter diet pills, I seldom registered bodily reactions. But now here I was, riveted, responding to this *YES, YES, YES.* The words were again audible. This voice seemed to know what it was talking about, but dang, it also felt otherworldly, maybe even extraterrestrial. *YES*, it/I affirmed, *Boston University is your campus. Go into the office of admissions and find the registrar, GG. Tell them you're coming.*

I followed the voice, unclear if it was mine, God's, or Dexatrim's (and perhaps unable to differentiate between the lot). I arrived just minutes before the campus office closed for the weekend and finagled my way through the door of the registrar. Once I had her attention, I spoke matter-of-factly in the future affirmative. Apparently, I already had a natural ability to speak life into actualization. *Yes, I am planning on attending Boston University next year. It's really, truly the only school where I've wanted to study. I sent in my application but because I never received a response, I took the day off of school and drove all the way here.* (In reality, we regularly skipped school, and had planned to be gone for Assembly Day. The last thing I wanted to deal with was a bunch of religious speakers educating us on Psalms. To me, Assembly Day was a golden cue for a vacation from school.) Of course, the conviction I affected in front of the registrar was a bit theatrical, but by now, I'd convinced myself that I'd been set on attending the university since *birth.* Even though just weeks ago I could barely budge to fill out my return address on the top of the school's application or check the spelling of my piecemealed essay, I was, suddenly, solely Boston University bound.

The registrar seemed impressed by my Giovanni-style, Italian determination. Her eyes widened. While I focused on remaining apparently unwavering, she picked up the phone and made a call to some office or another. Providing my name to the person on the other end of the line, she carefully enunciated, *Giovanni...yes. Giana, G-i-a-n-a.* She nodded, listening to whatever admissions official she'd dialed, and then looked at me with a smile. After her call ended, she met my eyes with sincerity. I did my best to pull off looking earnest and worthy of a great education. *Giana, on behalf of the university, I'm so sorry, dear. During the summer, we had a turnover of some of our most essential staff members. To say the least, it's been a bit of a challenge. It's possible we lost your application.* Bear in mind that this was the late 1970s. If you were a college applicant sending in an essay, you didn't print it out. At best, you typed up your formal submission if you didn't submit the whole darn thing in handwritten ink. There were no back-ups, hard-drives, proof of sent email. Licking a thirteen-cent stamp was a risk in the seventies, sending word via the USPS was at the mercy of fate; the item could be forever lost. There are wartime stories in which lovers believed they'd lost each other forever just because a letter of proposal had failed to arrive. My BU application could have been destroyed by inclement weather or sabotaged by a lonely mail carrier—who knows? I attempted to relay my greatest portrayal of dismay upon hearing the counselor's news. *Oh no! This is crushing! Since I was ten years old, I've wanted to attend BU because it was the first university to open up all its divisions to female students, back in 1872!* (I'd learned this fact just twenty minutes ago from a poster above a water fountain, while zipping down the halls in search of the registrar's office.) This seemed to impress the registrar, however. She wrote something down, then spoke: *Let me tell you what, Giana. I promise I will do everything I can to admit you, and don't you worry about having to take the time to fill out another application. What a bother!* She shook her head and rolled her eyes, obviously fed up with the failed admins; it turned out, I'd come at the perfect time. *We'll call your guidance counselor early next week and have her pass along to you our decision. How does that sound? Will that make you feel better?* I felt like I'd gotten a green light, a lucky roll of the dice. It felt natural, fun, and right. Looking back, this was my first breakthrough in accessing an effortless style of manifesting, something in which I'd continue to excel and *(surprise, surprise)* something I hadn't learned in school.

We did our due diligence in Boston over the weekend, celebrating our exuberant youthfulness by drinking excessively and sleeping little, the general protocol of the young and wasted. On Monday, we returned to the opposite extreme: our Catholic school prisons. Adam marched off in the direction of the boys' penitentiary—and I, toward the girls' school, bidding each other goodbye with a sloppier-than-usual kiss, both of us still hungover. Surprisingly, I made it on time to our Monday morning mass, mumbling through the Act of Contrition: *Oh my God…I am heartily sorry…detest all my sins…sin no more… Amen.* I washed the morning penitence down with two hits of Dexatrim and held on to my horses, riding between the extremes of heavenly prayer and hellacious debauchery, a bit dizzy after the weekend of *high* festivities.

No sooner than the end of first period, I was called to the office. I wondered if I still smelled of alcohol from my trip, since we'd driven right to school from Boston after partying most of the night, arriving just five minutes before the bell rang. I assumed I'd been caught for one of the various detention-worthy activities I'd surely committed the week prior. Over the past month, I'd been late for math class most days, if I hadn't skipped it altogether. I'd taken a few smoke breaks in the utility closet the week before, and I had an ongoing trade of Yodels for Anne-Marie Hollister's answers to our history exams. That was between Anne-Marie and me, however, and I'd surely defend our agreement if pressed. She liked Yodels, and I had the goods. I needed exam answers, and she was a walking encyclopedia. Done deal. I braced myself for attack when entering the office, expecting the front-desk attendant to direct me to the headmistress's office. Instead, she pointed me toward Academic Affairs, which left me confused. *Oh no. Did I flunk out of high school so close to my freaking last semester?* I was already figuring out how I'd tell Lia and Gino. Once I made it through the door, I found my guidance counselor smiling and shaking her head in disbelief. I was completely thrown off. *Giana Giovanni!* she enthused, *I have no idea how you did this, but I just got a call from the registrar at Boston University. She personally reached out to apologize for any inconvenience and wanted to let us know that the university would be pleased to accept you next fall. You can simply send them your deposit before Christmas break.*

I think I actually tossed the near-to-nothing contents of my stomach in the bathroom after exiting her office. I wasn't anxious about her news as much as I was suffering an elongated hangover—my stomach, burning with increasing acidity amplified by my double dose of Dexy. Though I was denying my body's natural digestive process on the most literal level, I was resolving to figuratively swallow something much bigger. *It's okay if Adam wants to find his future at Virginia Military Institute. I'll find my way in Boston,* just like the song *"We Go Together"* from the movie *Grease* (which would happen to be my go-to theme the very next year), *chang-chang-changitty-chang-shoo-bop, we'll always be like one.*

CHAPTER 12

A Crash Course in Basic Italian: The Many Ways to Say Arrivederci

I'd determined how to remove myself from Adam without falling apart, but now I had Frankie to contend with. My sister, no longer hidden in my shadow, would enter her senior year of high school on her own, finally able to live without suffering as my fall guy. Our relationship was more complex than we could comprehend or acknowledge. In doing our best to survive as the single unit *GG-Frankie*, we banded together for the benefit of collective strength. Two minds and two able bodies were better than one when it came to protecting ourselves from our parents' offensives. We nonverbally adopted a tag team style, athletically strategizing mid-move, mid-fire: *Frankie, stay in left field. I'll go full forward!* My sister and I sought relief together in our own unspoken way, numbing out to self-soothe, two bodies sharing one comforting couch. We compensated for our missing foundational pieces as resourcefully as we knew how, seeking first aid with whatever we could conjure from the metaphorical medicine cabinet, be it via Dexatrim, tasty Pop Tarts, or late-night TV binges. As much as we self-soothed together to an impressive degree, Frankie and I couldn't help but speak the same badgering language that had been used on us. Like our parents had done to us, we misinterpreted or often denied each other's claimed reality. A typical exchange went something like this:

What the heck, GG? That's not at all what Aunt Rosa said! Are you nuts?

What are you talking about, Frankie? You're the one literally out of your mind! That's exactly what happened!

We thought of ourselves as independent, though we knew our parents clumped us into a single *polpettone* (one big meatball), hence the shared moniker *GG-Frankie*. We outwardly claimed opposing positions in a dance of sibling rivalry.

The truth is, even to this day, my relationship with Frankie remains extremely nuanced. We've been entangled from the very start, so we've never bravely dared to adopt a different way of speaking to each other using a kinder type of communication. To meddle with our connection felt like brain surgery. One slight move in trying to finely separate our annoyances from our affinities, and we'd throw the whole system off, which seemed riskier than just enduring our dysfunction. With all our family has suffered, one might think we'd have considered the benefits of family therapy or an immersive healing workshop. Heck no. No Giovanni other than me, the lone GG, would be caught dead in a *healing workshop*. I attended these workshops because I had to forge my own identity away from my overbearing family dynamic. A *personal growth and development* seminar at the Hartford Hyatt may as well be an active minefield according to most of my family members, so within their walls, I could safely explore my individual identity. Also, since no other Giovanni would dare tread into the ballyhoo of publicly touted self-improvement, I would do the grunt work for us all. I'd go in like a firefighter for the rescue. No wonder I accrued dozens of hours in sessions, analyzing dreams, and praying for my parents' health through creative visualization. I put a whole new spin on the idea of family therapy. Could it be successful when done alone? I wasn't sure, but I'd try.

Frankie certainly has her opinions about me, and I understand her perspective; I get it. I can imagine what it felt like for her to be punished throughout childhood as a result of my devious behavior. I've listened to her reflect on what a *pain in the butt* young GG was, both in front

167

of the family and mutual friends, which is always *so lovely* to hear. She'll wear that same hard-to-read smile our father has plastered on his face. *GG was just so bad.* Frankie often repeats this line, usually adding, *and she dragged me into her every plan*! Her assessment, I admit, is spot on. It's true that I was the culprit in all reprehensible naughtiness within the Giovanni household, but I don't think either of us could comprehend what was really going on psychologically in our family. Even with all my learned Italian defensiveness and hotheaded self-determination, I am filled with enough shame about myself to start a whole new branch of Catholicism. I could have been a modern Catherine of Siena, the patron saint, doctor of the church, had I not continuously focused on my self-assessment of being bad and reiterated my Declaration of Worthlessness. I believed in my wrongness religiously, it was my real *holy confirmation*, the actual dirty waters of poor self-reflection in which I baptized myself on a daily basis. And my negative self-talk set the metaphorical table (or, more accurately, dashboard) for my *reservation for one*, where I'd consume half an aisle of Cumberland Farms in my car.

I don't blame Frankie for harshly assessing my childhood behaviors. I often feel they're nearly too complex for *me* to comprehend. Frankie hasn't spent years, like I have, unpacking the core components of my psyche, which, let me tell you, is no job for the weary. What Frankie considers my *badness* was more complex than that. I dragged her into all of my rebellious plans, but this wasn't because I wanted her to take blame or suffer on my behalf. It was because I needed her there as the representative body where I couldn't feel mine. If Frankie hadn't been around to reflect my every odd-turn, I wouldn't have been sure I physically existed at all.

All deep psychological justifications aside, I admit Frankie endured some of my worst sisterly behavior after I'd been accepted into Boston University. As brave as I made myself out to be, subconsciously I was scrambling to figure out how I'd get through this next transition without my sister. In all honesty, physically separating from Adam seemed a far simpler uncoupling than detaching from Frankie. Frankie and I had leaned on each other so deeply that, to me, even the idea of regularly eating dinner without her seemed bizarre. She was kind of my domestic partner, and we were, in ways, more successful in this relationship than were our own mother and father. It was incomprehensible to conceive of a life in which Frankie and I weren't living under the same roof. How the heck would I manage to do this? It may have been my subconscious attempt to cut the cord of our codependence that led us to the Bridgewood hospital sometime in January of 1979.

It was the same week my parents submitted the college deposit to Boston University. The roads were icy and, while I'd learned how to drive my dad's old BMW 320i stick shift, I wasn't prepared to traverse the winter roads. Back then, the youth didn't get taught many things, like, for example, how to drive on ice. I guess this level of education fell into the mysterious category of *stuff we'd have to learn ourselves.* I hadn't taken any kind of driver's education, unless stalling about fifty times on a street's incline during my first month of having a license counts as training. Regardless, on a wintry Thursday morning, Frankie and I headed to Adam's house on our way to school (one of the more responsible trajectories I'd make in my teenage years, as most others involved some form of truancy). As we took the exit off the highway onto Post Road, the car wheels skidded on black ice. While an educated driver might know not to accelerate at such a moment, I was not privy to this logic. I tried to brake but was losing control, which was my worst nightmare. Giana, as we know, doesn't have a moderate level of relinquishing control. As soon as Frankie and I started to swerve and careen, I was submissively stunned into total wipeout mode. We struck a large cement barrier head-on.

The world spun around us in circles, disorienting me beyond my status quo. I'm able to function while in a state of general disassociation, but in this case, I'd truly entered a next-level altered state. I had been thrown out of the driver's seat and was now alone in the car. My first response was to locate Frankie. I mustered the ability to focus my eyes and glanced around. I spotted her outside, stumbling around and looking stunned. My car (what remained of it) had found a little plot of land along a snowy bank to declare as its own. Here, the monochromatic colors of the season and unusual perspective of life stopped along a random exit gave me the strange sense of being tucked into another world, one made of clouds. My body had retired its impulse to move forward; I couldn't resist its heaviness. This is what it took, evidently, for me to land.

My vision of Frankie, who was white as a winter-sky zombie, began to blur. I blinked to retain my focus on her, to make sure she was okay, but the view from my left eye was turning a dark red, covered with something warm and thick. Any initiative felt exhausting, but I managed to bring my hand to the side of my skull and discovered a hole there. Rather than registering pain, I simply became aware of a heat emanating from the hole, blood steadily gushing out of it. Everything felt confusing and too difficult to deal with. I let my view of Frankie dissipate and promptly blacked out.

Turns out, the car had been folded nearly in half, right on top of my head. Someone sent for an ambulance, and we were rushed to the hospital. We were sent to radiology and put through diagnostics. I was lucky, as the outcome could have been far worse. I'd escaped with only a concussion, whiplash, and a pretty solid gash down my face, worthy of fifty-or-so stitches. Frankie, as usual, received the brunt of my reckless action, with injuries more substantial than mine. Gino and Lia quickly arrived at the hospital. Though I couldn't move my head much, I was alert enough to hear my dad's voice, and noticed the unusual emotional reaction I had to it. For the first time, Gino's words sounded like safety, like an assurance we'd be okay. *Oh my God. How are the girls?* Gino asked the medics once reaching the doorway of our shared room. His voice was tinged with an unfamiliar tone, something similar to concern. I could hear Lia repeating a prayer under her breath.

I was admitted to the hospital for a few days of bed rest. After getting stitched up, I didn't spend much time reflecting on the accident. Instead, staying true to my nature, I simply tuned out the traumatic incident. I assumed my typical mindset: *It's done; move on.* Frankie, however, required more significant rehabilitation than I did, as she'd chipped a bone in her neck. For more than one reason, I couldn't bring up the accident with Frankie. Not only had my actions physically injured her, which was the last thing I'd ever want to do, but also, to me, the wreck symbolized our upcoming parting of ways. Ripping Frankie from my side via a cement block was inconsequential in comparison to our future split, the severance of our Siamese-twin-type attachment. Growing up, we had needed each other to survive, but now we'd part ways. Frankie would be free of me, free to find herself. She could venture unencumbered by her troublesome sister into her senior year in Bridgewood while I'd attempt an adult trajectory in Boston. Maybe I couldn't bear leaving Frankie in any other way than to literally knock us both out and then cut us apart, removing Frankie from the role of my partner in crime. According to the doctors, Frankie was only one or two vertebrae away from having incurred irreparable damage. My sister had gone out on a limb for me before, risked her neck, so to speak, but this was the final out-of-control Giana bad-girl move. She wouldn't have me behind the wheel again, metaphorically speaking. She would learn to take control, discreetly reminding me of my shameful behavior. Frankie needed three-plus weeks of recovery time in the hospital and was in a neck brace for six months following our accident. With the help of physical therapy and willpower, Frankie found her own stability. She'd emerge, brace-free, and forge her own rules from that point on. My sister didn't need me to shield her anymore, not if I'd be running such a madhouse, forever living out my getaway plan. Frankie didn't need to get away from anything except my shadow.

My sister is a smart woman, like our Aunt Rosa: capable and analytically mathematical. She's also dependable, witty, careful, clean, organized, and strong. She is such a minimalist that it's sometimes befuddling to me that we come from the same parents. While I sucked up all the troubled history of our frenzied Italian Catholic ancestors, my sister seems to have been blessed with the gentlest of our genes. Even though the closest thing to an apology I knew how to give Frankie after our car accident went something like, *Holy cow, Frankie. I can't believe what happened to us*, I hope that young Frankie knows that I'd never want to hurt her. In general, I needed a better sense of where I began and ended in order to take ownership of any of my own actions, to even begin to understand how I impacted the people I loved. But I was sorry then, and Frankie, I'm still sorry if I ever sent you spinning or if my own overwhelm and post-traumatic behavior affected your peace of mind.

CHAPTER 13

College (Cafeteria) Bound

When it was time to set out on Interstate 95 north to Boston for school, Frankie came with me, risking her life as my passenger again. It was sort of an unspoken gesture to mark the closure of our conjoined adolescent years. I know she was also dealing with the stress of the separation. When two children in a family with complex interpersonal dynamics (which—let's be honest—is, like, every family, right?) stick it out together, they forge a strong and uniquely empathetic bond. Some children grow up in *mixed families*, but my sister and I grew up with *mixed messages*. We'd found our strange ways to stay alive, equations that would only relate to the two of us, like Stove Top + *Father Knows Best* + GG-Frankie = Saturday night. In the future, that formula would be obsolete, no longer our personalized bill of comfort. We'd trade it in for other healthier (though sometimes more neurotic) rituals. As we drove to Boston, we left our childhood rites behind; a cork was put in the bottle of our *life until now*.

As sisters, Frankie and I share similar knowledge. We are aware of the subtle differences in personality of our grandparents—Nonna and Nonno—and each of our wild aunts and uncles. Without having to describe it, we'll always know exactly what Lia's expression means when she tightly scrunches up her face to the right versus to the left. And while we determine similar constructs as reality, we'll each always hold firm to our own interpretation of what that *actually* means. Though, in ways, we were headed for two different worlds, we'd manage to remain in relatively short range of each other since we had to maintain our own end of *Reality Rope*. When crises ensued or business got hot, we'd each keep a tight grip on our opposing position—same rope, different opinions. Neither Frankie nor I will ever let go of the rope because, simply, we need each other. Our differences confirm our identities. Bouncing contradicting perspectives off each other encourages us to rise to the occasion with defensive stubbornness and secure our individual identities. Frankie's the cold-pressed olive oil, and I'm the balsamic vinegar. We make sure to stay starkly opposite while forever remaining a classic combo.

When Frankie and I arrived on the BU campus, it turned out that I didn't yet have a residence hall to roam through because I'd secured my enrollment later than the rest of the student body. The school could only offer me temporary lodging for two weeks while they figured out where they could house me. Sent to a rather sterile nearby hotel, Frankie and I lugged my wares in from the car: boxes of bedding, shoes, and makeup—plus posters of bands, including The Moody Blues, Lynyrd Skynyrd, and Styx. I decided to leave most of the things I'd brought from home in their boxes until further notice. Afterward, we found our way to the dining hall, which was quite a trek from my temporary lodging. After filling our trays, we sat off in a corner of our own and silently blew on our soupspoons, trying to cool the university's version of minestrone. After we were finished eating, we headed back to the odd hotel room that was now my home. Within the hour, Frankie left; she had an early shift the next day at the Grill.

Here's what's amazing about how Frankie and I do intimacy: we don't. I'm not sure we even hugged goodbye before she got in the car. Instead, I filled her empty arms up with whatever stuff I'd decided was extraneous or couldn't fit into the miniscule space of my temporary lodging. As per usual, I gave orders to Frankie: "Tell Gino Jr. to stay out of my room. Also, mail me the pillowcase I left in the bathroom!" That translated to: *Thanks, Frankie, for bringing me today. I'm totally nervous, even though I know Dad has never recognized that emotion as acceptable. Also, I have no idea what it's going to be like living somewhere without you!* Frankie said, "Okay, gotcha," which translated to, *I have so many mixed feelings about you, Giana, that they cancel one another out. We've been through more than most can ever imagine. And I'm not sure if we'll forget about these years or if we'll forever struggle with the long-term impact of them, or both, but I guess we're going to find out, Sister.* The whole moment of departure was quite difficult to get through, and it's likely Frankie won't ever know this, but when she left, I sat on the bed of my hotel room. I folded my summered Italian legs up to my chest and rocked myself back and forth on the thin mattress, eying the unpacked duffels, the cheap composite-wood drawers, the ugly blue Berber carpet. I put on my flip-flops and walked to the snack machine down the hall, put in a quarter, and hit D11 to release my only familiar, a Tab.

Processing saying goodbye to Adam was a bit easier. I simply ignored the fact that we were heading in separate directions until the day before he left for Virginia Military Institute. Fortunately, Marianne, Adam's mother, had left for the afternoon on some last-minute errands for her son before his imminent departure. Though Adam was heading off to do heavy-duty training and stand up for his entire country, apparently, purchasing boot-camp toiletries and last-minute military-school-approved items was a job too tough for a young cadet. That meant we could make out in his room and feel completely free. As we curled up like wintering animals, I tried to memorize the moment, to somehow capture the effortless ease between us, so that I would always have it with me. Just as I found that one perfect notch in his shoulder upon which to rest my head, Adam got up. Watching him as I lay there, the lone spoon on his taupe sheets, he took his nicest poster off the wall. It was of Styx, his all-time favorite band. He mumbled something like, *I probably won't be allowed to hang this up, but I'm bringing it anyway*, and started to roll up the poster evenly, meticulously. Adam touched everything with precision. Something about watching him pack up whatever he could of his identity left me feeling hollow. *Why is he being so careful rolling up his Styx poster, so committed to having it in his dorm? Why can't he leave a poster behind, but meanwhile, he's unconcerned about leaving us? What made him decide not to go to school near me in Boston, and how is he okay with the fact that we're going off in our own directions?*

I had one strong feeling that physically registered, a nervous racing sensation. Surely, my Dexatrim days had set me up to easily access anxiety as a substitute for almost all bodily reactions. I started to cry, *Adam, Adam*...I repeated his name, trying hard to find some kind of logic or reasonable one-liner to follow suit, something that spoke to my fear, my feelings, my attachment. There was nothing I could find though. We were kids; this is what kids did. If we finished high school and if we had the means or interest, we went off to college. Adam looked at me, and for the first time, saw my face truly upset with him, filled with tears over something other than my parents yelling at me, something just between us. *GG. We're going to be okay,* he assured me. *We'll talk. We'll write. We'll visit. Don't worry.* Despite his having a rigid emotional desert of a mother and a penchant for guns, Adam had a decent emotional vocabulary. He soothed me; the only person who'd ever reached me this way. He brushed my hair back, gently wiped a drying tear from my cheek. Out of all the hands I'd encountered, only Adam's had been granted permission to touch my face this way. I lay my head on his muscular thighs and he folded his upper body over me like a tent; together we made a tiny world. In that shape, I felt so safe, *at home*, actually loved. With Adam, I was present, or as near to it as I'd ever known. This was as close as I'd come to having an emotional dialogue. We wordlessly remained in that position for an extended period, and just before Marianne returned from her duteous outing, I left for the night.

I returned to Adam's the following morning to give Adam a long hug and one last kiss before he drove south. I brought a little gift for him: his favorite of Giana's baked goods (two Nestlé Toll House chocolate chip cookies glued together with a generous portion of Pillsbury vanilla icing). I also gave him a short love note and a framed picture of us. He handed me his Styx poster as though he was presenting me with a Holy Bible. *GG, I figured you should have this one.* And that was it. Two weeks later, I'd leave for my own collegiate experience at Boston University, the school I'd decided last minute that I'd *always wanted to attend.* I mustered conviction and placed all my bets: Boston would be enough to stimulate me, fill my heart, and keep me driven.

College life didn't exactly start with a bang. In fact, my entire freshman experience was like a long blur, the kind that blankets a whole year like an Italian smears Nutella on...well, anything, really. I don't remember a single one of my classes, and I'm not sure if I was fully present at any of them even then, during my so-called attendance. Mostly, I flitted around awkwardly on campus, off-kilter, to say the least. After enduring two weeks of temporary lodging, I was housed away from the rest of the freshman class in a residence hall filled mostly with older international students. I had a few roommates, and they kept to themselves. The only thing that got me through was my weekly call with Adam. Ours was the era of phone cards and landlines, and we'd take turns calling each other to split the steep long-distance fee. To budget, we decided we'd have one call weekly, and even then, we dropped serious bucks for less than an hour of catching up. Interestingly, in an economy of inflation, my monthly phone expenditure that freshman year was about three times more than what my current unlimited cell phone plan costs.

During my *blur* year, I occasionally sent Adam letters. It was a one-sided correspondence. I justified that his hands were too preoccupied with learning to fire guns for him to be able to pick up a pen. For the first month we were apart, our communication felt *manageable*, but by month number two, I began to feel an unresolved pain every time we'd speak. While I was holding on to the coordinates of our past, Adam was finding a new center of orientation in military school. In our earlier phone calls, Adam sounded relieved to connect, as though

I was his connection to home. But like a Doppler effect, Adam grew more and more distant each week. He was immersed in his drills, his curriculum, and his life with fellow students—all of which I had *about zero* ability to relate to. There weren't girls around him, so I didn't feel concerned he'd meet someone else, especially because I faithfully believed in our unbreakable bond. But I wasn't connecting to my school environment in the way Adam seemed to connect with his new life in military school, which made me feel more depressed. As he submitted to extreme calisthenics and responded to his commanding officer's calls in high salute, I traded in popping Dexatrim for popping in for free refills at the dining hall's soft-serve ice-cream machine, saluting the vanilla flavor with my repeat service. Adam was *dropping and giving twenty*, while I was dropping in at the cafeteria and gaining twenty.

Ever the one in control, I took the initiative to visit Adam during our first fall semester apart. Adam enlisted his friends to come up with a plan for him to sneak out of the barracks so that we could have our privacy during my visit; this was his first real, covert military operation. We reserved a hotel room in Lexington City, his new home base, which was about as interesting to explore as a bag of rocks. I wasn't going there to check out Lexington City, so I didn't care. I only wanted to be with my love, my best friend. I was nervous in the days before heading south to see him, worried that when we'd reunite, Adam might no longer seem like the guy I knew. But I justified my concern about our physical separation with our theme song from the *Grease* soundtrack, which provided legitimate consolation. Adam and I would always go together like *rama lama lama ka dinga da dinga dong*. Olivia Newton-John's character, Sandy, assured me that real high school sweethearts make it work, as she lived in Australia, while her boyfriend, Danny, lived in America. Who knows how far apart she and Danny would be after high school? Comparatively, Adam and I should be able to deal with a measly few hundred miles between us.

Because we don't yet have the twenty-twenty hindsight of our later years, it's likely that when we are teenagers, our minds can't grasp how much we're still in utero, undergoing radical changes. We're old enough to rent a hotel room, pass as adults. We can drive, vote, file taxes, and—back in my day—drink by eighteen. We can fight for our country, shoot a gun, donate blood, make a baby, or take birth-control. Massive responsibility is put in our hands, but meanwhile, we're still attempting to get a foothold on who we are. I'm no early-childhood psychologist, but *coming-of-age* seems to me an inherent contradiction, like a flaw in our human design. Teenagers rife with hormones plus unknowns, paradoxically entering adulthood.

For the collegiate, academic years are not so much about getting through Advanced Chem and Spanish Literature as they are about coping with a figurative growth spurt, a kind of existential crisis. Coming-of-age growing pains don't involve the aching of bones, but instead an often uncomfortable stretching of the ego. Surfacing or retreating, shrinking or swelling, the young, erratic personality moves through extreme calisthenics in hopes of one day landing on a functional middle ground for itself. Dramatically exploring the outermost edges of personhood—whether going for the gold or landing in the red, the college student wildly pushes the capacity for consumption; how much partying, keg-tapping, fraternizing can be had? Meanwhile, it's during these unruly years we are confronted with the obligation to name our major and minor life focuses. No wonder it's so easy to run into the same dominant demographic in the dormitory: *the Young Undergrad in Flux.* With piqued interest, we perk up for the promise of greener pastures, weighing the influence of the stories we've been told against the stories of our souls, and migrate through friend circles and philosophies as we try to figure ourselves out. Once we settle on a formal academic path, we then *declare* ourselves through it. It is like a tribal ceremony, but one that can often leave the initiate feeling isolated. While we might sleep only feet away from our roommates' snoring faces, we now lie alone in our metaphorical beds. Amid the mayhem, we maintain the hope that we've chosen a major worthy of long-term commitment, lest our parents kill us. At this point in our lives, however, most of us have little experience with anything like long-term commitment outside of having watched every *Star Wars* episode back-to-back with a bottomless bag of microwave popcorn.

For me, left on my own at school, I wasn't ready to form my new identity without Adam. I wanted to regress, to find the one security blanket I'd claimed, my boyfriend. For Adam, though, he'd willingly trade in clutching a security blanket for fingering the trigger of a gun, aiming to powerfully impact the world. Meanwhile, I'd handle the trigger of the soft-serve ice-cream machine in the cafeteria in dreamy denial until I was ready to confront a deeper kind of identity, way beyond my college years, one that I could feel from the inside out. This identity I sought would be far less ready-made than either the soft-serve machine in the cafeteria or the multiple majors available at my school. While I likely flopped Economics 101, I aced honors-level self-denial, doing my best to cover up how lost I felt during my freshman year at BU. However much I blocked out, I couldn't shake my hunger for a kind of soul food, and nothing edible would placate this call, it turns out, not even the faux-vanilla soft-serve. Far past my formal student years, I'd continue the journey of sating my soul, on the path of the seeker, which was sort of my college major.

It was after my first bombed year of college that my real education began. I'd spend the following four decades attempting to untangle the complex knots I'd tied during my first decade or two. If you told me during my freshman year, when I was already scholastically exhausted, that I'd spend something like forever in a spiritual grad school, I might have actually checked into San Sebastiano's nunnery, the vision my mother once had for her own life, and surrendered myself to covenant piety. Instead, though, I was spiritually scrappy. Throughout my years, I'd wander the avenues and streets of the world, seeking mystical experiences, spiritually attuned networks, and places where I'd retreat, detox, and dismantle my darn identity. I knew, ultimately, that my real profession, my declared major, was beneath all the other titles I held—not daughter, not first-generation Italian-American of immigrant parents, not emotional eater, not restaurateur, or even healer. My heartfelt humanity would be identified in my locating, finally, my *feeling*—my feeling of presence, life, vulnerability, and connection, all degrees, titles, and statuses aside.

There I was, though, landing in Virginia, rife with the zeal often afforded only in those young years of so-called self-discovery. I arrived from Boston on a morning flight, direct to the tiny airport nearest to Adam's school with just a carry-on. I'd landed earlier than expected, so after deplaning, I took my time in the terminal bathroom, freshly applying my lipstick—my favorite pink of the era, Revlon's Lilac Champagne. Then I pulled my little wheeled bag to the curbside pickup area outside the double glass doors, where I enjoyed a Virginia Slims cigarette. Turns out, I'd go a long way, baby, to fly to Virginia for the *slim*, but possible, chance my boyfriend and I might make it last forever.

Before I took my last drag, Adam arrived, smiling, with a handful of peonies. His standard military school buzz cut made his eyes look like steel, like bullets in contrast to the pink peonies. Even when he broke into a recognizable grin, Adam seemed different than the kindhearted boy I'd spent so much time with the year before, under our favorite band's poster, making out on the plaid bedspread his mom had picked out for his Connecticut bedroom.

"GIANA AND VIRGINIA SLIMS"

As per Adam's instructions, I'd managed to fit a conservative dress into my weekender bag for his military gala, where I'd be smack-dab in the middle of his new world. Frankly, I would have been content to have spent the weekend alone with Adam, relaxing, talking, kissing, watching movies on the room's "Pay-as-You-View" channel, killing the contents of the minifridge, and ordering room service. But Adam seemed set on attending the formal, so I didn't argue. I was curious enough to meet his brigade, the ones who were now getting all of Adam's attention and time here in Bumblefudge, Virginia. All military academy boys were considered *rats* in their freshman year. This was standard protocol in military school, the hierarchal way of showing superiority, true to the patriarchal top-down strata of importance. First-year boys were to be reduced to nothing, considered worthless filth, and then their identities would be built back up. Cadets were conditioned to fit the preferences of the system after being successfully destroyed, the same strategy the young men would later use to control their foreign enemies. You'll *do unto others as you have been done unto*, or something like that, right? *Forward...march!*

Amazingly, regardless of the brainwashing, Adam was still able to be romantic with me with the same vigor I'd remembered—pretty good for a reduced-to-nothing freshman military *rat*, impressive for a man who'd endured the Catholic conservatories and the school of soldiering-up. While I recalled the language of our physical closeness after months apart, Adam sweetly held my hand, giving me time to reorient myself to him, to his smell, to our connection. I'd been more comfortable with Adam than anyone I'd known before, but I had to admit, there was now a different feeling between us emotionally. We were bonded through our shared experiences, he and I, but our certain future didn't seem as secure as it had before. Instead of the thrill of being in his arms, I more-so felt an urgency to return to what we had (in truth, by that point, my nervous system had basically been set to feel urgency as its default mode). While in ways it was satisfying to return to each other, I think we both sensed the shift we'd undergone in our weeks apart. In life, there are some basic things we can't deny, one being the inevitability of change. In this case, Adam and I were now independently forming; we weren't changing in the same way, at the same rate, together. Perhaps, if we had been more mature, we'd have recognized this as the next threshold, a deeper invitation into love, but we weren't even twenty years of age. How could I have grasped love as something to cultivate when I hadn't yet labored to grow anything in life other than maybe my hair, which I'd managed to grow by two-and-a-half inches since graduation. Deep questions about my relationship with Adam made my head ache, so I did my best to ignore them, to shake off any concerns and just enjoy our weekend.

I missed the whimsy of our previous years together, when I didn't think much about something called *the future*, didn't concern myself beyond going to a rock club or catching a film, like the horror movie *Carrie*. This was the last flick Adam and I saw during our senior year, a weekend date we'd made sometime in the fall. Suitably, *Carrie* was a perfectly patriarchal horror movie, with the central plot involving a girl who, after her first menstrual period, goes violently mad; *ya know*, just simple, innocuous, 1970s entertainment. That was it, though, for the future, nothing planned beyond a few days' advance notice for a date with Adam and Steven King. In high school, we were wrapped up in the ease of it all. Now, I was no longer lost in the moment with my knight in shining armor. I felt more like a stranger in a strange land, a stranger missing her distant lover.

By the time I'd returned from that first fall visit, I am certain my roused intuition already knew the end was near. I made a mixtape that included the likes of Fleetwood Mac's "Landslide" (*I've been afraid of changing, 'cause I built my life around you. But time makes you bolder, even children get older*), the Bee Gees "You Should Be Dancing" (versus, say, shining rifles—sigh), and, of course, "How Deep Is Your Love" (*We belong to you and me*). Then there was "Free Bird," the Lynyrd Skynyrd classic, which was basically our song. *If I leave here tomorrow, would you still remember me? ...I'm as free as a bird now, and this bird you'll never change.* A bunch of other sappy lyrics captured what I'd never be able to say out loud. With this, more or less, I crafted a musical survival kit for the emotional *grotto* I'd be in until the next year. (And when I did eventually emerge from my cave, I'd remain perpetually disoriented, unable to know what to make of daylight.)

The fall turned to winter; Adam became increasingly engaged on his campus, and I, meanwhile, felt exceedingly lost. My mixtape wasn't enough to soothe my senses, my anxiety, my fear of losing Adam and everything that came with it. I may have been struggling to pass my classes or make friends at BU, but as an Italian, I could call on one sure-fire resource with certainty: I know how to eat. So I stocked up on the old colorful companions. Trustworthy go-tos, whose disappearance I could monitor. Half a bag of Fritos left, check. One-third of a bag left. (Look! Somehow, I can compute culinary math!) One-fifth of a bag remaining...then the crumbs. Shall we kill the whole thing off, allow all traces of substance to vanish, to leave us? Sure. My mouth was in control of it all. Meanwhile, I couldn't get a handle on Adam's escalating distance. His Sunday calls began to peter out because, he said, he didn't have the money to spare. I then took it on myself to be the caller, to help him save cash, but he often wasn't even around when I rang. And for every time I reached out to keep our connection strong, I caved in weakness and reached out for a bag of Oreos, Kit Kats, or *Nestlé Freaking Crunch*. That was the year that Nestlé Crunch and I became good friends, basically entering a courtship. I was lost on campus and lost in myself. Nestlé Crunch was only twenty-five cents and just down the hall, a stable housemate. With a single push of a button, one turn of a wheel, she'd submit to my hands. We've been together a long time, Nestlé Crunch and I, and her slogan, "For the Kid in You," was entirely appropriate, even then. There was Giana, growing up—or, at least, growing larger—with no sense of inner anchor. She hadn't even learned how to tread water, how to breathe, how to self-soothe, any of the elementary stuff.

Months before the end of the year, I began to count down the weeks until summer break. I was so excited to go home, to be with Adam, to strengthen our connection again. I expected to live out the very best version of my fantasies; we'd spend nearly every day side by side. Then Adam called to let me know that he had decided to take a job on the Massachusetts coast, where his family had a summerhouse. His decision was based solely on his need to make money. Since school was expensive, he explained, he had to work to afford the cost of his sophomore year. I couldn't understand how Adam could forego the opportunity to be with me as much as possible over our break. Call me thick, but at the time, I didn't compute that his decision to be an entire state away was also a direct statement to me: *GG, my life has moved on. Our relationship is not my priority. In fact, GG, it's not even happening, and I'm not prioritizing a plan to make it happen.* I definitely didn't hear anything like that. Instead, even though I was disappointed, I rationalized that Adam was being responsible, choosing hard work over his desire for recreational fun with his girlfriend. My family valued hardworking, self-sacrificing individuals above any other kind, so this made sense to me; it even seemed attractive. Adam was of solid caliber; of course he'd work himself to the bone, *duh*. I didn't put it together, however, that he could have just as easily gotten work in Connecticut, right down the street from my house. Heck, he could've been a manager at the American Grill if he'd wanted to, and I bet Lia and Gino would have paid him nearly double my wage. Instead, all summer long, Adam hardly took the initiative to come to Connecticut. The joy and fun I'd hoped to have during our break had not actualized. Summer, at least on my end, offered little warmth despite the sunshine.

On the one weekend Adam arranged to come to town, he decided to invite a handful of his friends to join him. It seemed less his priority to spend quality time with me, and more to party with friends for a superficial summer romp. I was kind and friendly to his group; I'd already met most of his Massachusetts friends over the previous years, friends he'd made during the many holidays his family spent at their waterside getaway. During the weekend, I tried to get a sense of our coupledom, analyzing every move he made. Adam put his arm around me. *Okay, everything is totally fine*, I thought. *He likes me. I'm just going crazy, like Carrie, the menstruating telekinetic killer.* Then, the next minute, he left for the liquor store without even telling me he was going on a keg run, and my mood took a nosedive. *He's over me. What was I thinking? He doesn't want to have a girlfriend anymore.* I had transferred all of my self-esteem and emotions into our relationship like it was a container. If I allowed *Adam* to control my feeling troubled or joyful, I didn't have to be physically flooded by my own sense of anxious overwhelm. I didn't have to deal with destiny or define my ambitions and independent desires. Adam could be my sentient body; he could handle that. Over the weekend of Adam's visit, although I was more insecure than an ice cube in a Negroni under the summer sun, as a young Italian woman, I still had a hearty sense of territory. I could tell Adam was being eyed by a girl who'd come into town along with his Massachusetts tribe. Her name was Monica Bell, or Mimi Bell, as she introduced herself. I could tell by the way dippy Mimi Bell looked at and talked to Adam that she liked him. *Well, well, Monica Bell*, I remember Frankie and I casually mentioning later that night after first encountering her, our nostrils flaring, a typical response of teenaged girls. Later, we'd jeer, *Mimi Bell, Dumbbell!* We'd sometimes sing this in the same melody of the Beatles song that had come out about ten years before, the one with the French and English lyrics, "Michelle." Frankie and I shared a weird sense of humor, and that summer, it actually felt really comforting to be with her, especially after a year of living in a sterile residence hall.

My sister was getting ready to go to school at Connecticut College in the fall. Her desire to *get in shape* for her new life, and my need to find something I could control allowed us to again team up with a plan to lose weight—this time, without Dexatrim. We somehow knew that the pill approach to dieting wouldn't really be effective in the long term. The anxiety Dexatrim provided ultimately undid all of its advertised hunger suppression. Ultimately, the yellow-and-burgundy capsule confused my senses, causing me to mistake anxiety for hunger, defeating the whole purpose of popping pills. Frankie and I needed something more stable in our lives, at least when it came to food. Enrolling in a military academy of our own, we committed ourselves as deeply as first-year *rats*, but rather than training with physical weaponry, we went to battle with willpower of steel.

We opted for a variation on the good ol' Scarsdale Diet's rigid plan, the meat- and vegetable-based food-restricting diet scheme, the diet I use as my go-to to this day. In part, I revert to this diet because it is familiar, but also because it specifically forbids me from acknowledging the core foods of my Italian heritage, which, as we know, are pasta and bread. The diet then becomes a wonderful twist on self-hatred, with the unconscious rationale being that if I starve right out of my body whatever fat genes I inherited, I'll thus rid myself of my Italian pear-shape body. And if I can get thin enough, I might slip away like a sailboat gliding on crystal-clear tropical waters, no longer at the constant beck and call of the Giovannis. All of this, of course, is theoretical; it's what I've made up as the underpinning belief system that supports my surfaced intentions.

In ways, I could consider my introspective investigation to be self-absorbed, but even the ascetic Catholics point to Revelations as essential to decoding mystery, and so, however uncomfortable it can be to look beneath the hood of my dysfunctional relationship to food, I've reveled in doing so. Isn't it interesting how, while I go with the flow in so many areas of my life, I can't just freaking eat healthy food without putting myself under authoritarian control? How is it that, if I am so intuitive, I don't trust my gut instinct, can't even approach something like normalcy when dealing with food? My diet is either based totally in elimination—like complex-carb denial—or a hell's bells all-out binge-a-thon! What would it take for me to slow the heck down long enough to patiently listen to my core need, like *really* slow down? What if actually, from a healthy place, I just wanted to enjoy a frickin' cheese-and-mayo sandwich on a blanket under the sun somewhere? Does it matter, in the long run, what I'm eating if I'm always racing around in the car and shoving food in my mouth like I'm plugging an open floodgate? Does it matter, then, if I'm inhaling slices of turkey breast, something on my allowed food list, or a blacklisted gas-station grinder preserved with a variety of chemical flavorings if I'm *wolfing* and multitasking, tasting nothing? I remain frustrated about feeling both unacknowledged and unheard by my family, but this is the same damn thing I do to my primary need: shut her down, turn her off. What if I gently allowed myself to find my natural rhythm, my essence? What if I relinquished control in order to learn just who the heck I am? Might I learn to trust my food choices as a way to empower myself to feel good and worthy rather than overstuffed and in a food coma?

On paper, a plan to permanently let go of dieting sounds sensible, even enlightening, but the reality is that it's harrowing, and my success rate so far is *about zero*. If I *really* and *truly* stopped controlling food, I'd threaten my ability to remain functional, and I'd lose my total focus as well as any thread of self-confidence. The only times I have been able to recognize myself as successful are periods in which I've mostly followed my *Avoid-the-Gut Diet*, which is a pretty ridiculously named diet for an intuitive woman like myself. This denying of my gut instinct allows me to shut down all sensation below the belt, turning off most of my body. It's amusing how I've remained zealously committed to this diet of self-denial while simultaneously looking for myself in every workshop, every spiritual book. How did I manage to avoid realizing throughout all of these years that to spiritually discover where or what *I am* relies specifically on my ability to practice whole-person self-care? Through self-care, we can remain sensate and cognizant—not checked out or numb, dumbed down, wasted, or intoxicated (yes, food is a drug in the sense it can knock one out when ingested in excess). We unite our physical adroitness and spiritual strength through cultivating mindfulness practices. From this place, we forge healthy habits and transform limitations, whether they've manifested as physical disease or incessant, self-critical thinking.

That summer, however, I'd not yet exposed myself to anything considered spiritual. In fact, I barely had my basic thoughts together. At that point, the word *spiritual* only conjured up the memory of church hymns, or my baptism, which (*I must confess, Father*) didn't really penetrate my spirit. These were the closest encounters I'd had to anything spiritual up to that point. Outside of these variations, nothing considerably woo-woo had yet shown up on my radar by the end of my second decade. By that summer after my freshman year of college, the closest thing I'd experienced to smoky ringlets of burning frankincense was rummaging through my sister's dresser drawers, *incensed* that *Frankie* had borrowed my clothes again without asking first.

My sister and I did find spirit, though, in the form of fermented alcohol, and that worked. That helped us touch something that felt higher, effervescent. Frankie and I spent much of the summer drinking, an activity we included in our weight-loss plan, of course. Why be thin and sober? How dull! The only point of being thin was to be unlimited, and this meant being granted full access to festive nights filled with celebrating, dancing, and laughing. Being thin meant having permission to feel comfortable in clothes, to exude charisma. Alcohol conveniently served as a kind of food supplementation; it was easier to forgo eating dinner if we'd get to drink the day away.

On the night Adam came into town with his Massachusetts

gang, Frankie and I were quite wasted and spent most of the evening exchanging glances behind Mimi Bell's back while she attempted to flirt with Adam right in front of me. I knew the only reason Mimi even liked him was because *I* liked him. She was that kind of girl, the kind who only wanted what someone else cherished or valued. My sixth sense about Mimi Bell was so strong—be it from the Italian absinthe Frankie and I had gotten our hands on, or just my natural instinct—I felt I had to bring it up to Adam. *You know that little girl, Mimi Bell?* I broached the subject with my best emotional-communication language skills, which were probably then just a mark or two below where they rank today, so I'd say that at that point, they were *about zero* out of ten. Adam looked at me quizzically, almost sneering, a way he never used to look at me. It was subtle but distinct, the kind of look guys reserve for when their girlfriends are acting "crazy." *Acting crazy* is a perspective that has often been projected onto women for the last, say, five thousand years, anytime we've given voice to our instincts. Adam responded in a slightly irritated tone; he knew what I was getting at. *Giana, of course I know her. She just spent the whole weekend with us. Why?* I was feeling a bit reluctant to bring this subject to Adam's attention, hesitant to confess I sensed anything wrong between us, and Adam hadn't brought up anything directly. *She likes you*, I said. I knew it was true. I knew Adam was smart; there was no way he couldn't have known Mimi Bell was coming on to him. Men, and especially young men, can sniff out a woman's interest level like a good Italian girl can smell the bay leaf in her *pasta e fagioli. Mimi Bell is a family friend, GG, there is no way on Earth she likes me.* Adam, true to male form, dismissed my insight, denying the possibility.

As Adam grew more unresponsive throughout the summer, I became more anxious about my upcoming return to Boston University. Dexatrim had set me up well for having anxiety coursing through my body. Interestingly, it had been more than a means of halting my hunger; it was also a way to deal with my emotions. As uncomfortable as the anxiety effect of Dexatrim was, at least it covered up my raw feelings, repressed my primary emotions. I was sad, sure, but I would only feel nervousness and stimulation. It was better to tweak all my energy and remain charged up than down for the count, immobilized by sadness. I was confused, yes, but I was more running on high and tripping over myself than admitting to being at a loss. I vied for more foundational support as I prepped to return to school, somebody to vent to about my broken heart, but emotionally, I was alone. Rather than moping and feeling broken, I kept revving my system, running on empty with anxiety as my fuel. In a way, this can toughen one's emotional self, even more than the Virginia Military Institute can.

Adam and I had been so close for so long, and our communication was based on our intimate trust, which had so naturally occurred between us. With this closeness now missing, I wasn't sure how to communicate my feelings, wasn't sure where the Adam I knew had gone or how to share what I believed. I also couldn't find the feelings inside of myself, as there is only so long one person can singlehandedly maintain a relationship. I no longer had the ability to express myself easily and authentically within our connection.

Honestly, I didn't even know if Adam and I had a relationship anymore. He and I were overdue for a heart-to-heart conversation about how we each felt about our connection, but thanks to my insecurity, I stayed quiet. I'd inherited this quality from Lia; we were both experts at freezing in the face of despair. My nervous system had a black belt in operating while remaining in shutdown mode. Lia had turned that gene on during Italy's upheaval, hiding out underground until the danger subsided. Here, the problem was not necessarily a separation of nations, but the growing divide between Adam and me. Our situation was less historically significant than being under Nazi attack, but I felt tortured all the same. I hoped that something would shift our rapport, return us to the happiness that had been ours for so long.

In the last week of my summer vacation, just before my sophomore year began, Adam disappeared completely, went missing in action somewhere in the Massachusetts wild. My self-esteem and sense of value shrunk each day his mother played answering service to my calls, offering simply, *Adam isn't home, but I'll let him know you called.* His mother spoke to me as though I were a contagion she or her family could catch through the telephone receiver. Meanwhile, Adam had flown the coop without sharing any thoughts with me about how our next year apart might go. Last year it was so different as we were heading off to school. Now, as I prepared to return to Boston, the most unstable part of my life was our relationship. Our connection had been the only thing that felt solid and dependable to me the year before.

On the morning I was to leave for BU, I rang Adam again. I'd nearly exhausted my efforts to reach out, but I knew we needed to speak. As I was preparing for how to casually address him and then warm up the conversation, his mother answered the phone.

Hi, Mrs. Grant. This is Giana. Is Adam home? I said, pretending I hadn't already called ten times in the past four days.

Hi, Giana. Adam isn't around, Adam's mom replied, barely covering up her disdain for me.

Okay, do you know when he'll be back? I asked, knowing she wouldn't provide actual details but going through the motions anyway.

Really, Giana? Adam actually doesn't seem to want to talk to you anymore, does he? He's not really interested in being your boyfriend, in case you haven't gotten it, she said, flexing some genius parenting skills and exuding loving kindness (not).

I seriously did not know what to say for a moment. I sat back, blinked a few times, and immediately steeled myself against the blow. I was shot to smithereens, but I wouldn't let myself feel that, nor would I let Adam's mother reap the reward of her gunfire. Amazingly, Adam was the one at military school, but that year, his mother had learned how to shoot straight through the heart better than her son. I thought for what felt like half a minute. I was in such shock that I had to muster every ounce of courage in my body to come up with the right words to say to her instead of admitting loss and defeat.

I gathered whatever self-respect I could find, and responded, *You know what, Mrs. Grant? If Adam has something to say to me, why don't you tell him that he should call me directly and let me know.*

With that, I hung up. Adam felt lost to me, and more than simply missing in action, he was now turning out to be an enemy of the state. I was at a loss for words and feelings, in full freeze mode. I could barely find my arm to lift my hand to my face to wipe the tears that were streaming uncontrollably down my cheeks, splashing on my tanned, Fritos-fattened thighs. I barely had enough energy to look down, but when I did, I was able to cast my despair and hatred somewhere, right onto the roll of fat I saw folded over the top my jeans. *Giana, you are so disgusting*, I said to myself. This fixation on my body as *the thing that was wrong*, would become my anchor. I rekindled the familiar technique, but with new reinforcements. My disappointment in my body, its betrayal, this would never leave me. If things were fleeting, if safety was broken beyond my control, if promises turned up empty, at least I could attempt to master my physical self. I'd deal with life's unfairness through body hatred and body shaming. Honestly, in the height of modern civilization, it wasn't an original plan. Many other women did the same thing. We focused on what we could or couldn't eat as a way to determine our value, dealing with imbalanced politics, the economy, and even global issues through caloric restriction. If I could control the intensity of life by controlling my body, well then the disembodied GG, the one who is running around like a workhorse, *she* could remain unfettered, stable. The disembodied GG, whom I identified as, was holding it together. She'd stay constant and let her body go up and down rather than allowing for one single emotion. *How are you, GG?* anyone can ask. *Good.* That's literally what I always say, because it's always how I *am*. But in the case someone might be brave enough to ask, *How is your body, GG?* I'd have to take a moment. *Hmmm...*, I'd say, completely at a loss. *To be honest, I don't know.*

CHAPTER 14

Starving as Salvation

There was a form of anorexia popular in Italy, circa the fifteenth century. It was called *holy anorexia*, and largely affected Catholic nuns and other pious women. The concept was straightforward: Starve to honor the suffering of Jesus. Starve as a way to practice *devotion*, to touch the heart of *sacrament*, to find worthiness within the human experience. However much the canonical gospels differ, all in all, Jesus starved while enduring *passion*, and so devoted women aspired to follow his example. Hips popping voluptuously into the shape of an hourglass? Here's a cure for seductive puberty! Simply *whack-a-mole* all sensation and satisfaction via self-deprecation. In the context of the extremely religious, it could be said that passion tweaks the soul, warps it like a record. Even worse, carnal passion afflicts humanity; it thwarts human spiritual devotion by abducting the senses and taking over the whole body. Be honest: How many times have you said to yourself, *I'm going home alone at the end of the night no matter how well the rest of this date goes*. Then, four hours later, your peck-on-the-cheek plan has turned into a four-glasses-in drunken make-out session, pushing your date's hands away as they crawl up your leg. Welcome, *holy anorexia*! Starve that promiscuity right out of your body, and you're good to go. I don't mean to sound crass; religious self-starvation was no joke. It's likely that it was the ancestral predecessor of the various eating disorders that affect as many as ten million American women today. I *Wiki'd* the facts, which led me to Professor Rudolph Bell, a published expert in the area of gender studies and Italian religious history. We're not talking small numbers here; Bell reports that more than half of the devoted women of the Roman Catholic Church in the Middle Ages were neurotic religious anorexics. A substantial population of girls sought Roman Catholic convent life just for its promise of education. For young women, this arrangement translated to, *We are born with original sin. All physical pleasures are carnal crimes. Forbid me food, and forgive me, Father. Please grant me an education.* This repentance (however much the physical effects of it would later be celebrated by *Vogue* magazine) was accompanied by a slew of near-psychotic and superstitious behaviors. Devotional Dexatrim-like fear-based paranoia infected the cultural psyche of women in the Middle Ages. The starving girls' state of malnutrition was enhanced all the more by a lack of vitamin B_{12}, which only increased the probability of psychotic breakdown.

Even the first female doctor of the church was a Mad Hatter anorexic, Catherine of Siena. Awesome—anorexia endorsed firsthand by one of the top religious luminaries of the time. As a child, I'd glorified Catherine, initially drawn to her holy image found within the delicately lit Italian churches of my family's homeland. She was a saint revered for her dedication to upholding peace. In the twenty-first century, perhaps Catherine would have been just another self-cutting, calorie-counting, belly-fat pinching, walking bundle of insecurity. She'd fall, just like the other starving girls in her class, for a squarely built Anglo hunk named Adam. Nervously tugging down her size-XS miniskirt, she'd wobble in heels to the table. He'd pull out her chair for her on their second dinner date. She would starve in a different kind of devotion that night, one in which she'd make sure to order nothing more than a soup and side salad. For many of the young, modern *holy anorexics*, traditional church wouldn't catch the heart's fancy nearly as much as young men would. If we needed to confuse our appetites, they would do the trick. I was caught up, as well, in my own devotional holy narrative, fixated on one guy's rejection. I could somehow sacrifice my feelings of hunger, let them disappear like Adam had, even if only months before I'd given in to the gluttony of Nestlé and Twix. I would now take the vow. I didn't need to eat and didn't need to love. The young Giana basically set up her own crucifixion.

Adam called just hours after my conversation with his mother. It's as though she told him, *Adam, get it together, and don't be a little boy. Call Giana, and tell her, or I'm driving you to Connecticut*! It wouldn't surprise me if she did, in fact, give her son a General Grant–type order such as this. When the phone rang, I knew it would be him, and when I answered, my voice was already quivering. Adam delivered a simple and straightforward breakup line: *It's not going to work out for us, Giana*. No explanation, just a phone call, and only after I basically forced him, via his difficult mother, to reach out to me. How could it be that in the three-plus years I'd given my heart to Adam, it had taken just one simple phone call to obliterate the entirety of our bond? I had to leave for school the very next day. Understandably, I could barely get out of my bed in Bridgewood the following morning, much less figure out how to arrive on campus later that afternoon. I made it, however, three hours up the highway. Considering my energy level felt about as high as that of a squashed fly, it was pretty remarkable that I'd managed.

Partly because I couldn't sink any lower, my sophomore year at BU started much better than my previous year. My circumstances were better, for one. I'd been accepted into a socially vibrant dormitory on campus, in the same building as the cafeteria. This meant no icy walks to get to my *emotional safe house*, the trustworthy home of buffets and free refills, muffins, bagels, rubbery pizza, and burritos. (And my school ID granted me access to a bottomless bread basket!) I lived in a suite with six other girls—six different creatures with whom I could distract myself. I could alleviate my grief by dissolving my own remorse into their dramas, their lives, their affairs. Since I'd grown up losing myself within my family, applying a similar pattern within this relatively less explosive group of girls was seamless. I liked everyone

I lived with during my sophomore year, and found them to be diverse enough for me to be able to redefine myself, to step away from the Adam era, to bust out of that Eden like a runaway train.

My best friend from college remains one of my closest to this day: Josie. Josie has a quality I've heard people also attribute to me: a sort of eternal youthfulness of mind and body. Josie is always able to find laughter and remain poised, even in our strangest moments (and believe me, we've traveled to some exotic locales and laughed our way through some truly bizarre times). This is the stuff friendship is made of, I believe. Probably the best thing I got out of college was my friendship with Josie. In those first weeks of our sophomore year, the student body set out like termites claiming off-campus social turfs—infesting local bars, pool halls, live-music venues, diners, and coffee shops. One weekday night, I came home from a random social event and made my way to bed. The ceiling spun a bit as I attempted to fall asleep. I had an early-morning class to attend. After a concerted effort to retire, I slipped on my flip-flops and grabbed my shower bucket. My plan was to stand under hot water and see if I could sober up a bit, and then head back to sleep. I pocketed my pack of cigarettes as I headed out the door. In the last week, I'd traded Virginia Slims for Winston. It was something harder, something less vulnerable and hopeful, something that would not remind me of the state of *Virginia*, where Adam was, and the *slim* crack of light left on in my otherwise betrayed heart. I'd already made a habit of propping myself up on the bathroom counter late at night by myself, facing the showers, with my hair in a cap and a towel around my body. Legs crossed, staring vacantly toward the empty rows of shower stalls, I would light up a cigarette and let my mind go blank, dissolve into the smoke rings. As I walked to the bathroom in my pajamas, towel under my right arm, shower caddy and smokes in my left hand, a girl who seemed just as drunk as I was approached me.

Hi. It was Josie, my soon-to-be best friend. *Do you have any food?*

I'm a cut-to-the-chase person whose life—from how I've built value to how I've devalued myself—has revolved exclusively around food. I immediately appreciated Josie's directness, and I understood her objective. The girl was drunk, it was late, any potentially still-open stores were far away (especially for the inebriated), and a girl has got to eat when she's got to eat. *Yes, I have chips!* I said, saving her.

I turned around, put down my shower caddy, and grabbed my Wise potato chips bag. Josie and I plunked ourselves down in the hallway and devoured the entire contents. By the end of the bag, we'd spilled significant crumbs but also explicit details of our lives. It was the start of a great and easy friendship. She became my new go-to, and frankly, a far better one than Adam had panned out to be during my college years. Josie was available to connect, to explore, to hang out and laugh. Also, she loved the same junk food I did, and, like mine, her interests included barhopping, parties, and all other fun social activities. Together we made the most of our college priorities, which included everything but the actual academic work.

Within the first weeks of my newly formed friendship with Josie, we headed out on a Friday night to Cornwall's, a Beacon Street bar just a few blocks from our dorm that would become our second home. Josie wanted to introduce me to Patrick, the roommate of Curtis, a boy she liked. In college, pairs of girlfriends sought pairs of boys; it simply made things easier. Josie had already gone on a date with Curtis, so it was my turn to meet Patrick. Since Adam had executed our relationship as some kind of sick military school target practice, I'd been rapidly disappearing. Don't get me wrong, I wouldn't have voluntarily endured our breakup for anything, not even the promise of acquiring a thin body. However, losing my appetite was a welcome side effect. If I couldn't have Adam to hold, at least I could almost feel my ribs again. Without hunger, I didn't need to go so often to the school's epicenter, the cafeteria (but it was still nice to know it was just six floors below me, like a kind of security blanket). I tapped the university's soft-serve ice-cream machine less often during my sophomore year due to my heartbreak diet. The Sysco food truck probably had to slow down its soft-serve restocking schedule, peddling less corn syrup, emulsifiers, and milk fat to campus. For the entire fall semester, I remained in a kind of abstinence mode, *holy anorexia*. If I did hit the cafeteria for a single soft-serve, in relationship to how married I felt to the machine the year before, it wasn't doing much for me now. I couldn't manage to keep down more than a tomato soup and oyster crackers, and so this was often my only meal of the day. I'd pocket a few packs of oyster crackers for later, and between these and my Winstons (which did a better job of numbing my emotions than the old Whatchamacallit Slims), I kept the pilot light of my appetite broken. I subsisted for a season or more on beer and tomato soup, dry mouthfuls of crackers, and smoke rings—perfect for a girl lying in the ashes of heartbreak. I'd returned to a size 8, and, as we know, size 8 is great, according to the Giana scale, so I had something, at least, to feel motivated about. Without fixating on my shrinking size, well, I'd then be flat-out empty of purpose and resigned to actually confronting the hell of my heartache. So, like a good *religious anorexic*, I used starvation as a means to repent. Adam had been my heroic figure of a god, and without him in my life, I was forced to find salvation. *Forgive me, Father, for my body is so disgusting I could not keep a young man satisfied as much as the promise of war and weapons did. Forgive me for failing to be of sound form like the image of man you made to your liking.* Exhausted from having failed so hard in keeping a boy's interest, I had little power to do anything other than abstain from food. *That* I could do. That was something I had found previous success in making happen. I kept that going for at least a year before I allowed my nose to respond to the fragrance of french fry grease. Boys and other things might disappear, but some things, like GG's appetite, cannot vanish forever.

Since body size determined my self-worth and security, and since I'd arrived at the shape that fit my most preferred wardrobe, I tried to convince myself I was ready enough to meet a new boy. I headed out with Josie to find new livestock for our pastures. Patrick entered Cornwall's with Curtis, each wearing a version of the same outfit: trousers and a plaid, autumn-colored shirt. They sat next to us—Patrick on my side, Curtis on Josie's. Patrick was handsome enough, but there was little actual interest on my part. Honestly, I was still just too darn wiped out to be stimulated by the presence of a young man, however much I tried to be open to it. I struggled, trying to wrap my mind around the idea of even kissing a new guy. The only kisses I'd really ever enjoyed were the ones I'd shared with Adam, and my foolish mouth still felt devoted to my memories. Regardless, I entertained Patrick, tested the power of my gestures; that was fun enough. *May as well investigate whether I still have it*, I decided. *It* being that skill of rousing a man's interest. Patrick's assessment of me, it turned out, didn't matter. Within the first twenty minutes of our conversation, I completely ruined my evening. No, wait—let's restate that: I ruined my entire year.

We started innocently:

So, where are you from? I asked Patrick, politely making small talk.

I'm pretty local, Patrick said with a twinkle in his eye, probably already mentally undressing me, as per the norm.

Oh, you're from Boston? I asked, already thinking about returning to the dorm to chain-smoke and finish reading Jackie Collins's newest release, *Chances*. It's the first of a series in which I'd absorbed myself, along with the rest of the girls on campus. The book starred protagonist Lucky Santangelo, a young, take-charge kind of girl who ran her father's company. Losing myself in the page-turner while tucked under the covers, ignoring my own unlucky-in-love existence sounded way more snug and satisfying than small talk with Patrick over beer and stale popcorn. But I was patient, mainly for Josie's sake because I knew she had been eager to set up our double date.

Well, I'm actually from Marblehead, but yeah, it's close to the city. Just up the shore. Patrick replied, not knowing he was igniting the bomb ready to explode in whatever remained of my heart.

I hadn't thought of the potential danger before asking; it was automatic. I hadn't considered that out of the whole nation, Patrick might be from the same tiny oceanside town Adam had, basically, chosen over me. Marblehead was where Adam had been all summer. This was where his family's summer home was, on the beach. There was no stopping my further inquiry, my filter had been ripped out. Small talk time was over:

Oh, yeah, I know Marblehead. Do you know Adam Grant? He works at the Three Cod Tavern?

Yes! Patrick exclaimed, his face lighting up. We had something in common, which was always helpful for boys—something to talk about that was mutually understood, impersonal, and empty of substance. *I know Adam. He goes out with Monica Bell.*

That was pretty much all I heard, the end of my night. I froze. I think I repeated, *What?* enough times for Patrick to determine I was broken. I excused myself and headed toward the door. My stomach lurched into my throat, forcing the single drink I'd downed back into my esophagus for an acrid ride. Josie followed me, after saying goodbye to Patrick and Curtis, leaving them with our beers and the bowl of cardboard-flavored popcorn. Josie was the type of person who would always prioritize friendship above fawning over some irrelevant man. She rushed to my side and helped me get my head together. We made it to the dorms, and I lit up a Winston. I couldn't believe that Adam had lied to me, and worse still, I'd suspected it. I'd called him out on the whole thing, and he'd denied what I'd so clearly intuited. I made a vow to myself that night, even though I didn't realize it until recently. Maybe I had allowed it before, but I'd never again let anyone interfere with my intuition. Even if I stumbled, inevitably human, not always recognizing my gut instinct and truth, once I became aware of it, I'd hold on firmly to my *forza della natura*.

This was what hurt: Adam betrayed me because he discounted my insight, which is the strongest part of my essence, the core of who I am. Even if I was drunk at the time, rolling my eyes and flaring my nostrils over dippy Mimi Bell, it still felt almost sacrilegious that he had refuted my intuition. Adam, to his great credit, had been the first and only man I'd found gentle and real enough to trust with my faith.

I'm sure I inherited from my parents a deep sense of betrayal and deprivation. Lia and Gino both grew up in a country that disguised its economic interests and power platforms under the pretense of religious morality, for the good of the people. My mother's warring Sicily denied her the natural birthright of girlish fancy and physical freedom, the ability to be young and childlike. When the war, at last, ended, the economy faltered further. Lia's country still would not coddle her nor respect her family's hard-earned relationship to their land. Instead, her family risked losing their home under new imposing regimes, all for the sake of "economic development."

And then I came along, born with a hefty inheritance of that same resentment. In her first years, little Giana experienced her own version of betrayal, but she'd block that out for some years. All of these circumstances, both in my parents' lives and my own, occurred before I was able to have a say, but with Adam, I had chosen. I chose Adam by my heart's decree; I followed its guiding light. But as it turned out, Adam denied my intuition, which, to me, was worse than any tragedy I could recall. Adam lied to me. Adam left me. Adam didn't care if a wild lion consumed me in a cave; he didn't mind if I was in harm's way. In fact, he dragged me, unknowingly, right into the intersection of harm and hurt. When I called him out on it and braved sharing my fears and insecurity, he misled me. He lied to me because he lied to himself. His betrayal and denial was more than I could deal with, and because he had no phone at military school and remained inaccessible to me, I had to resort to writing him a letter.

Later that week, after I'd stopped crying and feeling sick to my stomach, after I'd mustered the strength to get out of bed, smoke a cigarette in the girls' showers, and go to the corner store for a bag of chips and a pack of Yodels, I wrote a letter to Adam. It wasn't that long, and halfway down the page I summed it up, letting him know he had been a complete lying jerk. I did so simply by articulating the following question: *So, Adam, does the name Mimi Bell ring a bell?*

Within a couple of months, I soothed my Adam burns with an insignificant affair (if we can even call unsophisticated college dating an *affair*). And, there were a few more ultimately challenging, intimate relationships with men scattered throughout my lifetime—all just ghostly particles of whatever remained of the effigy of my previous relationship with Adam. After I sent my letter to Adam, I knew everything was finished. Still, over that winter break, I reached out to him to invite him out for a drink. I wanted answers, I wanted to feel better about the fact that I'd spent a few years so devoted to someone who ended up being so meek, unclear, and dishonest. Adam had been a reflection of me, and I couldn't bear to consider myself someone who could sink so low, even if I'd end up abusing myself with food with far more deprecation than he'd ever shown me. I needed to see Adam to at least try to clear our karma.

We met near my family's Bridgewood house, at a local bar. I was so nervous to see him. He'd arrived first, and I bumbled my way to join him at a two top near the bar. I cut to the chase. I had questions and was ready for his explanation.

Adam, why Monica Bell? She seems so unlike you, so not your type.

Adam's eyes filled with something I could only interpret as remorse.

Giana, I don't know. She was just there. It was, like, a location thing. She was there, and you weren't. GG, dating her was literally terrible. Our relationship was a real low point for me, and it didn't last long. There is no way Mimi Bell and I had anything close to what you and I had. Giana, I'm sorry.

I accepted Adam's apology, but we were finished. My Italian

cross-you-off-my-list nature had no ability to reconstitute my now broken faith in Adam being my confidant, my beloved. Plus, we were in entirely different geographical locations now, and our futures offered no possibility of our sharing common ground again. Although Adam had provided me with his reason, explaining that his connection with Mimi Bell was, ultimately, worthless, I couldn't shake the effects of his deceit and betrayal.

If we look at our life dramas and circumstances as *little gifts*, contracts we create with others in order to teach ourselves both subtle and obvious lessons, the point of my relationship with Adam becomes clearer to me. He allowed me a safe place where actual intimacy developed. And there, in a kind of body–mind–spirit connection, filled with joy and passion, he handed me the crucible, the crux of the work I'd have to spend the rest of my life powerfully transcending. He gave me the philosopher's stone as a kind of orientation point. I knew betrayal and denial well, but before Adam, I'd known them only at such a young age, I couldn't recognize their influence. Now I'd learn to see what these parts were and how I could develop a healthy relationship with myself, whether doing so would take a biblical forty days, or more like forty years.

Honestly, in many mythologies, religions, and cultures, including Judaism, Yazidi, Islam, Sumerian, Sikhism, and Christianity, forty is an epic number. Forty days and forty years are oft-mentioned measurements of time in the Bible. There are multiple poetic layers to this number. In the book of Genesis, rain fell for forty days and nights, and that was before our current environmental climate change, before the invention of umbrellas and almanacs. That's a lot of rain, a lot of rain checks, lots of opportunity for *fair-weather friends* to disappear, so understandably, the historical event was Bible-worthy. Later, the Hebrew people were banished from their Holy Land for forty years. Moses meditated, sans food, on three different occasions for forty days and nights each. Jesus fasted for forty days and nights multiple times in the Judaean Desert. Sounds like they were listening to the same ancient podcast or had been persuaded by some sponsored social influencer on the positive super-hero benefits of fasting. There were all kinds of infestations in the world at that time; perhaps Moses and Jesus were trying to rid themselves of bedbugs or scabies. Anyway, the Bible, religious texts, and various fables often make mention of the number forty, from Elijah's life to Muhammad's and Gabriel's. At around age nineteen, I was given my own forty-year sentence. And here I am now, forty years later.

Adam's actions spoke to me, set forth a decree. I can picture him in the attire of an apostle or in the red sash donned by devotees of Saint Sebastian. *Giana*, my imagined Adam says now from that very last scene at the bar, except for now he is standing in the clouds.

Go forth until you are fifty-nine seeking outside sources to help you fix what you believe is wrong with you. Then you'll find a simplicity, a feminine way to look within with the clear, discerning eyes of self-love. Rather than attempting to kill off the symptoms, you'll learn that you can self-compassionately recognize the root causes. Here, you'll look beneath this betrayal and denial I am handing you. Only then, when you place these dominating influences on your life aside, will you ascend the mountain of your personal chaos, after forty years. You will go toward the mountain then, for forty days and nights, until you metaphysically meet your own body and take responsible ownership of your energy and essence, choosing self-generative, lovingly radiant survival. Here, GG, you'll stand to embrace all facets of yourself in full, and possibly transform your own pain. In this personal transformation, you'll stand for all womankind's relief from being controlled by the echoes of warfare, the pillage and rape of Earth herself. For forty years, you'll wear the religious cloth of your ancestral past. Then, forty years from now, you'll take it off in your own Mount Sinai moment. You'll learn how to look at yourself naked in the mirror; you'll trade in Frito-Lay chips for Freedom-Love of self.

You'll take this unrecognized pilgrimage blindly, says Adam-of-the-Holy-Robe, *along with the rest of womankind. You'll all meet on that mountaintop without knowing you were each headed there to commune. Together, you'll be part of an epic moment, transcending all historic tales of women waking up. You will all throw off the reins of your outworn genesis. You'll shine beyond all controlling dictatorial forces, evolve beyond all forms of punitive tyranny and internalized patriarchy. Got it? Oh, and Giana, even if you write your own nouveau bible post-trek, don't expect it to read like a story featuring male leads saving the world while their dedicated wives hold down their forts. Expect it to be filled with nuance and tender discoveries, with a badass female protagonist sharing her pilgrimage to self-compassion.*

Adam, of course, didn't really say anything like this. He just drank one beer with me, mumbled a sorry excuse about betraying me for the convenience of Mimi's proximity to his young sex drive, and then talked about getting back to boot camp and rifle polishing. Ultimately, however, Adam stood as a messenger. He sent me into my own exile into a desert of sorts, and for forty years I lived in a dream world of pushing, going, and bingeing. At fifty-nine, I'd surface with a readiness to be liberated in a new way, a way that would involve a discovery of my own body as my spiritual center, a source of grace, healing, and freedom. That would happen. But meanwhile, at twenty years old, I just had to get through two-and-a-half more years of college. I had to figure out who I wanted to be and how I would live up to the Giovanni standard of hardworking financial championing. I'd need plenty of plastic-packaged processed snacks and fizzy sodas to get through it. When I returned to Boston after Christmas break, I declared my major: business. It made sense; I meant business. I would never let another man have power over me. I'd make sure to get the job done myself. I'd develop *self*-control, an internal willpower.

From that point on, declaring *I meant business*, I would find ways to deal with my issues as a business. As if it were a full-time job, I would attempt to temper my longing, control my insatiable desire to have everything, to want more, more, more. While Gino and Lia had grown a successful external franchise, I'd try out my business prowess in an internal capacity. I'd found my first company, figuratively at least, within myself, and we'd go up and down in a kind of market analysis of our success, filing for bankruptcy or hitting strong strides. Like Gino and Lia, I'd gauge the value of my business empire through the commodity of food, although, in this case, I was a franchise of just one. One body with multilateral investments. Our equity was determined by all things *food*: how well we could stock it, store it, spice it up, or sauté it with garlic. Yes, our stock would depend on how we'd derived our sense of worth from our eating habits. We'd rate how well we'd staved ourselves off, suppressed our needs, successfully starved, or sacrilegiously sucked it down. Even if I'd failed to abstain from food like the epic figures of biblical lore had in their devotion, I'd still fixate on self-flagellating for what I ate. It didn't matter if I used an actual whip or simply found extremely self-critical internal language to repetitively scathe my soul. In fact, to cut my cost on needing outside abusive tools, I'd employ my self-berating eating words, which required no fiscal overhead. I was in business.

CHAPTER 15

Giana Giovanni Means Business

Makes sense to me, as the Giovannis built a franchise empire, all in the name of feeding the Northeast; I built my own interior franchise, all in the name of feeding my pain. It wasn't until I spent my forty years of wandering in my own desert, filled with all these splintered-off internal *parts* and *pieces*, that I'd learn to find an integrated mother ship of all of me, a whole GG who can focus on her breath. She allows pleasure and joy and simplicity through her nervous system. She lets negative emotions in and out, lets the past go. She accepts herself as the sole means of knowing herself. She is a constant work-in-progress. This is the wise-woman way, to *know thyself* goes hand in hand with accepting thyself.

I had lived for my forty years as a stranger in a strange land, but all along, that strange land was actually mine. In a way, from the get-go, I bought it, I manicured it, I gardened it, I capitalized on it, and I had let myself, all the while, remain estranged from it. All the parts I'd hired, the Escapist, the Obsessor and the others, they'd specifically been to deal with the main issue: I didn't know myself, I didn't want to feel myself, and I hadn't allowed myself to claim myself, so I couldn't figure out who I was. I was searching for something concrete, obvious, linear—but I was searching through lenses provided solely by an external system, not through the eyes of my own self-compassion.

The thing about being part of a deeply sewn-together Italian family is that, beyond having a proclivity for your own best-loved meal of Nonna's (mine, of course, was her meatballs), there wasn't much more room for personal identity. I was, more or less, a tool for my family's agenda. Lia wanted to keep her immediate family together, closely knit. In a way, this was to compensate for Gino's tendency to self-distance. Lia figured that if she wrapped the entire family up as tightly as possible so that they all relied on each other to professionally function, she could ensure the safety and survival of her family. As a result of her ambition, my mother determined she should hire me. In fact, since they'd paid for my education, conveniently, in trade, they now owned me like livestock. When Lia called me to reinforce her desire that I step into the family business, it was a fortuitous moment for her. Josie had just accepted a job offer at a top real estate agency in NYC, and I was painting my toes Pepto-Bismol pink, but feeling sort of dismal about the future and myself in general.

Lia spoke to me in her most coercive tone of voice: *GG, your father needs your help. The business is expanding all the time, and now we have the real estate. I need you to come and be a supervisor at the restaurants. No one else can do it, but we know you can. We got you the education, and you have all the knowledge from the university. You received the education we never got, and so, GG, we need you for the business now. It's time to come home. Let's bring you back because your father needs you.* Then she added the final kicker, the clincher that would force me to acquiesce to her request. *GG, your father's getting older; he can't do it alone anymore.* In our family, admitting an Italian man is losing any kind of strength is like declaring famine. This was an emergency. Subconsciously, I created an internal business contract, one between my family and myself. I had to go save us.

Often, the graduating girls who didn't have professional plans, in those days, had other kinds of plans. They'd found their mate, were bearing rings, and were getting married. I, too, was spoken for, but I didn't have a ring to show for it. Instead, I'd bear the stringent reign of Lia and Gino. There would be no room from that point on for any other kind of marriage. I'd marry my parents' enterprise and take on my father's vision as my own. The truth is, I was Gino's daughter. I loved managing, overseeing operations, living in a hot state of high intensity, i.e., the inside of a restaurant kitchen. I loved having staff, people to take care of, upholding excellent customer service, and earning more than our annual projection. However, left to the will of my soul, I'm not sure that flipping burgers and grilling steaks would be my most passionate offering to the world. But I understand the heart of my father's vision is an authentic offering, a way to provide regular people with affordable meals. I also liked the challenge, to be honest. I mean, I operate best under stress, however ashamed I might feel to admit it. I'd have to basically become a master of riddles, figuring out how to integrate my spiritual self on the job with my inner rebel. In fact, all my parts would have to learn to step in. As Giana developed the skills to assert herself, she'd learn how to run the family business, not just in the way Gino mandated. She'd run the company not only by his rules, however inspiring he was as a role model, but also in her own style of operation. *For at least forty years, she'd immerse herself in this. For forty years, Giana, you'll wander the desert of the American Grill.* In numerology, forty can symbolize a crossroad, a moment of deepening connection to the earth and the divine or the practical and the infinite. That sounds about right to me.

CHAPTER 16

Benediction of the Beef Patty

Within weeks, I'd returned to Bridgewood, and I set out to find an apartment. Since I was expected to start work right away, without much time to hunt for the right place, I rashly decided to live with a slightly nutty young woman I'd met through an ad in the paper. I then officially moved into my first *adult* home. The day after I'd moved into my little apartment, I was expected at 7:00 A.M. at a restaurant my parents were *transitioning*. This meant the restaurant wasn't called the Grill just yet, but Gino had purchased an entire franchise with my uncle, with the idea that they'd all eventually be absorbed into the collective chain. They'd operate each of these newly acquired restaurants under their previous name, Maggie's, until they were up to par, ready to be turned into one of the family's own, baptized and branded as the American Grill.

Here's the way a family business often works: when one comes of age and is inaugurated into the working clan, there really isn't one title, one role, and there's no direct plan for promotion within the company. Ultimately, I'd start by cutting my teeth, attempting to assert myself into the culture and be treated with a degree of respect. I'd have to adopt my dad's controlling *say-it-straight* language and take no BS from the employees, making sure they knew I had a handle on everything. I'd be sent between all of the restaurants, supervising along with the rest of my family members. There was no structure to my job description, and there was little sense of how to carry out our work responsibilities without stepping on one another's toes. In some ways, especially when Frankie and Gino Jr. joined the family operation, we were like a swarm of chefs in the kitchen, each yelling over crackling hot oil about who had the best technique.

In a position that had no formal description, I had to start somewhere. So, at age twenty-one, I walked into Maggie's, introduced myself as GG, and spent the next year trying to win the respect of the employees. Most of the kitchen crew at Maggie's had been at the restaurant for many years and found themselves in the midst of the changing of the guard, the shift in ownership. When the previous owner announced he'd sold his chain to the Giovanni Real Estate Group, his employees braced for a transition of management. The entire staff was under the assumption that my uncle and father would be overseeing operations. Of course, Gino gave no advance notice to the workers of Maggie's that, instead of being under his supervision, his twenty-something daughter, fresh out of business school, would be in charge of the establishment. Let's just say that my first season was a *killer*. The employees didn't even do me the courtesy of hiding their sneering judgment or give me a chance to prove myself. They just assessed I was naive, inexperienced, and thus incapable. I had to think on my feet, listen to how Gino spoke to the staff, and emulate him. To find authority in that world, the world of short-order steaks and mashed potatoes, I had to kill any inkling of softness, further shutting down my femininity.

I spent a single year mostly at one location, and in the process, I had to fire a handful of entirely worthless employees. On one night, specifically, I drove back to Maggie's a few hours after I'd left. I'd forgotten an essential book of recorded profits that I needed to drop off at my accountant's the next morning. That first year of supervising the family business was so exhausting that I wasn't sleeping more than four hours a night. When I got to the restaurant, it was around 11:00 P.M., and I was hoping to get home as soon as possible to my freakish roommate, curl up on the couch, and watch a rerun of *Happy Days* or *Flipper*. When I arrived at Maggie's, I was curious as to why there were cars parked in the lot and why some of the restaurant lights were on. As I entered the back door to the kitchen, I heard loud music and shrieks of laughter. I discovered a mini-mob of servers leaning against the soda machines, passing a joint around, along with a bottle of our table wine. No one paid any attention to me. Before figuring out what to do, I wanted to determine how outnumbered I was, so I walked around and counted. Nearly half the staff was on premise, standing around, snacking, drinking, and even dancing. It was a full-on Maggie's house party. I watched them for a few minutes, figuring out how to reprimand them for the mayhem. To be fair, they'd organized a pretty audacious event. On one hand, I was furious that staff would be so disrespectful to our property, taking the opportunity to steal provisions from us that we'd not offered them. On the other hand, the party looked super fun—like something that just two years ago, I'd have wanted to join in on. I felt a slight bitterness that all of my joy had been taken from me, between my new role of supervisor and the departure of my carefree, teenage years. I'd been forced into a position of being like a little Gino, a mini-Lia, expected to sacrifice all I had for the single purpose of growing the family estate. Still, if I was going to get the job done, I'd do it well, so I gathered my most hard-nosed, bitchy sensibility, and walked over to the group. I demanded first that they turn off their music, and then ordered them all to go home and report to me the next morning. I needed a night to sleep on everything. The next morning, I decided simply to request that all staff members hand over the keys they had to the restaurant. I didn't want them entering after business hours and using our restaurant as a free bar.

I gave my deviant employees another chance; amazingly enough it came natural to me, mainly because I'd given my own deviant self so many chances throughout the years. Many of the employees were more than a decade older than me and had been working at Maggie's for years. They were hardly keen to relinquish the reins of operations to a new owner, much less to his young daughter. They acted more like a mob ready to revolt than a collective of staff members concerned about their jobs. Each longtime employee who had a set of keys came up to me, and as though they'd all agreed on a protocol to respond to my request, practically *threw* their keys at me. *You can have our keys; we don't care. You think we'd steal from this place? It's been our home longer than it's been yours.*

The battle between employees and employer continued well into the end of my first year of working at Maggie's, until I decided to break down and ask my dad for help. He told me that I have to fire some people for real. I'd have to speak straight, like a boss, and let people know that they had one final chance to respect me, and if they blew it, their job was gone. I tried it out, emulating the Gino approach to business, and it worked. Within months, I'd implemented a plan I'd devised on my own—a plan for more efficient, successful operation. I got rid of a crew that was too full of attitude to fulfill their duties, and I hired a new team. Within the next year, that restaurant ended up being one of our highest financial turnarounds and became the next full-fledged American Grill.

Not long afterward, I earned an official spot (a small spot, mind you) in the family office and started to transition to other Grills, evaluating what was and wasn't working, making sure all along to use tough language. In restaurant mode, I spoke in bullet points, forgave very little, and effectively practiced *powering over* all the employees, as I'd learned from Gino. My family had a primal, aggressive communication style that we used both in our professional endeavors and our private family interactions. We maintained no difference between the two. It was all family-business mode; this was how we strengthened our bond. We had something of a short-order cook's short-tempered, fast-tongued system in place, forgoing formalities— no *hello*, no *goodbye*, not a single *How are you*. We spared ourselves small talk in the same way we spared boundaries between where one of us started and the next began. That's why what my dad endured, we'd endure, and what Lia wanted, we'd prioritize as our top desire.

We were one great conglomerate of an establishment.

By my second or third year in business, I knew I was going to die if I didn't find something—anything—for myself outside of my family's pursuits. I tried partying, seeing live music, and making new friends, but nothing seemed to answer the deeper call I had for release, for relaxation, for something that felt like a salvation. Church was off the table, as I couldn't handle the rigid suffocation of lines drawn, the likelihood of slipping into being wrong, damned, condemned. I needed something that made me feel loved, someplace I could know myself. I had no clue as to who I was. While most people were discovering that in college, I'd been barely surviving my own anxiety. After college, I'd just been figuring out how to bark orders and scrape together a living on the meager pay my parents provided in exchange for my more-than-full-time dedication to their creation, their company. I needed an escape, someplace I could go where no one in my family would find me, where they wouldn't *want* to find me!

Part Two:
The Mystery in the Marinara

In the early spring of 1984, I visited friends in Boston. The city had become a semi-regular weekend spot for me, a place where I felt comfortable going out without encountering anything that reminded me of work. This was the place where I remained anonymous, securely away from the American Grill, a place *where no one knows my name*. While I sought the opposite bar scene than the characters on *Cheers*, we found our social scene on the same streets. In Boston, I relaxed and enjoyed my time away. One morning, after a typical evening out, I headed out to meet college friends for breakfast at a diner somewhere on Huntington Avenue. I walked past a new bookstore on Newbury Street, called Trident Booksellers & Café. The sweetly inviting shop caught my attention. I peered through the storefront's window. I heard a distinct voice that, at first, I believed to be speaking directly into my ear. I soon realized the voice was actually speaking from inside of me. *Look down, Giana*, it said. This was, in fact, my second time hearing distinct direction, the guidance of my internal navigator: intuition. Strangely, the first occurrence took place less than a mile from where I then stood, smack-dab in the center of Boston. This was when I received or heard the inner voice that instructed me to go to BU. *Look down*, the similar-sounding inner voice insisted, so I looked down. At my feet was a flyer, which I picked up. It was slightly wet from street cleaning or morning dew or who knows what, and stained as well, but I knew it was mine to pick up off the ground. It read simply, *New York City, Shakti Gawain's Creative Visualization Workshop, April 21–22*. As this was the spring of 1984, people were wrapped up in Reagan's reelection, as well as the upcoming launch of *Miami Vice, Gremlins, Ghostbusters*, and *The Karate Kid*. The Olympics were about to take place in Los Angeles and Princess Diana was due to give birth to Prince Harry. George Michael was rocking the charts in Wham! No one I knew was talking about creative visualization, and I definitely had never met anyone named *Shakti* (which, by the way, is considered the feminine representative of divine energy, so—all in all—*Shakti* was exactly what the naturopath doctor ordered). Two weeks later, I'd convinced Frankie to cover my weekend shifts, and I headed to New York City. I crashed with Josie, who was busy diving into her new professional life in the city.

On a Saturday morning, I made my way to Union Square, to a place called the Realization Room, a place totally foreign to me. The only *room* I'd yet made for any kind of conscious *realization* was when I realized hot sauce made everything taste way better. Aside from that, I felt largely devoid of epiphanies. I was mostly just busy dodging parental bullets and trying to figure out how to assert my authority at work. I was concerned with successfully covering up the fact that I had no idea who I was by adopting a business personality that felt secure, intimidating, and demanding of respect. I was modeling myself after my father while denying the impact of his influence in my life, living somewhere in the middle of a contradiction. The Realization Room was, despite its deceptive name, not just a single room. Instead, the building contained a seemingly endless number of rooms and floors. I was disoriented in what felt like an architectural maze. Perhaps I was feeling a little overwhelmed or nervous. It's always been hard for me to gauge what I'm actually experiencing in the moment. Whatever it was, I was unable to navigate on my own to find the meeting room for the workshop. Fortunately, a gaggle of people entered the building and headed to the stairs. I joined in the ascension, and together we entered the largest room on the second floor. We sat, most of us silently, playing with our pens and notepads. (Of course, this 1984 weekend was long before cell phones, when being uncomfortable, anticipatory, or eager appeared far more obvious without devices to hide behind.) Having had no clue how to prepare for the workshop, I hadn't even brought a notepad. The only thing I had on me was the little flyer I'd found with the address and information about the event. Without even a spare Twix bar or can of Tab, I was as naked as Giana could be. Feeling strangely less fidgety than normal, I sat down at the end of a row of chairs toward the back.

Before long, our weekend host, Shakti Gawain, entered the room.

She wore a long flowing dress and carried a steaming cup of something aromatic. From the corner of the room, I caught a whiff of the floral fragrance. This was either the scent of Shakti herself or whatever holy beverage she was imbibing. I felt, perhaps, like my mother felt when she found San Sebastiano's nuns after the hardship of war, the sole female protection available to her in little Melilli, Sicily. Of course, New York City was significantly larger than Melilli but likely as devoid of feminine energy, all the same. I'd found this tiny tucked-away sanctuary, calling me toward a realization, and there was its centerpiece, Shakti Gawain, a woman unlike any other I'd seen. In this woman's presence, I immediately felt I could be in my body. The way she lit up was infectious, and she lit me up as well. Something in me, a muscle I'd unknowingly clenched throughout my lifetime, finally let go. Shakti appeared to me like a genuine, loving light. She spoke slowly and methodically, and just being in her presence was electrifying. I'd never been in such a focused type of energy before; in fact, I'd never been in the presence of something I would call *energy*. I'd never found a presence energizing, unless we can count being drawn to and seduced by a pack of Yodels. Here, I suddenly felt a charge inside of myself; this was different. I felt connected and simultaneously invited to be in my body. *Perhaps*, I thought, *this is considered resonance, a feeling of aligning with something rather than being possessed by it.* This would become the new muscle for me to refine in order to create my life. No businessperson, including my father, had ever taught me that.

Shakti's training was completely new territory for me. The fact is, I'd never been able to deeply focus on anyone or anything without immediately feeling that I'd lost what little sense of myself I had. I could only feel myself vicariously through others. Interestingly, Shakti's presence was so commanding that I didn't have to rush in and fill her up, abandoning myself in the process. Shakti probably didn't even have to say much; she just emanated safety, home, earthiness, and hope. Within the first few minutes of her arrival, I received more of a spiritual download than I had throughout my entire college career. I'd already learned something about how to not lose myself entirely around others. Jackpot, if you ask me! And Shakti's million-dollar mindset training sold, in the eighties, for probably around a single *hundo*. This was the era, mind you, when people considered personal growth and development to mean something like injecting steroids for Olympic training. I simply invested; however, I was an American pioneer, *darn it*. Like Gino, I knew a gold mine when I was sitting on one. This was gold. Over the weekend, Shakti shared with us some specific tools that I still use to this day, tools that have evolved with me in time. They have merged, shape-shifted, and even been shared with my own clients. I've passed down Shakti's teachings in the oral tradition of feminine wisdom, often citing her in my work. Interestingly, on the rare occasions I hear my own intuitive inner words, they've come to me in the same way, through oral tradition. Generation to generation, from one circle to the next, women have kept the conversation alive. We have shared stories like torches, listening to one another, passing truths from one to the next. In this way, we learn the unwritten ways of refining, honoring, and accessing the power of our spirits.

I admit that the first exercise didn't go so smoothly for me, most likely because it required *feeling* one's body. Shakti described the visualization as a kind of *charging up*, making contact with something beyond another person (even, as in my case, a container like my car or closet) as a way to become *energized*. She simply expressed, connection creates a charge, or energy, in its purest form. To Shakti, connecting directly to the earth was the strongest, surest means of accessing the greatest source of life power. Makes sense, as far as the basic scientific laws of conductivity go, right? Shakti called her exercise *Grounding Energy*. Conceptually, I was intrigued, but this method of grounding energy was a completely new idea for me. I hadn't been trained to *ground* anything other than the beef by Nonna, who attempted to pass down her meatball recipe solely to me. And as for energy? Outside of viewing *Mr. Wizard* as a kid, when nothing more entertaining could be found on the tube, I'd had little exposure to the concept of energy. But I went for it. I felt thoroughly compelled by Shakti to comply with her directions since she was so alluring to me.

I attempted to visualize the so-called "energy of the earth" and feel it in my body, but I was too new to this, and I couldn't *get it*. At least, not at first. Although I'd managed to eke out a college degree, I wasn't able to feel my lungs fill with breath and envision receiving the earth's energy at the same time. To be honest, I probably couldn't even pat my head and rub my stomach simultaneously. I'd be lucky, at that point, just to locate my stomach with my hand. I did, however, benefit from the focused attention of the group. Somehow, I could feel something close to *going inward* when everyone else was deep in his or her own meditation process.

Shakti helped us to go deeper, asking that we close our eyes, visualize an electric energy of the earth, and fill our bodies with it. She continued to support us, guiding us in simple steps. Suddenly, something clicked. I felt a wave of something. Was it the energy of the earth? The sensation filled me up, and immediately became too much for me. I didn't know exactly what I'd just let into my body. The only outside force I'd inadvertently let into my body was when I'd sleep-eaten most of the fridge, which was always a total bummer. This full body sensation wasn't caused by food though, and I wasn't sleeping. Rather than blissing out like the rest of the Shakti clan, I was led by the experience into a hyper-anxious state. I did exactly what my transpersonal acupuncturist, my "Gospel of Bill," described, the GG classic fight/flight and then stone-cold freeze, if not the inverse: freeze and then hit frenzy mode. As far as I could remember, feeling any kind of external energy source had always led me to some type of anxious reaction. Even over that weekend, I couldn't begin to comprehend my reactive patterns or believe that one day, I'd learn to cultivate receiving energy as a way to fill myself with tranquility and joyfulness—that this would be my best medicine for my well-being.

Shakti's information was just a beginning point for me on the long path toward cultivating the space to receive anything, which is pretty essential for someone who works as an abundance-mindset coach, right? My body had been trained to receive simply through bombardment: *stuff it, slap it, strike it, shock it.* In Shakti's workshop, as clear and enlightening as was her direction, filling myself up with the earth's charge, at that point, felt like when my parents were fighting in the next room. Remember, I didn't realize until about age fifty that my spirit could actually be inside my body. I didn't feel like a catalyst for energy, I'd barely located my pulse. If anything, I felt like a catalyst for Dunkin' Donuts advertisements. I could just imagine the marketing conversation inspired by my lack of willpower: *See that susceptible woman? She'd totally veer off the turnpike at exit 3W for a Bavarian Kreme or two.* Going within to feel something? That was impossible and foreign for GG in the eighties, certainly. The only going within I'd been up for was biting into a Reese's Peanut Butter Cup, admiring the perfect scoop of sugary peanut butter smooshed within the milk chocolate, or contemplating the architecturally masterful creamy filling inside an Oreo.

Fortunately, for spiritual seekers with complete body disassociation, which are probably greater in number than one might guess, Shakti moved on to a more doable technique, one that I've continued to practice since that very weekend. It's actually the most famous practice among her many students. This *Pink Bubble Technique*, lo and behold, didn't really require much of my body. Instead of my anxiety-ridden bundle of flesh, the container involved in this practice was an imaginary *pink bubble* into which I could attract whatever I desired. Inside my bubble, I could acquire momentum and materialize abundance in my life. I'd jump on the idea of acquiring the things I wanted without having to burn a calorie, and as far as I was concerned, that was a doable form of exercise.

From the moment I met Shakti in the spring of 1984, I connected with her guidance on a spiritual level and found peace in her calming presence, a total novelty for the newly adult Giana. That weekend, I

The Pink Bubble

GiANA the Visualizer

discovered a way to concentrate by extending my point of focus out to the stars, planets, and galaxies. Sitting in a room full of people who were exploring universal energy and imagining pink bubbles was so contrary to my pace of life in restaurant mode, which was filled with busy people taking orders, flipping burgers, barking at one another. Plus, if I could connect to the expansive pleasure of a pink bubble, why would I have to surrender to the skimpy affections of little boys? I could be caressed by stars! This was way better than any other pastime I'd found; I could disappear and remain fully in control of the entire experience. So, *check*, I was sold.

That weekend, I signed up to become a lifetime member of the school of personal growth and development. Having found Shakti's language, I now knew I wanted to cultivate this intuitive skill of mine, and, in typical Giana fashion, I went hard. I dove right in to my *third eye*, so to speak. My new insatiable hunger for spiritual learning worked well for my extremes. See, the thing about intuition is that, since it is immediate, it often rides along with fear. Fear, like instinct, also triggers an impressively potent response from the nervous system. This is why, in ways, the healer's intuitive work also offers her a discerning eye to see where her own trauma resides. As she sifts and sorts out her instinct from her learned response, she is inevitably forced to look at herself. She also might be prone to having a strong instinctual download followed by, for example, an undeniable hankering for a strong, smoked *provolone piccante* on Tuscan *ciabatta*.

One thing we didn't go over that weekend, though, was the possible shadows that energy work might bring to the surface for the practitioner. It was 1984, after all; even the spiritually inclined had some subjects that were off-limits in those days. Don't talk about money, politics, religion, or, God forbid, vulnerable fallibility. If one was spiritual, one would be as strong as Christ himself. We didn't discuss any possible side effects of exposing our limitations. Instead, Shakti emphasized how creative visualization was necessary to make things happen, and in the Reagan era, *doggone it*, that was what was important, *dreaming big*, as his campaign advocated. By the end of the weekend, not only had I gained tools essential to building a whole new mindset, I'd also connected with the other attendees. I experienced *resonance* and felt less like the outsider, as I nearly always had among others. The people at the workshop spoke with kindness, communicated in a way I could only describe as *heart centered*. I'd never experienced communication like this, but in the presence of Shakti, it seemed we could all reach parts of ourselves that previously had not been accessible. In fact, for the first time, I was able to get a sense of what I wanted in my own life, simply, perhaps, because the space felt so safe. Shakti's words were relaxing and filled with love. Literally, she could have been reading children's stories to us, and I would have likely been transformed just by the calmness of her voice. Aside from her tone, though, she delivered extremely substantial content.

After the weekend was over, I lay in my bed in my little apartment and applied her *Pink Bubble Technique*. In a pink bubble, I'd create whatever I wanted, and, better yet, anything other than what I wanted was unable to enter my little bubble, the ultimate protection. The visualization was the only time I was able to focus on doing one thing alone—no multitasking, no compounding of thoughts, no creating chaos. I zoomed in on an individual desire as I'd never managed to do before, unless, of course, we consider my getting hooked by a billboard advertising Arby's Meat Mountain Sandwich. *This* was some form of focus, as I'd suddenly find myself *self-actualizing*—or shall I say, *self-sabotaging*—at the drive-through, as though I'd lost all power to do anything other than submit in full to the Meat Mountain. In that case though, I was possessed in full by something removing me from my own command, while in Shakti's pink bubble, I was in control of the visualization. Here, I'd focus on what I consciously permitted myself to want (anything from a specific work relationship to a new apartment). I'd seal the deal by reminding myself that if my vision didn't come to fruition, I was then inviting something even better to emerge. Looking back, it is not surprising that in the rare moments when I'd conjured the image of a specific man in a romantic capacity, I could draw him into my imagined pink bubble, but I couldn't imagine more. It's as though I didn't really want to risk carrying out a healthy long-term relationship. It was safer to just call him into my pretty pink bubble, like Bubblicious eye candy. Of course, just as I suspected, *presto!* They'd respond to the effects of my visualization in real time, but once I'd gotten their attention, I acted like a child, still ten years old, with Johnny Marconi. In terms of love, I had no idea what to do other than let havoc rule.

Shakti's work was simple in many ways. She designed it to be something like Manifesting 101. She was an early adopter of the concept of the power of using our thoughts to bring about positivity, at least in the Western world. She named her work *Creative Visualization*, but these days, there are a significant number of similar manifesting protocols available to the seeker. In that era, though, practicing creative visualization was considered *way out there*, and frankly, being *way out there*, finding her own outsider faith, was the only way Giana could confidently build a sense of self, distanced from the daily grind of Giovanni governance. Going outside the norm was also the way of martyrs and saints, believing in something that could be perceived as heretical long before the rest of society adopts a similar viewpoint. Yes, we rebels find our faith in what is often dismissed by the rest of society; it's what pushes the envelope of the world. Nietzsche did it, as did Hermes, Copernicus, Einstein, and Moses, all envelope pushers with radical gumption. Meanwhile, I don't believe my own acts of revolt were particularly noteworthy. They definitely fell short of leading people to a promised land, and instead, were more about leading myself to a tub of Land O'Lakes and jam. In 1984, I figured since everything I ever did, according to my family unit, was certifiably crazy, why not add *spiritual seeking* to that list? While, in some ways, I'd strayed from my Catholic faith, I'd maintained the same song and dance as that of the Catholic martyrs: *die for a cause, sacrifice self at all costs, and never relent.* After Shakti's workshop, I felt secure in my faith for the first time. I believed in my connection to *universal energy*, which would never betray me. Universal energy was unwavering. It would never deny me of my greatest potential or call me wrong for "sinning" or forgoing mass. For once, in a relationship, I felt unlimited, even if my partner was, well, an entire galaxy. The great, expansive universe, oddly, became my surest sense of home.

$\mathscr{S}$piritual Pink Bubbles and Carbonated Beverages

Nowadays, the term *Law of Attraction* is typed into the Google search bar as often as *Laws of the United States Senate*, maybe even for those knee-deep in law school. But back then, it was unusual to hear about anything like it, so I was even more excited. Tell me something beyond how to get the crispiest potatoes from the deep fryer or how to deal with restaurant suppliers. Give me an opportunity for conversation that isn't focused on Gino's or Lia's needs, and I'd find relief. Before Shakti's work, I'd lived my life considering myself and everyone else to be just victims of circumstance, going along in life, affected solely by the luck of the draw. As I continued to hone the techniques Shakti provided, I noticed that life began to grow with a new kind of abundance for me. I experienced real moments of clarity and was charged with an appetite for discovery. It was, as Aladdin and Jasmine sang, "A Whole New World." Of course, I was also coping with the stress of restaurant life in ways that had less to do with visualizing pink bubbles and more to do with ingesting carbonated bubbles of diet soda. In the eighties, I consumed the latter in excess, along with half an aisle of the local Wawa (which was my first mini-mart sweetheart). In the *pink bubble* behavior, I consciously found my identity. In the carbonated bubble behavior, I hated myself. Interestingly, both of these behaviors (my newfound spiritual-visualization exercise and my *wolfing* of junk food) served the same agenda. Through both, I did not have to deal with my body, how it felt, or where it was physically located. Visualizing pink bubbles took me to la-la land, while junk food took me to Wawa-land. Perfecto! I'd experience my sense of self either in the *cosmic* heavens or in a wrathful, plastic-wrapped hell, but, by God, I'd bypass the whole darn thing. The adult Giana created a type of contract with herself: No one other than she would be permitted to inflict pain on her. She had to find the best form of punishment, so Giana chose food as her abuser. It was delicious and voluptuous, and deceptively pretty, like a lover. It seemed friendly enough to her inner child, as had her trusted adult guardians. However, once she'd succumbed to it, lost herself to it, it was able to play the punitive, sickening, sinfully reproachful trick. Isn't it interesting that we tend to hurt ourselves in ways so similar to the ways we've been hurt?

In the past, all the shame and guilt I felt came from actual living, breathing influences—you know, people. Now, since I'd decided to be both the tyrant and the victim, I could keep my punishments private. As both the protagonist and antagonist, the play was mine alone, and I could keep to myself the secret of my flailing self-esteem. That was safer. Plus, my nightly performance took me away from being available to the rest of the world, the rest of life's stage. Food, my scripted Shakespearian drama, served as a buffer between me and the rest of the world.

As I continue on my healing path and learn about the power of breath—as in, the effect that pausing to breathe has on our cognitive experience—I find that it's interesting to consider that food became nearly like breath for me in my moments of internal war. I used food as transition, a way to inhale. But rather than moving through the cycle of oxygen and carbon dioxide, with food, I shifted between cycles of feeling revved-up or flat-out catatonic. I'd use calories, carbs, and *wolffication* as my means of dealing with and relieving feelings; screw this breathing stuff. Breathing might actually relax my nervous system, and that idea was utterly foreign and threatening to me. What might happen if I stopped vacillating between a pressing agenda and a pressed panini? While it royally *sucked* to feel wasted from consuming an excess of Ho Hos, which had its own side effects, in the long run, the stuffed feeling would always be easier to deal with than risking close encounters with others and, ultimately, intimacy with myself.

In the first decade of my esoteric seeking, I integrated my American Grill work life and my spiritual studies with extreme caution. Because I am, by nature, a sharer, I divulged my spiritual interest to a select audience, careful to not expose myself to the wrong company. After Shakti's workshop, an appetite awakened within me (but one that I welcomed and allowed). This type of hunger was for crystals, angel cards, and essential oils. I feasted on self-help books, candles, incense, and connecting to realms I called *universal, cosmic, and energetic.* Spirituality promised unlimited means of discovery, ways I could relieve myself of my obvious birth defect, my tainted character. Eventually, I started to notice how my work in the family business and in spiritual realms naturally found their way toward intersection. Turned out, I didn't need a PR team or an HR hub. I'd lie in my soft, plush, luxurious bed at night and envision what I wanted to bring into my business. I'd see the perfect employees walking through the door, and *pronto*, just like that, I'd manifest it. *Si, prego.* I'd also conjure opportunities, envision scenes. I had a notably new feeling, a racing sensation up and down my arms, like a tiny battalion of light particles charging from my chest to my fingertips. The aftereffect of my energetic visualization had nothing to do with Dexatrim, but, like a stimulant, it also kept me awake and riled up, as I anticipated my best life on my pillow. The key commonality is that both my fixation on the pink bubble and my use of Dexatrim supported my intention of finding wholeness. Obviously, I was insufficient as is, but with these outside allies, I could sculpt a worthy, near-perfect version of Giana and a life where she was in control. This life was, of course, available only in the future, out of reach of my chubby, blubbery arms in the late-night hours. And, aside from these inanimate tools, I was so freaking alone.

One afternoon, I stood in line at my local grocery store, after having shopped *within safe parameters*. This *safe parameter* kind of shopping takes place outside of the mini-mart and in the earliest hours of the day, when I'm less prone to having an unstoppable urge to *wolfify* and can keep my focus safely on nonedible goods, like paper towels and laundry soap. I was next in line at checkout when the enthusiastic girl ahead of me struck up a conversation with the clerk behind the counter, who was apparently a friend of hers. The girl described a New Age workshop coming to town, led by someone named Angel Gale. As I'd felt my intuition rise in Boston, directing me to Shakti Gawain, I similarly felt pulled to the conversation between the two girls here. Without hesitation, I found myself interjecting, *Can I come?* Within days, I found myself sitting in a small circle with other women, learning from Angel Gale, my next strong female influence of spiritual inspiration. This was my first practical support for integrating the sacred into my life. Angel directly encouraged me to find a greater unification between my interest in spirituality and the family business. There was no real divide, she said, between my offerings, whether they involved serving sausage or spiritual maxims. For example, Angel divided her time equally between promoting her husband's budding vehicle-repair business and her esoteric spiritual-learning groups—very *Zen and the Art of Motorcycle Maintenance*. She insisted that the only way I would find my real prosperity and path in the world would be to speak my truth in every area of my life.

From that point on, I revealed my interest in holistic wellness both when I was in my supervisory role at the company *and* when I was with my family. I shared with confidence, offering employees or my family members the harvest of my immersive studies. While it would take some years before I would charge people in a professional capacity, I offered my learnings to my community free of charge. I called wellness—holistic interests and healing—my *hobby*, dulling it down. My healing practice lifestyle was something I practiced, so it seemed, to counter the effects of my inflammation-inducing lifestyle, its polar opposite. For years, I would not acknowledge my core dedication to healing and spiritual seeking mainly because there was no way the

Giovanni family would ever recognize my interests in this realm as valuable. Now that I'm nearing my sixth decade, times have changed, and my family and I have to some degree as well. I've learned that no matter what you do in life, acceptable or not, you've got to own it, and that the real secret to success, more than just *knowing thyself*, is to compassionately protect the essence of thyself. It's amazing how, now nearing my sixtieth year on the planet, I am still not sure if I've ever had a solid experience of feeling whole in my own body. Still, what I've learned to feel as my truth, I stand behind securely. I love cooking, and I love herbalism: nature, beauty, and natural medicine. I'll protect and defend these affinities. In a way, Gino taught me this through his strict response whenever I confessed to being scared: *GG! Don't show concern; it is weak. Don't fear others*, Gino convinced his children.

CHAPTER 18

$\mathcal{P}$ast Lives, Pasta Life

While I was most interested in calling on angels, referring to saints, and learning about backyard botanicals, my wanderlust, at times, edged toward extremes, even occult-like esotericism. I found myself sitting with mediums, people who allow other entities or people to speak through them. For much of the general public, I get it: this is (at least at this point in our cultural consciousness) still considered a bit *left of center*, but give the world another decade, and we'll probably have a medium running for president. There are, in current times, already some well-known mediums, ones who've made it onto *Oprah* or who've published *New York Times* Best Sellers, so, go figure. Obviously, more people than would admit it are open to wisdom from unconventional sources. My own interest in mediumship led me to inviting channelers into my house, hosting gatherings where people were able to connect to those whom they'd loved and lost. I became enthralled by past-life regression work. This was a great option for someone like me who, frankly, didn't know where to begin sorting out the emotional blocks in her current life. No, in those days, young Giana was a house of cards built on defending suppressed memories by deploying self-protecting weaponry. Her personality was merely the sum of traversable spaces remaining around the explosive places. What happens when a person avoids her hurt places, her internal landmines? Eventually, as she acquires years, it becomes more difficult to find safe avenues remaining around the high-voltage, highly traumatic areas. In this case, young Giana would have to unravel her own patterns, repair land, and make room for herself. She'd find *la forza della natura*, a force of nature, to heal her own inner earth—just as her mother had single-mindedly financed her war-ruined farmland in Melilli and just as the Giovannis had pushed to keep each olive tree functionally fruiting year after year in Abruzzo. Like Lia and Gino, I had to repair the land too, make amends, but in this case, the war-torn land was my body.

With regularity, I tuned into a spiritual radio show, hosted by Ronnie Gans. I gravitated to his infectious theme song, "You Read My Mind." As soon as the show's music came on, my brain perked up, ready to be enchanted by Ronnie's spiritual clarity. Ronnie was the first *past-life regressionist* I'd ever come across. He lived near one of our family's restaurants, so his office was a convenient stop on my way to work. I figured, make a pit stop at the hypnotist/past-life regressionist's, and then continue on to work, restock the condiments, order the chicken breast from the distributor, and contemplate the fact that I'd been a betrothed princess in the Victorian era. On the day of my appointment, I entered Ronnie's clinic in Winford, Connecticut, open to discovering what types of crazy things had happened to me in previous lives. In a way, until then, spirituality was a kind of *fun* for me. It was like a continual, playful Ouija board game. (In case you're not familiar with this game, it's one that's popular with schoolkids. Two people query their collective intuition while keeping their fingers on a planchette, which then moves around a printed board, spelling out answers.) I figured going to the nearly celebrity-status radio host's studio and being guided into my past would be a thrill a minute, the kind of esoteric high I liked to get from my foray into spiritualism. So, I arrived to Ronnie's waiting room humming his theme song, "You Read My Mind" and feeling gregarious. Once settled into his space, Ronnie lit some candles and led me into hypnosis to take an "inventory of my energy field." He didn't need to ask me why I'd come to see him; he was a seer, he could *read my mind*, like his theme song suggested, right? As I lay on his practitioners table, he hovered his hands over me, one near my head and one near my lower abdomen. I began to relax. *Giana*, Ronnie began, *what happened when you were six?*

This threw me off, despite my trancelike state. I thought, *What the heck? I came here to go into some past life—to figure out where I was in the Middle Ages or the Edwardian era, or learn about how I survived the Holocaust. What does age six in my actual life have to do with this?*

My inner vision went with him, beyond my control. I saw what he saw; he saw what I saw. He was leading me more vividly into something I'd never forgotten, but it was a memory that, when it surfaced, I'd hit hard with my best Eating Words: *no big deal.* All of the wrongness I embodied, plus the kind of secret eating behavior and guarded relationship I had to anything intimate—my response to anxiety—this was its nest, its place of origin, at least in this lifetime. I knew this feeling, but lived to subdue it, and now, here I was. I'd bought a ticket to what I'd imagined would be an amusing ride through my past lives, and I was being tossed and turned, trapped. I tried to dodge Ronnie's questions. I wouldn't tell him what I saw. I tried to get away from the memory, leave the visualization, but he wouldn't let me. Every part of young Giana that knew deviance, escape, rebellion and intensity had to be brought forth in order for me to muster the strength for active revolt. Little girl Giana hadn't been able to say *no*. Now, though, newly adult Giana was being led again into this vile scene and was even paying with her hard-earned cash for her return into it. For the first time in my adult years, I saw it all vividly, and, to top it off, I was again in the company of a male who had subdued me in a supine position. I didn't know it then, but Ronnie was my catalyst. He pulled the wool, the skin, the fascia, and sinews off of the skeleton and made me look at the bare bones, the stark past. I reacted by jumping off his table and bolting out the door. I may have tossed some cash by the entrance to his office on my way out. Regardless, I breathlessly fled until I got to my one safe haven, my *grotto*: the car.

Despite how frozen I had been in Ronnie's office, I figured out how to start the car and drive away. While there are state laws against driving inebriated and numerous tests to tell how impaired someone is, there are no tests to determine how under the influence of PTSD a vehicle operator may be. If there were, I would likely fail on a regular basis. Certainly, on that day, I would have been considered a significant danger to society. But with my eyes glazed over, I assembled myself as best as I could and set out on a familiar path of travel. I hit Frankie's house on the way to the family office. I needed to hear some filler information, the usual overexaggerated stresses of building a dynasty: who was doing what wrong and not doing whatever else. I'd gladly give my attention to anything outside myself, anything other than what I'd just seen on Ronnie's table. The radio was on, and fortunately, Ronnie wasn't on the air. It was a song by Tears for Fears (in my case, No Tears and No Recognized Fears), "Everybody Wants to Rule the World." *Okay, Okay. I can do this.* Pit stop for Doritos and even a real-sugar Coca-Cola. On to the family office. Over the hill and through the woods. This is how I'd continue to keep my internal chaos under control. I'd brush over the discomfort of what had just taken place in Ronnie's clinic. I'd wash away the bad taste in my mouth with Doritos' orange fake-cheese dust. Upon deciding that my experience at Ronnie's was the entirety of what was upsetting me, I would forget about what deeper memory had been conjured there.

But *holy crap*. There was my bedroom in our first house in Bridgewood. *Holy crap.* I'd thought I was just playing. It was fun. He was a trusted visitor in my home; he was safe. Then something felt wrong. Was it my fault? They knew, but it was denied. It never happened. We all ignored it; that was our family tradition. *Ignore the pain. No big deal.* It didn't happen to us, so we wouldn't be taken down. No one did anything to us Giovannis because we were the *doers*. We were the bosses. We were the survivors. We organized our positions within the family unit, functioned in roles. Giana would be the tainted one, the wrong one. Let her think she'd been born wrong, no big deal. Let her bury the memory; that's fine. Let her hide it in the secret sauce. Ultimately, it will just be the slightly funky flavor in our famous marinara. Giana can be the wilted flower, the damaged one. Lia and Frankie, they'd remain the compliant women of the family, always upholding the opinions of the Giovanni men. The men in the family would always determine what, in fact, was reality, and so if a male in our family ever revealed a dark, defeated, marred part of himself, it would never be acknowledged. For if the Giovannis had tarnished blood in even the furthest reaches of their extended family, what would have been the point of all their historic and ancestral history spent outrunning evil oppressors? That wasn't how the story would ever go. We were the ones who fled, who fought, who were the very definition of *hypervigilant*. Look up the term in an Italian dictionary, and you'll see an image of the five of us.

If we were to identify with the dark enemy force, as though we'd swallowed some of it, as though it had stained us, what would have been the point of our survival? How would we get into heaven, be considered saints or martyrs? (These were considered to be one and the same in our particular interpretation of Catholicism.) Ultimately, even though we had traded our devotion to the church for the American dollar, ritualized placing circular slices of salami on the tongue instead of holy wafers, and sipped real wine rather than the blood of Christ, we were not going to hell. Self-respect (while lacking for *me*) was the impenetrable essence of the Giovannis. So I acclimated to the collective tribal sense of *self*. I knew how to survive the situation: I'd just eat it away. I swallowed my secret sense of being wrong, being an inventor, a fabricator, a dramatist, someone who couldn't be trusted, someone unworthy of acknowledgment. I wasn't told outright that my experience didn't happen. It's just that no one ever brought it up to me, even though I knew that everyone knew. I knew that it had affected each of us. I understood, however, that it was better for me to avoid acknowledging it. Even now, as I write this, I ask myself, *Wait, did it even happen?* I've felt delusional for so long. Throughout my life, I've repeated a giant *NO* to myself. *No it didn't. No, I can't. No it won't.* Out of this dynamic, I set up my whole life modality of function. I am in tears right now as I go through this. It isn't easy for me to bring this up.

If no one talked about it, then it didn't happen. This became my personal illness, my scar tissue, the hidden but gaping wound. *No worries. No big deal. Work it out with some Ho Hos, Giana, Stove Top, fast food, donuts.* We'd all ignore the heavy weight of the whole thing and, in exchange, I'd be the heavy weight. At least we knew that in our immediate family, however unspoken our emotions remained, however buried, we could depend on one another. Together we were safe. That was the deal. In our family, there are things we acknowledge the heck out of, and things we don't ever mention. It's safer to immerse ourselves in the chaos of the present moment than to deal with anything difficult from the past, be it war, demolition, or even the twisted character of an extended family member. This was the agreed-upon pact of our immediate family unit.

My story is the tale of an emotional eater, car bingeing and coping with life through a singular state of being: hungry/not hungry. This isn't very original, is it? For women, sadly, it's not mind-blowingly unique. *Thin is in! Go from fat to fit! Get ready for swimsuit season!* Yep, for women in modern culture, swimsuit season has been the closest recognition of our cyclical connection to nature's rhythms. The media has long ignored discussing the wonders of menstruation, pregnancy, and menopause, but we just can't seem to escape the blaring adverts for the season of swimsuits. Somehow, we accept this strange, streamlined reductive reckoning of our whole entire lives. Meanwhile, we hold our families together, accepting our husbands' prolonged boyish behaviors while providing fortifying meals and handling all things from baby diapers to the bills. Still, being influenced by Mrs. Cleaver and wrestling with my waist size as a way to avoid feeling worthless doesn't make me unusual. I'm definitely not one in a million in this area, and frankly, I'm not even one in ten. Every other woman in my neighborhood has befriended Jenny Craig or one of her ilk, and then been two-faced (open sandwich), talking behind her back, or burned her at the stake (and eggs buffet). I've been around long enough to know that many families deny their daughters' assault allegations because the "shameful" information is injurious to the collective family psyche. It's the same in my case. The last thing I want to do is disrupt my family's functional disorder. I love my Italian tribe; they are everything to me. Through and through, my family has always come first. I mean no one in my family any harm, nor do I wish to project blame upon anyone. My sole intention to share my tale is to attempt to make sense of it *for myself.* Believe me, living in a topsy-turvy state with a rapid-firing mind at age fifty-nine doesn't make it easy to digest life. I would keep it all in the closet if I hadn't been convinced by members of my community—healers and friends alike—that in sharing my story, I might liberate myself, and even help others to take a similar inventory of their own lives. As much as our high-tech lifestyles have estranged us from one another, the internet has strongly supported the rising tide of sisterhood. We are creating a giant shift by letting our voices be heard, and I know that decoding my own self-sabotaging food addiction will help turn the tables.

In processing this, I've uncovered some statistics. For example, up to 75 percent of girls who tell their parents or guardians that they've been violated by someone they know have their claim invalidated or dismissed. This doesn't only affect their personal lives, but also the lives of their children, the people with whom they work, their siblings, their future spouses, and the list goes on. Until now, conventional America—well, actually, *much* of the world—has *shushed* the voices of women who speak up for themselves in this capacity. It has silenced them before they could even begin to express themselves, before they even knew the sound of their own voice. Aside from the denial of assault on girls within their own homes and families, the actual criminal justice system reports that 95 percent of sex offenders actually walk free, and that only accounts for the ones who've been reported. It is estimated that 75 percent of sexual assaults go unreported. There isn't data on how common it is for parents to fail to protect their child or deny their child's admission altogether. Evidently, as much as we've modernized our world, we've been long stuck in the confinement of societal shame. We've deemed it easier to strip a young girl of her sense of reality than to figure out how to actually repair the damage. How is it we can figure out how to build rockets to propel ourselves into space, but haven't been able to figure out how to deal with the global epidemic of sexual abuse? If there's anything I can feel in my gut in the moment (beyond a hankering for apple pie à la mode), it is how society *must support* the empowerment of young girls. This wakes me up. This is a priority. *I can feel this.* Yes, we must encourage the voices of young girls and staunchly protect their paths to maturity. We must teach girls to listen to their intuition and support them in honing their inner knowing. I do not stand alone in this assessment, but rather alongside the many individuals, organizations, and leaders of all genders who recognize the same need, who believe in this wholeheartedly. In all of my years working from my instincts and working to help others hone theirs, I am certain that intuition is a legitimate sense. Developing it is a skill. It shows up naturally if we feel safe enough to hear it and brave enough to follow it. If our intuition is undeveloped or has been ignored or ridiculed by our culture, we are starved of our most essential power. Of all the navigational technology I have in my life, there's no tool more essential to my sense of direction than my own intuition.

As we continue to culturally recognize our power as women, we can better understand our way forward by reviewing how far we've come. For example, from where I now stand, the brainwashing television of the 1960s, like *Make Room for Daddy* and *The Donna Reed Show*, seems truly ridiculous, but there can be no liberation without our freeing ourselves from the limitations we have unknowingly swallowed. I think this call to liberation is why, in part, I picked up that withered, weathered flyer in Boston. I saved the flyer, and its contents saved me. I began to understand the voices in my head that were telling me to cover up my pain with more sugar. I began to comprehend how, along with the bags of Lay's potato chips and the pounds of artificial sweetener and processed food, I was grappling with complex falsities. I went for artificial, processed foods because they had served me as a child, allowing me to ignore what was real. They became my baby blanket, my comfort. *Let's pretend everything is okay. I know the equation:* Mister Ed *plus toaster-ready pizza boats by Stouffer's.*

At this point in my life, I feel fortunate to understand how the fluffy synthetic filling of Twinkies might eventually be replaced by the soft gentleness of self-love. I've begun to grasp that Giana, when loving herself, doesn't have to fit into someone else's version of *perfect*, nor any prescribed size. She might simply be okay as is, her own strong container. She doesn't need to be larger than life, but rather, present in her own movements, *checked in*. She can inhale and exhale. She can feel her curves, let her stomach be, and accept that she isn't made like a man. Now, after all these years, I understand my struggle to feel my body and why I turned off considering my feminine self. Unfortunately, I'd confused being a girl with being a victim.

My twenties passed into my thirties in a haze of healing-energy intensives and high economic incentives. I continued growing my expertise in natural medicine, energy work, and transformational modalities of healing. I also expanded the scope of my business. All of the courses, weekend intensives, and multiple-year schools of initiation I've gone through is quite impressive, if I do say so myself. In total, I have completed many dozens of methodologies of practice. I'm a master of Reiki and a practitioner of Emotional Freedom Technique (tapping). I've studied neurolinguistic programming and have completed more than a decade of education in shamanic journeying. I hold a master's degree in spiritual psychology, have completed over four years of training in decoding belief systems, and am versed in working with multiple states of *brain waves*. I'm certified in hypnosis, past-life regression, and channeling the nonliving (yep, I've gone further *out there* than some may fathom, but it's all shoptalk to me at this point). I can as easily help heal a client of long-term Lyme disease using herbs and vibrational medicine as I can remove an entity that is causing dysregulation of the biorhythm of their large intestine. While I could tell you the distinct difference between an olive oil from the Italian region of Apulia and one from Calabria, I don't differentiate much between the normal and the paranormal. I'll work with people where they are. The main thing is how ready someone is when they show up for a session, and I know what it looks like when someone isn't ready to alter their relationship to a habit that's been working for them, believe you me.

I didn't use my healing work for the purpose of living in some far-out bohemian realm. I applied it directly to how I flipped houses, invested, and became a day trader and property manager. I didn't feel I could financially thrive on my restaurant salary alone, so I capitalized on having good family credit, and bought my first house with basically zero down. Then I flipped it and bought more. I became friends with contractors and their crew; it was in my blood to recognize the ones who worked like fiends, as I did. Aside from my ability to channel the frequency of flowers and saints, business was my currency. Honestly, I didn't see a difference between material and energetic wealth, which was surprising to me since I obviously couldn't recognize the material worth of my body. Supervising multiple restaurants alongside my dad evolved into a role of lead supervisor and manager at all of the American Grill locations. I borrowed my father's cunning endurance and managerial nature, and built my own branch of Giovanni success. While Gino communicated with his employees, inspiring their betterment by modeling business prowess, I exemplified power as well, but also provided my employees with salves and remedies.

The next step in my esoteric spiritual evolution was my years of studying with Dick Sutphen, a remarkable healer who is, to this day, considered the world's foremost psychic researcher. Dick, like Ronnie Gans, used hypnotherapy to focus on untangling past-life karmas. There is surely a significant place for this perspective in the world of wellness and whole-person healing. The problem, though, is that I abused my learning in the same way I abused my palate *wolfifying spaghetti alla chitarra*. I gorged on spiritual info, pretending I'd processed and digested what I'd consumed. Whatever remained, rather than sitting with it or trusting it, I would pawn off on my coworkers and friends, new and old alike. I handed out spirituality the same way I gave the rest of a *panettone* cake to my restaurant staff the day after I'd spent the night eating the better half of it (in minutes). It would take me some time before I could patiently, mindfully engage in spiritual practice, and even longer before I could shift out of the vicious cycle of mind–body disassociation.

By intuitive instinct and fortunate circumstance both, I met Dick Sutphen at the New Life Expo in New York City in 1985. This is one of the oldest, longest standing spiritual events, where healers, guides, holistic retailers, and anyone in the world of all things mystical convene yearly. For me, each booth at the conference caught my attention in that *thrill-a-minute* style, maybe even more so than might all the hamburger pitstop billboards in the world. Dick's wisdom came at the perfect moment for me, offering me possible answers as to why I'd been born so darn wrong. For my entire life, I felt wrong to be the single family member who stuck out like a sore thumb—or, I should say, a sore elephant. Since I couldn't seem to understand what I had done within *this* lifetime to be so obviously different and, accordingly, downright bad, I figured I'd done something before, perhaps in another life. When trauma surfaces, the patterns in the mind can be ornery, they've worked hard to keep troubling memories suppressed. I kept asking myself, *What did I ever really do to become this messed up?* Fortunately, the underground New Age scene provided opportunities to dive into the concept of having multiple past lives, inherited from long-held belief systems within various religious faiths and cultures. Of course, the concept of any significant time before the moment of one's baptism is largely lost in the Catholic faith. Like pretty much everything else I'd found interest in at that time, I'd have to keep this one in the closet too—along with my silvery-white sequined size-6 halter top. After I met him at his exotic booth, I bought all of Dick's books, and throughout the rest of the week at the exposition, I picked up enough flyers to poster a whole town on my own. I now had a library's worth of material to discover all of my previous lives and enough phone numbers of healers to help me find an alternative take on each one of these lives. I ate up all of this material, Giana style, without much self-control and hungry for more. In the weeks after the expo, if I ever felt a descending *darkness*, I'd pick up my copy of *Past Life Therapy in Action*. With new friends, ones who were also invested in the circumstances of their past lives, I could analytically talk for hours about repairing something I'd manifested centuries ago. It felt way more feasible to fuss over myself in untouchable, foggy past centuries than to tenderly confront and heal issues stemming from my formative years in this body.

Here's what's interesting about the modalities of healing to which I felt called: I started with the modes of spirituality that kept me entirely subdued, taking over my body in various power plays. I could physically disappear while becoming mentally engrossed in imagining my pink bubble. Or I might try to relate to energy in terms of being earth-sized. *I am filled with all of the power of the entire earth!* This was a perfect appetizer for the statement that often came only an hour later. *I am so full from this large stack of IHOP buttermilk pancakes!*

I'd also keep my physical self out of it when it came to healing sessions of hypnosis. I only had to be there for a few words, and then, just like that, I was under. (Truth be told though, even if you give me a few words when I'm involved in one of my dozen-plus multitasking endeavors, which is always, I'm gonna, at best, give you a vacant *mmm-hmmm*.) Evidently, long before I got my first certification with Dick Sutphen, I'd been living, effectively, as a master of self-hypnosis. Just let me repeat to myself, *Cooookieee Doughhh, Cooookieee Doughhh*, and, I'm out. Past-life regression was, in ways, like fortified hypnosis for me; let's call it *Hypnosis Plus Vitamin P*. Vitamin P, of course, stands for *past life*, rendering hypnosis *new* and *improved. Go under, Giana, with a little narrative entertainment on the side! Conk out, more or less, with the bonus of justification for why I'm a major mess and failure? Uh...check, check.*

After exploring the promise of past-life purification, I spent a few years toe-dipping in mediumship. While I certainly recognize the masterful teachings offered there, it was a bit too much for me, logistically speaking. Never mind my arranging to have the landscaper, cable guy, and personal organizer come over all within the same afternoon; now I had people both alive and dead knocking on my door, trying to locate one another between lifetimes and realities. It was hard enough to deal with the parts of myself that were longing to integrate. I didn't have room in my life to manage anyone else's missed connections. I'd leave that kind of service for Craigslist and the *Connecticut Post*'s classifieds section.

The turning point in my spiritual journey was when I began to understand that I could be a conscious part of a two-person form of interaction that lent itself to healing. I'd never realized that, while there was a *practitioner*, on the other end, there was a client, the one *practicing*. To practice taking part in my own therapeutic experience while under the guiding light of a professionally trained person was a defining moment for me. The only kind of transformational experience I'd had before (for better or for worse) entailed escaping my own consciousness. As I learned about myself through the prism of holistic neuroscience—rewiring thought patterns, exploring states of consciousness—I became more like an internal explorer than someone who self-ejected to get to outer space. Though I still remained largely based in my mental states and cerebral orientation,

I had begun the journey of embodiment. Only three decades later, I would begin to find a way to explore the land below my neck. As much as I had always believed that I'd refused to buy into a hyper-religious divide between good and evil, I'd actually divided both foods and my own body parts into these kind of categories. For most of my decades, I'd had my own version of what it means to "cross myself," a self-crucifixion cutting off feeling in most of my body and sucking on homeopathic pills like mini-rosaries. I also had my own type of religious-like recitations, subliminally reinforcing: *God forbid, Father, that I acknowledge anything devilishly south of my shoulder girdle.* For most of my life, I existed in my mind alone. That changed recently, when I decided to brave the snake-filled waters of my own inner Amazon, like a female Crocodile Dundee. (Or should I say, *Crocodile Done-de*valuing myself?) To my credit, all this time, I've been doing the best I can to be a real expeditioner, however much I avoided feeling my body throughout my years (at least, in this life!). Ironically, my life's mission required exactly that: experiencing my full physical form. Being embodied, it turns out, was the buried treasure I needed to discover.

Speaking of Dundee, from the beginning of my spiritual sojourn, I heard the call to travel. My first trip was to Sedona, Arizona, where I wanted to meet anybody and everybody. Sedona, for me, was the opposite of my Boston trips, where my intention was to have a party-weekend escape in total anonymity. Here, in Sedona, I wanted to *know everybody's name*; this was my own *Cheers* theme-song town. People who were awake to the healing power of crystals, angel reading, and lucid dreaming, these were *my* people. While I'd found that many people tended to tire me, I somehow had no sense of fatigue when in this level of company. Before long, I found myself going on international travels to study with my new colleagues, as well as hosting healers for weeks at a time in my own home. Interestingly, as I explored the islands of Greece in group retreats titled "Treks of the Ancient Goddesses" and sat with shamans in Peru, sipping plant teas,

I never felt radically transformed when I returned home. Mostly, I felt jet-lagged upon my return with a few suitcases full of rare antiques from far-out flea markets in various parts of the world. In recent years, in fact, I've realized that some of my trips were less about taking *purifying sojourns*, and more about getting *permission slips*. That is, I felt that in foreign countries, I had permission to eat whatever I wanted. Whether on spiritual voyages or heading to the Italian farm where my family's land flourished, I gave myself a permanent hall pass. *Eat, eat, eat.* I love food, and at least while we were on vacation—food and I alone together—like most good lovers, I could forgive the daily strife of our relationship. *Baby, I know we've been fighting, but when I take you to Argentina, we'll forget all about the blackouts and aggressive consumption. We'll eat multiple meals, fully on board with each other; we'll be one. I'll slowly caress your plate, using actual tableware. I'll taste you and tell the whole place about how beautiful you are. I'll never toss you out, discard your untouched parts in the trash, or leave you on the side of the road.* Yes, when I went traveling, I treated food with special attention, and she reminded me why I'd been so damn married to her for all of those difficult years.

Still, there was very little mercy and *about zero* amount of vacation time allotted to step away from my 24/7 job of reinforcing negative self-talk. With my wonderful self-berating record player on repeat, I was afforded little room for any other relationships, especially ones with men. I could deal with having a boyfriend for no more than two years, and more realistically, on average, no more than two weeks. My girlfriends, my spiritual schools, and, my main squeeze: my work—these were my healthiest *significant others*. I treated these parts of my life well, nourishing friendships and business connections. I could take care of my employees and allies, though I still struggled to gather enough self-compassion to rise from the ashes of my own pyre, phoenix style. All the while, at my best, I studied with chefs, even attended Geneen Roth's body-love workshop, a silent retreat aimed to help connect women to their relationship with food.

Despite her impeccable, poster-child-for-transcending-diet-gimmicks coaching mastery, I still emotionally ate. I remember, in fact, being at Geneen's workshop, waiting for the meal break in utter discomfort, feeling unsettled and ready to bolt. I read through books of gourmet chefs, Giana style (mostly flipping through the pages and looking at the pictures—though surely absorbing something throughout). I also studied with Martha Stewart, who, to this day, I revere as a masterful businesswoman and artisan. But no matter what, no matter what master I sat with, from Shakti to Martha, I seemed to fail when it came to having confidence around food. The only way I could feel any semblance of self-worth was by starving myself of all the foods of my cultural heritage, which is pretty insane, if I think about it. No pasta, no bread, not really any carbs at all—nothing my ancestors relied on to survive. Go figure. I'd just return again and again to that flimsy Scarsdale Diet, the one created by the man who was murdered by my school's headmistress. For whatever reason, it worked for me. Like a prisoner's diet or that of a dog, Giana gets meat and a few pieces of celery, *va bene*. I never had a sense of my body size being beautiful, heck no. In fact, I never had a sense of my body being anything other than *too big*. Gino's reflection on my fate, his single premonition, (*You girls are going to get fat if you keep eating only the foods you like)* was obviously true, because, well, *Father Knows Best*. That message stuck. Therefore, whenever I ate something I liked, *boom*: my body got fat or headed in that direction, true to Gino's word.

Sometime in my forties, I started to take more trips with a mystical focus, traveling with groups of healers I'd discovered through some branch of the spiritual grapevine. Many of these sojourns fell short of being as life-changing as promised, despite the fact that I'd geared up for attaining some level of enlightenment. Mostly, I'd walk around and shop, breathe the air of an entirely different part of the globe, sleep in the location's best establishments, eat fantastic fare (of course), and then return home feeling reasonably ready to go back to the grind of self-flagellation. I'd also come back feeling my waistband was just tight enough to yet again get started on my restrictive diet. Work was my confessional, where I'd redeem myself for having redeemed my frequent-flyer miles.

While I've chosen to take most of my travels to explore mysticism, often the deep learning I walk away with looks entirely different than what I'd imagined when setting sail, so to speak. Case in point: In Nepal, something extraordinary happened. My experience was something like a religious awakening, allowing me to see how powerful cultural perspective is and how deeply societal standards affect our sense of worth. The Nepalese children flocked to me, affectionately hugged me, and treated me as though I were a female version of Santa Claus. No matter what, they wanted to be near me, to touch my face and my body, to be in my arms. This felt incredibly bizarre to me and rather unjustified. What had I done to deserve all of this affection? When other women in my group walked next to me, they were mostly ignored. Meanwhile, I was hounded, surrounded, and more or less pounded on by dozens of adorable Nepalese children. I was kissed and coddled, and they even asked for my autograph. I was fameworthy to them. By the third day, as I was walking with a local interpreter, I mentioned this awkward situation. He laughed, explaining, *Miss Giana, you are a symbol of beauty here, because you are of a larger size. Here, if you are bigger, you are considered wealthy, special, gifted, spiritually enlightened, and anointed with power. The children hug you because they are hoping your large richness will rub off on them. They find you gorgeous. Understandably, they wish they looked just like you.* The interpreter looked at me with a gleam of admiration in his eyes. I had no idea what to make of what he'd said. I probably looked at him with my nostrils flared and eyes slightly crossed in a flippant gesture of disbelief, *not pretty*. However, it seemed the Nepalese didn't care about my cheeky expressions. Meanwhile, no one, at least no one sober, no one I could ever comfortably take home to meet my parents, had so directly called me beautiful. Or maybe they had, but in that case, there was no way I'd felt safe enough to listen, so I'd never heard it. I'd successfully dismissed any part of myself that could be considered sexy or appealing as solicitous, problematic, and susceptible to pain and hardship. I didn't want to feel pain or hardship, so *that was that* for allowing myself to feel desirable.

Something about little children considering me beautiful, though, changed my life, at least for that week. In Nepal, I allowed myself to feel the appreciation, to carry myself with pride. I figured that one week of feeling worthy—even gorgeous, darn it—wouldn't *kill* me. So, I basked in the love a bit. Children were so innocent, and I realized their attention could do me no harm. Here, I accepted the attention, probably because I couldn't understand the language of the Nepalese kids. If I had been able to understand them, I'm sure I would have found a way to negatively interpret their affectionate remarks. Instead, on that Nepal trip, I achieved something by letting my body be as it preferred to be, and I was happy to share the abundance. This was my first sense that my own body might support the promotion of another's sense of abundance too. My body could be something that wouldn't rob me of prosperity, but instead could be a representation of positivity for others. It could be something other than *in the way* or an entangled mess of misunderstood flesh. In Nepal, I felt kind of like a mother of the world. In fact, one of the oldest discovered artifacts of that region is a voluptuous clay sculpture whose body is shaped somewhat like mine. When I think of this, it does not surprise me that I had to go to similar coordinates to feel that someone, somewhere found me a symbol of beauty, of something good. Of course, I returned home to the world of Kate Moss models and tabloids reporting on every famous woman's weight gain or weight loss, and before long, I'd returned to avoiding whatever I saw in the mirror. Back to status quo, I forgot about Nepalese dumplings and temples, and, more distinctly, the feeling of experiencing my body shape as something considered beautiful. Back in the land of milk and honey—or, in my case, the land of Milky Ways and Bit-O-Honeys—I acknowledged my physical body only by registering what shade of lip gloss I liked, and left alone everything under my neckline.

Just like I mentally separated my head from the rest of my body, for a few solid decades or more, I kept my financial life and my healing life completely disconnected. If you know me, or know someone who knows me, or even know someone who knows someone who knows me, chances are, you've been handed one of my homemade salves, aromatherapeutic body sprays, or massage oils. I've doled them out like direct mail from your cable company, addressed to you or *Current Resident*. Over the years, I've been known to give anyone in need free energy clearings, archetypal dream analyses, and individualized reports on the spiritual roots of one's physical maladies, all at no charge. To bring in the cold, hard cash, I concentrated on flipping properties and day-trading (turns out, by the way, my intuition yields heavy returns). For profit, I focused my efforts on *concrete things*. I mean, I'm Gino's daughter. For years, I couldn't imagine being paid for something outside of the world of classic business. I'd revamp the buffet at the American Grill or invest in a new parking lot, but I couldn't put a price tag on my transformational coaching, even though I'd hear again and again how I singlehandedly helped someone turn their financial life around. More than just being a boss, I felt my role was to encourage people to see the abundance available to them. This is what kept my skin in the game, what made it worthwhile for me to break a sweat at work, in the heat of the kitchen. I'd hire dishwashers or hostesses, but from the get-go, I'd envision them eventually rising to a higher position, such as head grill chef. I'd learned that the richest gift in life is one's personal evolution, so in all my efforts, I applied the same manifestation energy work I'd learned through the many healing modalities in which I'd submerged myself.

At the American Grill, I was freely playing healer like a Steak Florentine Nightingale, but I started to feel that I was cheating myself. I'd been studying healing modalities for a very long time, had so many certificates, and had hundreds of hours of experience. I was disrespecting the entire holistic practice of healing by offering my skills for free. Enough women have been healers without pay over the years, like the nameless woman in the woods who took care of Saint Sebastian. I owed it not only to myself, but also to all womankind to recognize that my gift was worth a professional position in the world. Of course, it wasn't easy for me to actually start charging for my services. About a year after deciding I needed to make money for my work, I was still procrastinating in taking the initiative, but in my weekend workshops and healing retreats, I began to feel something resembling restlessness. This was different than the typical Giana restlessness, which is basically my standard setting. Really, I was feeling irritated with myself. I knew that I could organize retreats that were impactful, effective, and healing-centric, where people would walk away with something truly life-changing. It's said that a person will keep herself ignorant of something as long as she can, until it becomes a necessity or a real desire. I couldn't ignore the call anymore; I couldn't remain ignorant. If I didn't step up and take *myself* seriously, how could I encourage anyone else to be empowered?

I was forced to be honest with myself. It was time to deepen my commitment to self-care and leadership. On a trip to the Greek ruins, I received the message. I heard *that* voice, you know, the same one I'd heard in Boston that had led me to Shakti Gawain: my intuition. I chose to spend the afternoon by myself in Athens, leaving my group behind. I longed to connect with the essence of the images of the goddesses there, and I didn't feel like I was interacting deeply enough with my group. The rest of the women mostly wanted to eat and shop, which was fine, but I knew I was there for something more meaningful. I walked through the ruins as the sun hit its highest point, shielding my eyes at the feet of a statue. The goddess Athena had stopped me in my tracks. Athena is the goddess of war and courage, and her motto is, essentially, *Conquer and fearlessly go, go, go*. These are the two fundamental strengths of the Giovanni clan (as well as the two dominant qualities of Giana's inner joint chiefs, the Escapist and the Obsessor). I consider

Athena a kind of distant Mediterranean relative of ours. There, in front of my Greek sister, I heard the direction: *Giana, say yes.* I'd run *no* through my mind when it came to controlling everything in my life, including my emotions and diet; in fact, I'd always been one giant *no* to myself.

It had never occurred to me to accept hearing *yes* before. I couldn't say *yes* to feeling desire, to my romantic longings, to recognizing the real hunger of my soul. I couldn't locate *yes*, the place where I felt enough. Rather, I found places that killed *yes*, where *yes* keeled over in another *death-by-chocolate* binge. My inner rebel, strategizing like Athena in war, had unfortunately applied excessive force; she'd ended up taking me down along with my parents. My intention was to prove to my family that they wouldn't limit me, couldn't make me feel small. I'd show them. I'd eat the entire menu, let the unlimited buffet be my haunt. I'd find my comfortable weight (i.e., my safeguarded size) well above a dozen stone, and darn it, I'd ignore stepping on the scale to spite them all. All of my behaviors were responding to their *no*, but in the process of refuting my family, I hammered *no* into my cell walls, master-carpenter style. I tucked their *no* away, but its echoing reverberations burrowed in my bones; that *no* is a tricky thing.

I'd proven the naysayers—the *no* sayers—wrong; they couldn't limit me. In the process, though, I'd ended up proving to myself that my entire existence was wrong. I'd swallowed *no* right up, *wolffied* it. My parents' *no* was contagious. I thought I'd rebuked theirs, but I'd merely replicated it, taken its spores into my own system and spread that self-limiting virus throughout my being. Giana, she calls the shots—no worries if she shoots herself in the foot in the meantime, proving no one can trump her skill of self-sabotage. There, with Athena, I felt the courage to consider, if these Greek figures had lasted for so long, these ancient goddesses who were often chock-full of contradictions themselves, how might I flex similar strength? What if I learned to hear a *yes*, my own *yes*, and create for myself a life that is unlimited? What if I could help others do the same?

CHAPTER 19

Medicinal Garlic and Olive Oil Salves

While contemplating exactly how I'd brave stepping more deeply into my work as an intuitive guide, I made an appointment with a medium, recommended by a friend who called her both clarifying and insightful. I understand it might seem ironic that as an intuitive, I sought an outsider to confirm my own inner-knowing. However, over the years I've learned that often the best *seers* are simply clearing away the cobwebs over one's own instinctual knowing. I needed to access a higher source, a trusty etheric energy less boggled down with anxious concerns than Giana Giovanni. On the phone with the medium, I told her a bit about myself, explaining how I'd found relative success working in my family's business. I let her know that I loved helping people, watching them open themselves to unlimited possibilities and thrive. After we spent some time going over the modalities of healing practices I'd studied over the years, she asked me to lie down. I reclined into the beanbag pillow on my couch, keeping the medium on speaker phone while she connected to my highest self. *You know, typical Friday night stuff.* As mediums do, after a moment or two she'd attuned to my *guides*. I might best describe these guides as higher dimensional soul allies—sometimes named as saints, angels, or even animal spirits (and, in my case, I definitely have a guide or two in the realm of culinary spirits, as well, as I swear I am led by garlic and olive oil). After some minutes, the medium spoke: *Giana, I'm getting a strong message here.* She sounded a little choked up, continuing slowly, as though translating or straining to hear something. *Yes, I'm sorry, but I am definitely hearing your guides tell me that you actually are not a healer in this lifetime. It seems that you've been one in many other lifetimes, but this one is really a time for something else.*

Every part of my body curled up, cringing, gesturing in a hard sense of revolt. An immediate nausea overtook me (though, admittedly, I could have been nauseated from the salami grinder I'd hurriedly consumed just half a hour before our call). I wanted to verbally explode on this woman, to let her know, point-blank, that she was so completely full of, let's say, *hot air*. I was fuming that I'd trusted—even *paid*—this woman who was so completely bogus and that I'd divulged my life story to her. What did *she* know? I was ready to accost her in a bitter verbal attack, but my higher guides must have kept me from going straight-up haywire on this woman. It wasn't worth the karma, so I kept my cool. Though I'd gone silent, the medium on the other end of the line obviously felt my tension. Finally, I started in: *What are you talking about? No offense, but...that's a load of garbage!*

I heard the voice on the other line draw a deep breath and then exhale with a delighted laugh. *Oh, Giana! I'm so sorry to tease you! she confessed. But your guides knew that your rebellious spirit would only find the real answer if I gave you the very opposite of what you already know to be true. They informed me that if I told you directly that, yes, you are a healer, you would revolt, run from the truth, and disallow this part of you to emerge further. So I did what your guides asked. They told me to give you a "no" because you'd find your "yes" in that. I went with it, and I denied your inherent essence, and they were right! I watched you revolt! My gosh! I'm glad I wasn't there in person; you sounded more than ready to pounce!*

According to my guides, I was evidently ready to share my years of study and practice with others more publicly. *Gulp.* I'd already chosen some outlandish life changes, was I now supposed to come out as a sort of professional-level healer to my family? For example, in my mid-forties, I decided I would become a competitive dancer. In fact, I moved to New York City to pursue my new passion. I found a dance partner (an especially hot young man, I must admit!), and we had rapport. We practiced multiple times each week while I commuted to Connecticut to work. With sneering smiles, my brother and my father finally got over my dancing phase. No matter what I explored in life, if it didn't fit into their spreadsheet of what was *normal*, I'd be the brunt of their jokes. Now I was supposed to come out as a healer? I'd already given them salves for their illnesses, their indigestion, their heart conditions, and other maladies, however much they tended to roll their eyes at my offerings. Now I'd have to find a way to slip in my soulful business while being a restaurateur, but I'd do it.

After deciding to launch my healing-centric business, I found a top online professional development guru who offered a course in how to *manifest*, targeted largely at spiritual entrepreneurs. Since by this point, I was literally a *workshoptilyoudrop-aholic*, I signed up. Out in California, during the second of the multiple weeklong immersions spanning the course of a couple of years, we were given a specific exercise in which we would work with a partner with the aim to share our biggest professional edge. I had no plan to do much more than say whatever I could come up with about myself to the woman sitting in the chair in front of me, but something took over when she began to speak, a process of its own spilled forth from me. The woman profoundly reacted to the insights flowing from me. She later shared that our experience together was more positively transformative for her than any other mode of therapy she'd encountered. She didn't know it, but it was women like her who helped me access my own inner confidence to share my therapeutic offerings at-large. I had all the tools, more than enough, the only thing I needed now was faith in my own physical form. This is the same faith I needed to possess in order to heal myself. I realized then that my body was my truest companion, the very expression of my embodiment. It had come with me on this healing journey and would be with me until the end. The more I could accept the essence of my work in the world, the more I'd have to actually feel being in my body.

I went home and immediately began buying domain names. I couldn't be Giana Giovanni in the world of healing, so I'd be Giana *Gemma*. Gemma was my grandmother's first name, so it worked for me. Plus, in Italian, it means *gem*. Gems are my personal symbol of abundance, and anyone who has accompanied me to the Gem Show in Arizona each year to scope out the newest crystal geodes can attest to that fact. I knew exactly what I wanted to offer the world through my group work and individual client sessions. I wanted to help people actualize the life they most desire and help them to feel what I called being "limitless," living without a sense of limitations as to who they could be or how they could feel. After all, I was quite masterful at manifesting what I wanted, a skill I'd inherited from the Giovannis. I'd created my own version of abundance, and would now use it to help spread love and goodwill. I'd been blessed in not having to starve like Lia did during World War II, in having more than enough. I wanted to help others feel nourished in their lives and activate the potential of their own inner resources. I wanted to help other women believe that they, too, could feel the richness they rightfully deserved to feel. In order to more seriously take on the role of supporting others, I'd also have to step more fully into practicing this same healing work on *myself*. I knew somewhere, then, that I'd have to get to know the part of myself that denied my own abundance of life, that part that manifested a whirlwind of confusion in the measurement of calories. I'd have to confront my fear that I'd never *actualize* who I am, in regard to both of my identities: Giana Gemma and Giana Giovanni.

Meanwhile, as I grew my healing profession, I continued to travel and aggressively work in my restaurant and real estate businesses. I stepped more fully into supporting the work my father was used to doing, as he needed to slow down a little bit in his older years. It took me some time to see the correlation between Gino's becoming more frail and my own increasing sense of health concerns, but it really hit me when I was in Italy. I'd regularly go to Abruzzo during harvest time to oversee the bottling of the Giovanni *pure gold*, the fresh, cold-pressed olive oil from our one thousand five hundred olive trees. The land had once been my grandfather's, his father's, and his father's father's, going as far back as anyone remembers. Acquiring property ran in the blood of the Giovanni men. Gino and his siblings inherited the Abruzzo farmland. My father bought out his siblings and then divided ownership between Gino Jr., Frankie, and me. The three of us would go to the farm each year to harvest the oil. Sometimes it would just be Frankie and me along with her two sons. I'd bring extra suitcases and fill them with Bell jars of heavenly olive oil, and ship another dozen of them home, supplying a few local kitchen stores and specialty markets. I'd also give them to my friends and senior staff members. Additionally, I'd go to Abruzzo at various other points in the year to see relatives. My travel agent and I were on an autodial basis. Siri, my virtual assistant, heard her name more than she heard my mother's when it came to verbal cues for telephone calls. Over the years, while I grew my database of clients seeking peace with their ancestors and heritage, I found myself increasingly called to do the same in my own life. Therapeutic work often works that way, we attract others who are going through journeys we've either trekked or are in the midst of approaching ourselves.

Two consecutive visits to the Italian farmland, specifically, hit home for me, marking a major point in my own personal revolution. The first occurred during a trip on which I felt, for the first time in my life, *winded*, as in, straight-up exhausted. Regardless of what I ate, I'd always been able to take on a ton of work, sleep minimally, and repeat. Now, as I walked up a hill to the *piazza*, the center of the village, I felt my legs were too stiff to move effectively. Meanwhile, I watched women nearly twice my age, thin and agile, climb the hill with their tiny dogs, swift and carefree. I was hit with a major realization about my physical condition: *If I don't do something about my health and diet, I'm going to die.* This concern for my general survival while visiting my ancestral homeland hit me hard, and when I came back to Connecticut, I sought out a personal trainer. I decided I needed to get fit, like *really fit*. I wasn't going to do it halfway. I'd become a racer, a real runner—why not? If I was going to exercise, I figured I may as well learn how to appease my Escapist. Likely, my subconscious determined that if I *had* to be in my body, I may as well figure out how to run myself right out of dealing with it. I set a goal; that's the only way I operate. Even though I'd previously never run more than a hole in my stockings, I'd now learn how to pound serious pavement. My plan was to finish the Thanksgiving race in my town. It was just a simple five-mile run, nothing Olympic level, but for me, this was Mount Vesuvius. Five miles was about the farthest I'd drive to satisfy my hunger, but I had no clue how to travel that amount of distance on foot. To my ears, five miles sounded like five oceans, five mountain ranges, five planets far. Still, I didn't want to settle on training to jog down my driveway, around the neighborhood track, or on a treadmill while watching reruns of *Friends* on the overhead TV. I needed fresh air and to feel wind on my face. So I trained Giana style. I took myself from zero to pedal-to-the-metal acceleration. For me, there's never been a middle ground. So while I couldn't remember ever having completed a single sit-up, I figured out how to run five miles within a month. *No prob*, even if the idea of working out was foreign... beyond, of course, working out how I could justify consuming five pork buns and eating a half gallon of ice-cream. For me, the term *workout* only applied to how I could work out eating a double burger on my drive home while steering with my thigh on I-95. I hadn't applied willpower to my athletic health before, but I would now. I wanted to walk up the little hills in Italy when I was even older than the fiery eighty-something-year-old women I saw acing the ascent. Competitive motivation I *did* do, and only, of course, if someone told me all odds were against me. To add fuel to my focus, as soon as I mentioned running the race to my family, just as I'd expected, they refused to believe I was capable of succeeding. Therefore, I geared up to go. I trained, I sweat, and then, on the day of the run, I got my hair and makeup done before heading out. I wanted to feel ready to rock! Once I felt prepped in the only way I knew how, my best face made complete by my favorite lip gloss, I ran the whole darn race. I didn't finish first, not even close, but that wasn't the point. I did what everyone said was impossible: I kept my word, and I finished. For better or for worse, whether in holding lifelong grudges or committing to keeping our businesses thriving, keeping our word is one thing *all* Giovannis can do, and I called on this skill to get past the finish line. Once I'd done so, I was sure I'd never care to run any significant distance again, *definitely not*. I'd still aim to workout in some capacity, I'd jump on a trampoline and do crunches and other core-strengthening exercises, but only with my trainer on premises. Otherwise, the single strength training I'd bother to carry out was when I needed to haul cases of meat into my garage from the delivery truck, and pack sirloin into my freezer.

Here's the thing: all my various trainers, from my piano teacher to my Italian tutor to my therapist to my naturopathic doctor, they all encourage self-care practices. *Giana, you have to do X, Y, and Z daily, even for five minutes, to maintain, to discover, to change.* I can easily pop some herbal pills, but I've been less willing to understand that true healing comes from my own willpower. I think, for willpower, my entire brain has to get on board, meet in some internal family den, where all my inner parts have equal say and participate in teamwork. If real transformation requires a willful practice, why, when left on my own, do I seem to resist committing independently to even the slightest shifts in my behavior? Since it takes literally one minute to stop and drop into my breathing before, say, *wolfifying* a salami grinder on Connecticut's Route 130, why do I resist? Why do I need to hire someone else to hold my hand and hold me accountable?

Evidently, I'm happy to discuss my revelations for hours, reiterate variations of contemplations that all arrive at the same conclusion: *I need to love myself!* I'll process for hours with the world's best analysts. At the end of my process, most of my practitioners, whether weight trainers or energy workers, leave me with homework, likely secretly questioning if I'll actually ever choose to *live* the change I want to see, as in, actually *do* the darn thing. Do we all suffer so much to maintain discipline, keep our word, and create new habits? And if so, why the heck is this the case? How can we be so advanced in our evolution of thinking, and at the same time, remain primitively animalistic, like 10,000 BC level? Why would I stubbornly resist breaking habits while dropping big bucks to try to create change? How can I have ordered enough personal growth-and-development literature to open my own metaphysical bookstore, but, these days, fall asleep after reading a single page? I've developed thousands of metaphors to describe how I collapse into poor behaviors and manifest distress in certain areas of my life. I find it funny to refer to my typical Giana behaviors as *classic*, laughing at myself in the same way Gino scoffed at my ambitions when I was young. Why do I allow myself to maintain such bad behaviors, hurting my own body through extreme diet swings and staving off nearly everything I'm craving or else eating exorbitantly, abusing my system? Believe me, I *know* I don't want to eat Oreos. I mean, I could deliver a freaking TED talk on the science behind how much I don't want to eat them. I know I don't feel good about myself after consuming them, that's for sure, but unfortunately, I have *about zero* boundaries. Boundaries are for self-respecting people, people who feel good about themselves. Long ago, I decided that Giana wasn't capable of having boundaries.

When I decided to ready myself for a race (other than the *rat race*, for which I'd already received a gold medal), I didn't make the connection between training for endurance and cultivating energy, even though I was physically working out. While I intellectually understand the idea that *bad food* makes me *feel bad*, it seems I can't register the *energetic* repercussions of consuming it. I don't feel the effect because the way I experience energy is through creating external pressure. I feel an energetic charge only in having to struggle to survive, in having to plow through things, in having a mental list to check off, a full schedule. This is my form of inspiration. *Power up; power over*, I was taught by the dominant culture. Retract my senses. Rarely stop to smell the flowers I grow in my garden. Cook like the famous Italian chef Massimo Bottura, but don't register taste. It doesn't matter what's on the radio, because I won't hear it, along with the one hundred alerts sounding on my phone, because use of the senses requires a body to receive the stimuli. Sensing with the body requires feeling, nerves and impulses, energy, a rate of response, and active signals. I only recognize energy input if it has nothing to do with my body. Better to leave my body in disarray, in an entangled mess of *never-minds* and *doesn't matters*, in numb operation. Running the Thanksgiving five-mile race, however, helped me begin to shift my long-standing body numbness to embark on a type of physical transformation. However, such a shift of self-care would ultimately take much longer than clocking a five-mile run. During my training, I didn't lose weight, but I didn't really care. I was more interested in how I gained muscle and physical strength. I also gained a sense of my own legs and their capability. Even though I experienced a new type of connection, something close to a functional alliance (gasp!) between my body and mind, once the race was over, I dropped all interest in doing anything like that again. Perhaps I wasn't physically exhausted, but rather, scared of the concept of committing to a functional union. After the race, my body was left at the altar—my mind, a restless, runaway bride.

The next year in Italy, on my grandfather's land, which now belonged to the Giovanni children, I experienced yet another kind of breakdown/breakthrough. I should have expected something like a freak-out since I brought a crew of female healers with me and parked us on land that had been run by men for around a dozen centuries. My impetus for bringing these powerful women with me to Italy was to get a sense of how we might turn the space into a retreat in the following seasons. Heading to the homeland, I thought I was in high gear, filled with professional vision, but instead of stepping into the role of event planner once I got to the land, something broke inside of me. *Bravo.* Perhaps I melted because I'd never felt so immersed in female energy within the borders of the Giovanni farmland. Plus, I had to admit, maybe I was confronting my own edges here; it was a bit bold on my part to consider creating a nourishing retreat center on land that had been the nucleus of the male-driven complexity that riddled my own psyche. Once I had the company of a handful of strong women and their honest assessment and vision in Abruzzo, there was something we couldn't avoid that was present there, looming over us. Don't get me wrong—our family farmland is a haven, a rich cornucopia of olive trees and fruits endemic to the lush region. Still, one of my healer friends, after taking a lone walk on my family's land, let me know that she felt the earth there was writhing in pain from enduring so much warfare in the past. Whosever pain it was, the land's or mine, my grandfather's, his father's, or that of the Nazi soldiers who'd lodged there, I spent the week crying, nearly hysterical. I could barely get out of bed. I'd never done anything like this before, and certainly never in front of other people, but then again, I'd never been to the throne of my father's Italy with a potent posse of holistic women.

As opposing forces often work together, somehow, in surrendering to my own inner darkness, I found a new desire to more actively embrace the light. My Italy, perhaps, had been waiting for me to bring a dream team of healing women to its land. On that trip, I was given a harvest of a different golden shade than the olive oil we bottle yearly. I reaped a kind of bounty from my sorrow and reframed my personal commitments and sense of mission. Rather than my life's purpose being to avoid my own feelings at all cost and bark orders at myself until the very end, perhaps, I considered, life was made for something different. *Could it be that rather than plowing through it, getting up that Italian hillside now or at age ninety-five, my life was about pausing to connect to the horizon and committing to myself in spite of the obstacles in the road?*

$\mathcal{T}$he Big Fettuccine Alfredos

My self-confrontation in Italy took place not long after a family trauma. In the years before these two specific trips to Abruzzo, we nearly lost my father. The thing about Gino is that he has endless energy, even more than I do. I knew I'd been asked to come home after college to, more or less, walk in Gino's footsteps, and that I'd be presented with a challenge to find my own calling within the dynasty he'd created. Everyone pales in comparison to Gino; his survival instinct and business brain are unmatched. I often felt that there was no choice other than to accept my diminutive position as compared to my father's, and I did so (at my finest hour) with sincere appreciation. I knew I was lucky to have a parent who modeled endurance and tenacity, and imparted these values to his children. As a result, I was given the opportunity to lead a team and to step into a budding business with the knowledge that I, too, could build real financial security for our family. As unconfident as I make myself out to be, at least as a businessperson, I had an unwavering belief in myself, all thanks to Gino's and Lia's escape from Italy. Though it was never spoken of, the Giovannis unanimously agreed to never bring up that one day we'd reach the end of an era. We didn't let ourselves think about the fact that, at some point, Gino would no longer be around to tell us what we were doing wrong, to make final decisions, to advise us on how to grow, expand, and take the upper hand.

Then one night, at a dinner party of extended family and friends, Gino felt light-headed. He gently complained (something he rarely does) to my brother, Gino Jr. Shortly thereafter, he fainted. Rather than coming to, he remained unconscious, and paramedics were called to rush him to the hospital. Once admitted, Gino, still unconscious, was declared septic, which meant that his stomach had erupted inside his body and was now contaminating his entire system. My family and I rushed to the hospital just behind the ambulance. I did whatever I could, praying to Padre Pio, the Italian saint of healing miracles and, specifically, a benefactor of hospitals on the Adriatic coast. Padre Pio died in the late 1960s, and some people say he is still active in helping to heal people; this is his legacy. My entire family went into shock when Gino fell sick. This was the biggest calamity we'd ever faced together, and without Gino there to guide us directly, we were all at a loss. What could we do? The Giovannis, while uniquely skilled at doing everything to avoid calamity, had little experience in coping with situations in which nothing could be done. On the first night of my father's hospital stay, I chose to sit quietly, continuing to pray to Padre Pio. A woman approached me with a small handout similar to the flyer I'd picked up off the ground in Boston. It was just a thin sheet of paper, but still, it somehow felt transformational. There on the paper was a printed image of Padre Pio, the exact saint I'd been praying to. I heard my inner voice: *He'll be OKAY, Giana.* I knew the woman with the handout was a good omen, and my intuition told me that my father would be all right. I understand that to many, this way of handling things might sound irrational, but truly, it is in moments of desperation, that faith becomes essential. There I was, fully believing that my father still had years left to chastise me in the only way he knew how to love, and throughout his time of illness, I didn't let go of my certainty, not even for one second.

For three excruciatingly long months, my seventy-eight-year-old dad remained in a coma. Doctors told us it was possible he would never recover, but we had faith. Italian Catholics know how to get good with God when they've got to, that's for sure. But, during these months, I also got good with Gino. I cleared all of the air between us that could

266

use a little dusting and did a little *feng shui* on our father–daughter duo. I *Marie Kondo'd* our connection. I talked to Gino, and maybe it was easier since his eyes were closed and he couldn't make light of my sincere confessions. Still, I knew he could hear me, that he could feel my compassion and belief in him. I could feel his love for me, too, and I truly recognized the richness of our bond. I certainly wasn't ready to *lose* my father, especially because I felt like we hadn't even really *found* each other yet. I couldn't be sure there would ever be a clear line of open communication between us, but I knew I wanted to see his eyes again, keen, alive, and taking it all in, processing the world in his own enigmatic style. One morning, at the end of my father's third month in a coma, I squeezed his hand, and he squeezed back! Before long, Gino opened his eyes, gave us a look not too dissimilar to the look he'd give us when he'd walk by an area of the restaurant where we'd just stocked a shelf or filled a dressing, questioning our competency. Rather than feel scorned by his gaze, however, I felt a massive rush of relief. Just months later, Gino was walking around again at the Grill, chastising us with his eyes once again! My father was back in action, telling me how to run the business, what to invest in, and who to promote. I welcomed it all though, and even found sweet humor in his unique way of showing affection. After he recovered, Gino, for the first time, told me, *I love you, Giana*. It was under his breath, but I am pretty sure I heard it. By this time, Lia was well versed in the phrase and recited it regularly, usually at the end of family phone calls. Then, the words were safest to utter since she could just hit *end call* and be done with the vulnerability of the sentiment. Ever since my mother had found the Serenity Prayer at her Christian Weekend Workshop, she'd changed. My nephews and nieces all know a different Lia, their kind and soft *nonna*. Frankie and I, of course, still remember a more stern version of our mother, one whose style of reprimanding was quite intimidating.

After Gino's recovery, I doubled down on bingeing as a means of coping with everything. It was then that I became determined to build my healing home, a way to counter my dysfunctional behavior and create a real *forever residence*. I knew this home would be a place I could focus on acquiring radiant health, but I still felt like a bundle of contradictions on my own wellness journey. I'd developed one part of myself that clearly declared I was ready to heal, who planned to even support others in my forthcoming healing space. Meanwhile, I also threw logs on the fire of another side of myself, the half that remained determined to hoard, eat in excess, and continue to knock myself unconscious by way of terrible food choices. I felt full of shame (which, next to hot pepper, is obviously my favorite spice in life). I knew I had to seek a different kind of help in order to truly resign these long-held dysfunctional coping mechanisms of mine. I now understand that embarking on the journey of writing this book was my moment of bravery. But at that time, I felt convinced that revealing emotions or any other vulnerabilities (*especially publicly!*) would be a direct recipe for making a fool of myself. I wrote down the title, *Eat Your Words*, in numerous notebooks and tucked sheets of scribbled-on paper in various places, including the glove compartment, one of my three lip-gloss drawers, my bulk-goods cabinet, behind my Audi's sun visor, and even the laundry room drawer next to the detergent pods. I started to write down chapter names: *The Buffet and* something-or-another, and then a pun on *prix fixe menus*. I'd write things down and cross them off, spending some stream-of-consciousness moments trying to surface the stifled scream inside myself. Finally, after some seasons spent settling into my home, I realized that I definitely had a book in me. Its contents were buzzing in my brain, and it was ready to be born. Perhaps it's easiest to organize my life changes on the pages of a book. This way, I can retain some distance and close it when it gets to be too much. *Brave, like a lion, right? Big and fierce, and then scared of a mouse. Scared of a Yodel. Scared of a Nestlé Crunch bar.*

I do believe Gino was protected by Padre Pio, and I remain close to the image of the saint to this day. In fact, as spiritually skeptical as the Giovannis make themselves out to be, saints have shown up in weird ways for my family. Take, for example, my grandfather, who passed down a kind of vendetta that lives on to this day, one that influenced my father and then his children. Here's how the family feud started: When my father was about ten years old, my grandfather's cousin came over for a holiday meal. This was just before the war broke out, in the early 1940s. The Italian farmland was flourishing, and the business of agriculture was booming for the Giovannis. My grandfather confided in his cousin, *Good news! I'm going to purchase a plot of land down the way. It's being sold at a very good price, and I'm going to expand our farmland there.* The cousins toasted my grandfather's anticipated acquisition. A few days later, when my grandfather went to purchase the deed, he found it had been bought just the day before. My grandfather declared that this was impossible; he was sure he had been privy to the availability of the land before anyone else. The estate representative told him that it had been, in fact, bought outright by his own cousin. At that moment, my grandfather felt such a deep sense of betrayal, he was shaken to the core. For the next days, he could neither sleep nor eat. He paced the floors and pounded the walls, declaring he would seek vengeance. He was in such a frenzy of anger that he nearly lost his mind, as the story goes. Land was holy, and when one man shares his business plans with another, this a sacred exchange, especially between men who share blood. In my grandfather's eyes, his cousin's betrayal was sacrilegious, so he felt God gave him a green light to seek revenge. My grandfather seemed to really buy into the notion that *all is fair in love and war*, and when it came to breaking vows of confidence, violent retribution was not one's last resort, but the rightful action to uphold one's integrity.

The story goes that my grandfather descended the farmhouse staircase that evening, determined to seek revenge after having received the disturbing news about his cousin's betrayal. The house was dimly lit by gas lanterns, as was common in 1940s Italy. Before he reached the door my grandfather was stopped in his tracks by the image of Saint Anthony, who is considered the finder of lost things.

(Though the men in my family are against superstition and spirituality, they still believe in saints and apparitions. *Go figure.*)

In the world of religious lore, Saint Anthony was known as a pure devotee who had a small group of followers in Italy, and, specifically, one troubled follower who stole his sacred texts. Up until then, the thief had been one of Anthony's greatest disciples, but he was struggling because he was destitute, so poor he couldn't eat or take care of himself. In a state of tumult, the devotee decided to steal Anthony's holy book and sell it at the market for money so that he would not starve. He'd trade in belonging to his religious group in exchange for feeding himself. Anthony's betrayer made his way to the market a few towns over, which was known for buying holy texts. When he got to the market, the merchant looked inside of the book, recognizing at once that it belonged to Saint Anthony, as Anthony's personal notes marked each page. The merchant returned the book to its rightful owner and dragged the thief along with him to repent. Rather than scold the thief, the venerable Anthony said to him, *I have my book back now, but what about my disciple? Will you return yourself to me as well? Can you find redemption here, with God, for the fact that, because you were starving, you fell out of alignment with yourself?* (This doesn't sound much different from the same question I've been asking myself lately.) The great Saint Anthony, because of this specific pardoning, is considered the symbolic saint of forgiveness, of returning to us what has been lost, whether it was stolen by someone once trusted or missing for reasons that are harder to explain. Catholics call on the saint when they wish to have an item returned to them, specifically some*thing* tangible. However, I've interpreted this idea of having lost something to mean something more, like good spirit, compassionate understanding, or childish innocence. My grandfather, quite rattled by having encountered Anthony's image on the staircase, was influenced by his vision of the benevolent saint. He decided right then to spare his cousin of injury, to turn around and head back upstairs.

CHAPTER 21

B̶eta Waves, Theta Waves, and Creamy Waves Mascarpone

In the last years, I feel extremely lucky to have been exposed to a mode of therapy called ThetaHealing®. Working with my master teacher, I've undergone multiple levels of training, which have benefited both me and many of my clients. It's safe to say that theta work has been the most transformative therapy for me, specifically when it comes to supporting my awareness of my relationship to eating. My teacher is a truly masterful healer herself, and is versed in a variety of body–mind systems of transformational work. She was trained directly by the founder of ThetaHealing®, Vianna Stibal, who developed the technique by fully healing herself from a nine-inch tumor. ThetaHealing® works by relieving clients of their limiting beliefs by accessing theta brain waves, which are the waves we're neurologically riding in the first seven years of our lives. In a theta state, we are highly receptive, taking in all we experience, like sponges—whether it's coming from the media or our mothers. In theta mode, our subconscious is at its most programmable. We're like microchips here, shaped through deep-ultraviolet impressions that set up our lifelong operative functions. Amazingly, 95 percent of our reality emerges from the theta realm. Both harmful and supportive habits are engrained in us through this type of brain wave, which means the theta state offers us the opportunity to either evolve or devolve our behaviors. This is why ThetaHealing® provides us with the opportunity to form new rituals and habits by accessing our subconscious and reprogramming behaviors. ThetaHealing® fits my healing requirements too; if I can fall asleep during a form of therapy, I'm all in. If you can put me out to transform me, like they do with anesthetics before a surgery, then I'm up for it. If I can forget about it after our session and just let some *other* part of myself deal with the discipline necessary for change, I'm sold. Meanwhile, you can find me, until then, eying a ribeye or biting into a meatball parm sub. Theta totally works though. Not just for me, but also for all of my clients and the thousands of people in the ThetaHealing® community at large. How *nutso*, though, right? Our brains work mostly by operating beneath our consciousness? No wonder I've spent so many years avoiding this crazy house of physical embodiment.

Every ThetaHealer® learns about the frequencies of the central human brain waves in order to become fit as a practitioner of the technique: beta, gamma, alpha, theta, and delta. It's like sorority *rush week* if you were a firing neuron. Theta waves are special because they specifically help us to access our intuition or supernatural aspects of ourselves, which are sometimes less readily available. We have our deepest, dreamiest imagination here, but also a direct door to our fears and traumas. Because we have access to such a wide spectrum of impressions in this state, approaching healing work on a theta level can be key to transforming our limited patterns. It was specifically in my own ThetaHealing® sessions that I was able to truly recognize the voices in my mind that were punitively demanding I eat, *wolf*, binge, and stop everything to stuff myself into oblivion. When I explored these Eating Words from a place of deeper consciousness, I saw their root systems and how, like invasive vines, they coiled around my lush essence. However, since they've been part of my operating system from my earliest years, I'd just absorbed these words as part of my physiological nature. That's why I didn't even recognize them for so long.

Through this therapy, along with other supportive techniques and practices I've continued to source, I've begun to transform some of the fears that formed the foundation of my entire identity. I took on considering who Giana Giovanni might be if she weren't always filled with shame about being *fat* and focused on trying to *not get fatter*. Who might Giana be, I wondered, if she weren't trying to fix her clinical condition of brokenness? What if she weren't broken; who would she be then? *Does anyone else go through this? Am I the only one who feels like Humpty Dumpty, taking myself apart but always somehow putting the same broken, dysfunctional pieces together again?*

Truth is, I've expected healing to happen like electricity, because that's how I operate: I make commands and get it done. Giana's Rome wasn't built in a day, it was erected in under an hour, *doggonit*! Plug this in here, push that over there, torque this converter, tweak that wire, sprinkle this seasoning, and spark that fire! Healing doesn't always work that way though. Of course, there is always the mad scientist kind of healer, the one who can remove mercury toxins straight out of your liver by simply touching some part of your body, or obliterate a brain tumor in a flash. There's also the radical-transformation weekend workshops, which sell out because they're effective in many ways. Even if a physical shift doesn't personally occur for the attendee, to walk away with a new perspective on life or an improved mindset is worth the financial investment.

Still, certain kinds of transformations, like changing addictive thought patterns, learning to love ourselves, forgiving our trespassers, or getting over certain losses—these can actually require a significant time investment, and this healing path is not necessarily laid out in an A-to-Z fashion. When we're working toward our projected goals, Impulse says, *Do as I command*, but Healing says, *I'm here to listen and be led; take your time.* In response to sensation, Impulse says, *Better put up your guns.* Healing whispers, *I trust you.* Impulse takes the highway, while Healing gives leeway, allowing rest for the real road to recovery. Healing leads with curiosity, invites new energy and impetus, eventually allowing Impulse to rest. Throughout these last years in my healing home, kicking my own ass like a strong dose of homeopathic medicine, I've learned that you can't pay someone to do your personal growth work for you. It's got to take place from the inside out, but meanwhile, you can avail yourself of some great guidance, that's for sure.

Speaking of guidance, the business of Giana Gemma as an intuitive guide has been flourishing alongside the business of Giana Giovanni, and life in my healing home has been filled with all kinds of abundance. Recently, I've had the opportunity to speak in front of hundreds of people at conferences, host multiple healers (including my own mentors) at workshops in my home, and also build an interview series with a large following. With the help of my amazing virtual designer, who works with both my restaurant business and my healing career, I've been able to bring in some of my own personal heroes to be interviewed. There have been full days when I've recorded videoconferences with handfuls of interviewees back-to-back, covering all topics from binge eating to limitless money mindsets to powerfully claiming our sovereignty as women. I've had nearly one hundred interviews to date, featuring many inspiring guests. Creating my web series has been a massive learning experience for me. I'm so much better of a person for the incredibly gifted people I've had the chance to meet in this capacity. Plus, I am genuinely thrilled to conduct interviews, staying hyper-focused and super in-the-moment with my guests. The best part is that I can remain in the comfort of my own home during our recorded conversations; this is where I feel truly dialed in to my best expression. All of the crystals in the world, the pink bubbles, the trips to Sedona, theta waves, and ocean waves aside, creating a life where I'm truly, actively in a state of gratitude has charged me with a sense of authentic well-being. As cliché as it might sound, I've witnessed how creating a life where I am most often in an appreciative state benefits all aspects of my health and supports my best integrated offering in the world. I've come to realize that we, especially women, are not designed for cookie-cutter conformity (although I admit I've eaten my fair share of cut-out cookies). But seriously, for those of us who have extreme interests, contradictory personality traits, or a wide spectrum of professional skills, it can sometimes feel particularly challenging to find our place in the world. These days especially, our roles are so vastly different than they were over the past five thousand years of human existence. In ways, each of us is a Picasso in our own right, determining the shape of life beyond presupposed limits. As Maslow's widely accepted hierarchy of needs shows, securing a sense of who the heck we are in this giant universe is vital to our survival; well, anyway, at least it's vital for not feeling like a major nut-job. Especially for truly diverse women, like myself, it's all the more important to build a life that uniquely allows us to express our many facets, the multiple selves within our self. For years I tried to shut off one voice or another, rejecting various parts of myself, but I've learned through healing (or have *begun* to learn) that I won't get anywhere if I try to remove parts of myself; that only leads to more war. We've had enough wars in the world based on attempts to control, remove, or imprison certain types of individuals. If peace has to come from within, then *by God*, I've got to allow all of myself be welcome here on earth. *I'll keep you posted on how that one goes.*

A friend of mine took the kind initiative to connect me to someone she described as a *voice coach*. She'd introduced us because she believed this New York City–based voice coach might benefit from working with me. This was how I met Sofi. She signed up for a phone consultation, as most of my clients do before we book our first immersive session. On the phone, Sofi sounded confident, connected, and articulate, describing how she helps others tell their story, discover and hone their expressive strength. Originally a professional composer and performance coach, Sofi works all over the world training performers; providing creative direction; ghostwriting; and, in general, being a deeply effective creative therapist. While these *arms* of Sofi's might sound unrelated, she is a woman gifted with many facets of self. She has figured out how to interweave her diverse aspects through an interdisciplinary profession. Sofi told me about her twenty-plus years developing a voice-based methodology of healing. While I listened to her sharing her story, I was wondering how I might help her, when my intuition perked up. That *voice* awoke, just like in Boston, or when I was at the feet of Athena, and then with Padre Pio. There was my *yes*, so I jumped in. *Sofi, I need someone to help me tell my story!* Frankly, I'd never before had an experience like this in a client consultation, but our connection clearly felt like a mutually beneficial match. Sofi lit up, loved my shared ideas, and we arranged for our first immersive weekend together. She'd come to my house in Connecticut, and we'd get to work. She'd help me recall the details of my life over the last fifty-plus years, and together we'd create continuity from all of the pieces. We'd put the puzzle together breath by breath and see the picture, and through the work, we'd learn how to feel, *by gosh*, we would finally let Giana feel.

"GIANA ·The· Puzzle·"

CHAPTER 22

The Subliminal Spaghetti Sabotage

Meanwhile, I was vacillating in and out of dieting. I'd have a month or two of *bingeing cessation* under the guidance of a kind of *otherworldly* hypnotist. The hypnotist was led into a large gathering space, and we piled in en masse. It really was quite a scene. We were the *overweight underground*, groups of devout followers gathering in cities worldwide, fitting into spaces big enough to accommodate our *bigness*. The hypnotist would promptly put us under her spell. We were all well accustomed to *wolfifying*, and so we heartily devoured whatever she relayed to us in our quasi-conscious state, regarding what we would and would not eat from that point forward. The effect of her programming did not, however, have an unlimited expiration date, and so while it worked for me for a period of months, eventually, my hunger returned. But in the weeks directly following one of her large sit-ins, food became a nonissue for me. This was like the mother of all painkillers and offered me a much-needed respite from my *anything-but-happy hour* five o'clock trips to Cumberland Farms. I lost inches and was convinced I was *feeling great*. Soon enough, however, my true Giana brain regained control, breaking all holds placed on my dysfunctional eating patterns, and bready carbs again found my mouth. I then counted down the days until I'd return to my hypnotist to be, again, subdued, making sure to arrange my social calendar and travels around whether or not I'd be under the effects of the hypnosis. For example, I didn't want to travel to Italy if I'd just been put under; what a waste of money! As we know, pasta smothered in porcini cream sauce will always out-hex any other incantation. After my version of *holy exorcism* with the hypnotist, I planned to piously follow her program and watch the inches disappear from my hips—a sure sign from God. My hypnotist was nearly a canonized saint, the single mystical force, evidently, able to *get me good with grains* again.

The thing about hypnotism is that it only works if we're willing to suspend total judgment, so even as I began to consider a more sustainable, long-term way of coping with my eating issues, I avoided questioning this acceptably functional method for as long as possible. Still, smartly, I coupled my hypnosis therapy with the hiring of a two-person neural-networking team who came to my house overnight. These ladies helped me bring some of my subconscious patterns into a more conscious light, and their warm demeanor alone served as a long-needed motherly salve to quell my anxieties. As they led me into a different kind of trance state, we investigated past traumas lodged in my brain's neural network, which was still firing in response to my current everyday life. With the guidance of these *neural nurses*, I was able to see more clearly why I operate in certain *less-than-optimal* ways, and, through observation, begin to offer healing light to my systemic responses. With their two sets of hands collectively on my head or on my shoulders, I spent hours going deep within my psyche on my massage table, returning to various ages of my early life while they shared their insights. Really, to even approach what is often the *perfect storm* of a kind of addictive dissociative condition by employing multiple therapeutic approaches at the same time is like attending a healing-centric Lollapalooza. Having therapists in my home felt as though I'd brought a crew of unrelenting spa attendees into the eye of the storm. It might sound crazy, but I highly recommend this approach. Working with the neural network duo was an utterly unique experience for me. I mean, it's not every day I have a couple of well-trained women come over to my home to assess my brain patterns. With their help, I began to actually *feel something* in my physical form. Before I could label the *feelings*, I allowed myself to just safely be supported in feeling them, exploring the sensations of my body and discovering—for the very first time, in many ways—my female form.

Then there was the creative wellness work of Sofi (whom I call my therapeutic *storytelling coach*). Once Sofi understood how I'd used food as my place to check out, we set forth like lab rats, testing out how various eating explorations might affect the mind of Giana Giovanni. Sofi put me through a new kind of agony, a custom-made exercise that consisted of slowing down and finding pleasure in eating. *Sounds like hell, right?* For me, a person raised in the fast-paced restaurant business, slowing down and feeling deliciously calm while prepping food was not my *thing*. Instead, I tended to take on preparing food like a high school football team takes on winning the homecoming game.

One evening, while I was cooking, Sofi asked me, *Giana, while you're over the stove, can you feel your hips?* It was then that I realized out loud how, particularly while eating, I stay far away from feeling anything physical in my body (other than how physically close my hands are to the fire, a sort of inherited Italian animal instinct). I managed the high-flame sauté on my six-burner Wolf rangetop (appropriately branded and conveniently built right into my kitchen island for *wolffication vacations*) and tackled my broccoli rabe with a heavy-hitting dose of smashed garlic. Meanwhile, Sofi simmered in thought on the barstool across from me, planning our dinner ambiance for the night. Sofi shared that, frankly, she was baffled by the fact that I had created six eating areas in my downstairs alone—including three large tables, a living room, and a lounge area—but I hadn't sat down in any of them to enjoy a relaxing meal on my own. I eat standing up or else moving from one point of the house to the other. I also often have a phone and keys in one hand, heading out to my car with a sandwich in the other, organizing a meeting mid-mouthful. Sofi refused to honor these habits of mine, and demanded we arrange a specific eating nook for our soon-approaching mealtime, and turn a section of my living room into a mealtime fortress just for us, with candles, lush pillows, and a low table in front of a mirror. Without further ado, she determined, we'd create a ceremonious space, with the intention to *feel* while we ate.

Having to look in a mirror was actually one of my biggest nightmares. Other than to apply lip gloss, a mirror was only for one thing: to check my outfit. Otherwise, I avoided it—even to see if oncoming traffic was approaching. (I relied on my intuition for that while driving with my thigh and eating take-out chicken wings.) But Sofi wanted me to look at myself while I ate, to confront my inherent, self-confirmed negative self-image

Sofi lit candles, and we placed our still-steaming plates on the table in front of the mirror. Then, Sofi led us through some simple moves before she allowed us to eat a bite. Obviously, feeling anything from my neck down before eating a meal wasn't something I was used to. At most, I might take note of my activated salivary glands, and then—*mangia, Giana*. Sofi told me that sensing my body sensations would be a crucial factor in gaining ability to eat using my *intuitive response*, to recognize what tastes good and realize when I've had enough. Even though I attempted to meet her level of passion on this subject, I more honestly felt like saying, *Okay, Sofi, that's enough. Now let's do the equivalent of turning on some real entertainment. Since tonight's imposed eating practice prevents us from watching TV, can we at least zone out or talk about something non-food related? Please, can we get off the subject of how it feels to freaking chew? Puh-leassse Sofi?* But I said nothing because I knew Sofi wouldn't relent. Sofi then presented a more challenging assignment. *Giana*, she said, *I'm going to speak into the mirror about myself, then eat a bite, breathe while I chew slowly, and then put down my fork. I want you to do the same.* I watched her and then mirrored what she'd demonstrated: I picked up the fork, took a small mouthful, chewed slowly, and breathed. Sofi, leading by example, supported our journey into the body, the opposite of the way I usually consumed food, which involved vacating my body and, bite by bite, accruing more distance.

Looking in the mirror while I ate was so freaking *intimate*. I'd never realized how vulnerable this act of eating was, how sensual, even exotic, how absolutely extraordinary it is when one actually *experiences* it! It's blatantly obvious to most of humanity how darn intimate actual physical contact with another person is, but honestly, food is equally as personal. Entering through the mouth, food travels a deeply intricate path through our whole being, assimilating into our systems through a complex vortex and maze, telling our cells its story of the whole process. How's that for relationship drama? I couldn't help but think how culturally underplayed the eating process is, how much we ignore the intricate tenderness of the experience. We do it in front of televisions and drown it out at the pub. At best, we give quick thanks to the farmers and say grace, but then we often forego mentioning much about the food while we eat. Maybe if something shocks us, we cry out, *Holy mother! That's some spicy Calabrese peperoncino!* But that's about it. Typically, the marvel of eating, like breathing, often goes unnoted, unless it is a remarkable experience, for example, when one is breaking a fast. If one has been living on prison food and is then released, there may be a moment of recognition for the earth's gift of nourishment. Monks have written about the sacredness of a meal, the meditative invitation to nourish the self. Maybe this was really the idea behind the Last Supper, Jesus's feast of the senses. It requires that one wake up to give presence to the flavor of what one is consuming, not just pass over it with an empty grace. Maybe at Jesus's Last Supper, everyone was actually mindfully eating, putting down his bread between bites to breathe. Maybe when they chewed, they silently reveled in kinship, sharing in the savory experience, waxing poetically about every bite between mouthfuls.

It's much different than *wolfing* (head down, one or two chomps, and a quick swallow) to ride the thrill that starts with the excitement before the first bite. Then, once we're eating, we have the joy of determining how much more we want. We can decide we're satiated. We can choose to put down our fork and clear the table. The whole thing is a massive spiritual journey. Every meal. Like the biggest one we've got.

I thought about the fact that we are mammals, that we feed ourselves, that we have a fancy method of consuming food, that civilizations have been created and destroyed around agriculture and ownership. It was all somewhat mind-blowing when I slowed down with Sofi. No wonder I rushed all the time. Rushing lets you not have to deal with how fragile and precious life is. It's as if in the *rushing*, we're trying to keep up with the fleetingness of it all, but forgetting we, ourselves, are made up of particles of light. When Sofi and I ate that night by candlelight in front of each other—we were forced to acknowledge ourselves in the act. Maybe the shame I felt as a result of eating wasn't coming exclusively from my individual trauma. Maybe it wasn't an affliction exclusive to me in particular. Hadn't we all, as a species, gone through a food-based evolution, filled with trial and triumph? Wild plants became the staple of our agriculture, under our stewardship, on property we determined was ours to have, where we decided we belong. Governments, militaries, and institutions were erected to preserve and control nourishment. Hunting transitioned to buying livestock, and the world shifted from everyone growing their own garden to relying on the provisions of a few town farmers. Most people live in cities where often the only thing known as *The Garden* is the franchise on the corner, a price-per-pound salad bar of mini-corn and soggy artichoke hearts. We don't know what these things look like on a stalk anymore, so why would we talk about them while we eat? They just arrive, well beyond the moment of their harvest. We pile scoops of same-tasting foodstuff onto our plate and wolf it down while watching Hulu or whatever's on TV. This isn't true for everyone, but it's pretty intimidating how political eating is. All of us, more or less, choose what we support by how we eat, what diets we keep, and what brands we buy. At this point, eating carries the trauma of our complex history, our hopes and losses all served up in the day's special—*how appetizing!* It makes sense that we'd prefer to talk about our latest business acquisition than the path our asparagus took from seed to fork. No wonder I chose this daily eating ritual as my time to check out. Realizing that food had not only been at the center of my existence, but also a core component of human life, at the heart of expression, of innovation, and even the evolution of thought was nearly too much.

The simple act of chewing, rather than *wolfifying*, was a serious time suck. It required genuine presence, patience, and poise, like unbuttoning a Victorian bride's dress on her wedding night. Sofi even made me breathe between bites, rest my fork on my plate, and, for that matter, use a darn fork. *I mean, really!* By the time I finished eating this way, I'd surely be asleep. I missed the drive-through, the easy in, easy out. It made sense to me that just as I'd shunned the expression of my feminine curves, I'd also stopped being present when I ate since nourishment is what grew my female body in the first place. But like Saint Anthony, I would focus on regaining lost things, however hard, I'd figure out a way to reclaim lost consciousness.

The night we ate in front of the mirror by candlelight was the first of what ultimately became multiple weekend immersions in my house, just Sofi and me. Each weekend we spent together was filled with unique eating explorations, and embodiment experiments. In early autumn, before one of her visits, Sofi called to forewarn me. *Giana,* she said, *this weekend, I want you to eat bad food in front of me, food you normally consume in private. I think it's important that I experience being with you while you have what you consider an out-of-control binge or, at least, a splurge.* Part of me was thrilled, like one might feel if her new boyfriend asked to see her in something more risqué, but another part of me felt nervous that I'd be perceived as tainted, or even worse, that I'd lose it completely. What if I forgot about Sofi altogether while consuming some high-calorie buttery treat? Would I be held liable if I kicked her to the curb in order to make room for a baker's dozen from Dunkin' Donuts? Should I suggest she purchase travel insurance before we set out to *Bingeland*?

When Sofi arrived, I made sure to let her know who was in charge; I was already upstairs folding something, hustling a project, buying a ticket to someplace. This was how I'd territorially lay down the law, so that at any moment, I'd be free to check out and plow over whatever I felt like plowing over. Throughout the next hour, as Sofi went over her vision for our day together, reiterating her request that I go on an eating binge while she held space for us, I made sure to let her know that I also had errands and appointments to get through. She knew well the cards I tended to play though, and did a decent job of keeping the upper hand. Truly, this was why I'd hired her. I only hire *tough cookies*, because it takes one to know one. Sofi raised her brow when I rattled off my agenda. *We'll see, Giana,* she said. *We have a lot to do.*

We went to the farmer's market, and on our way, stopped for coffees; let the sugar-fest begin! I was pretty sure I wouldn't go on a full-out binge, because if I did, I'd be catatonic for the rest of the day. Definitely not effective. Plus, an act of bingeing can't be embarked upon voluntarily; it has to be triggered on its own. And up to that point in my life, it had been solely a date-with-myself experience. It's Giana's private version of *Romancing the Stone*. No wonder I've not trusted myself to actually do any of this breath-heavy mindful-meditation work on my own. I've reserved my time alone to be terrified that I was soon to floor it to the next drive-through window and sink my ship. But the thing about bingeing, regardless of how unhealthy a behavior it is, is that it's legitimate; it can't be faked. I'm not sure an emotional eater ramming the majority of a Pizza Hut Double Cheesy Crust Pan Pizza with sausage into her mouth in the duration of a single red light or two has ever felt like she was faking her experience. At least bingeing has that going for it: it's *authentic*.

At the window of my local coffee-to-go spot, instead of getting my typical black decaf coffee with a little splash of cinnamon coffee in it, I asked for two sugars and cream, letting just the front paws of my *wolf* out of her cage. Sofi got a decaf with almond milk, making sure to stay "sober" for us both. As an afterthought, I added a croissant sandwich with bacon, a foil-wrapped version of the French classic. As I unwrapped my sandwich and popped the plastic hood of my coffee cup, we ventured out on our trip to *Bingeland*.

Like the spiritual saying goes, the journey of a thousand bites starts with one illicit mouthful (or something like that). In *Bingeland*, everything the pious part of myself deemed off-limits was up for grabs. Nothing sumptuous was too large for me to place bets on, to fight for. I'd forge ahead until I'd dominated whatever food I'd determined to be my property, like Hannibal of Carthage raiding Rome, if Rome was, say, fried, greasy, cheesy, and doughy. Well on our way to *Bingeland*, I pulled away from the coffee drive-through in my car like *veni, vidi, vici*, with my destructive and arrogant food attitude.

Perhaps the fault of my food behavior lies in biological coding; when I eat, my animal brain still recalls how my Italian family was forced to give over their kitchen-table provisions to invasive military guests in World War II. Top science journals have conducted studies that reveal that stressful conditions are, in fact, passed down to future generations. Our *stress pathogens*, so to speak, are similar to autosomal recessive single-gene diseases, remaining dormant through one life cycle and surfacing in the next. Prolongedly elevated cortisol levels or certain sequencing in genes that determine appetite, depression, and anxiety can be passed down, just like eye color, from grandparent to parent to grandchild. Ample research ascertains that the physiological effects of starvation or concern over food scarcity (for example, as in World War II in Italy) can be expressed in eating patterns generations later. So if your grandparents were starving in the Holocaust, it's certainly possible that their neurological trauma is informing the choice you're making tonight at the mini-mart. You may be eating to stifle the screams of *their* gut bacteria as well as your own. *Just buy the Ring Dings, darn it, and do your best to make it out of here alive!* I've often tried to figure out why I've had eating issues throughout my life and where they, and my Eating Words, originated. Even before she refused to open her mouth at her mother's command, baby Giana smugly decided, *No one will out-tough me*! And now, how was I to discover a poised manner of eating? Why would I risk relinquishing my card-carrying status, quit collecting those *no-rewards* travel miles, barreling again and again to *Bingetown*?

Eating with Sofi that afternoon would, again, be anything but poised. There would be no cloth napkin across my lap or salad fork in sight. Sofi wanted to see me binge, and as her compliant client, I made our getaway from the coffee-shop drive-through, flooring my accelerator while reaping the bounty of my croissant harvest. I'd conquered that little Connecticut coffee shop like Napoleon took down Italy (perhaps he was fueled by a reserve of French croissants and café au lait). With a wide smile, I told Sofi that if she wanted to see *wolfification* in action, I wasn't going to play games. She asked if I planned to park; perhaps expecting me to take a moment to formally initiate my binge. I laughed at her assumption: *Are you kidding me?* Nope. I ate while I drove, steering with my thigh; how else does one travel to *Bingetown*? Did Sofi think I'd mindfully consume sinful food in a parked car, narrating my process throughout? Uh-uh. I turned the radio on, the blinker on, the AC on, and put my sunglasses on. I picked up my cell phone as it rang and placed what remained of the croissant on my lap while I rattled off directions to a cashier at one of my restaurants who'd rung with a credit card machine emergency. I steered the Audi around a bend, still cruising in *thigh-control* mode. Clearing random jars of salves and a few backup tubes of lip gloss from my car's cup holder to make room for our newly scored beverages, I temporarily handed off my coffee to Sofi. I didn't ask; I just assumed she'd now simply take my orders. I was in charge, the pilot of the mission. I multitasked, operating anything with a dial or a knob, blasting my atmosphere like a militant skunk about to conduct an air raid. I did all of this while pointing my long, pink-polished fingernail toward the farmers' market and mouthing to Sofi, while still on my call, *Should we go there before we head to my kitchen supplier?* I'd give her a choice. Why not? Sofi nodded. She looked excited, writing down her observations like Freud on a safari, exposed to a new breed of animal. I pulled up to the curb, parked, and ended the call.

I parallel parked in under ten seconds, still steering with my thigh. *Okay*, said Sofi, taking a deep breath, *I'm not just going to encourage you to eat foods you typically forbid yourself and call it a day, Giana. I want to see if we can work a little embodiment into the process.* I knew I'd hired Sofi, but to be honest, at that moment, I started to feel she was sort of becoming old news. I didn't want anyone to actually slow me down, make me feel or taste or acknowledge my *sins* in the moment. Wasn't the point of sinning to slip from integrity on a free pass, to leave everything behind, relieving my cares and sense of self? Later, I could confess. *That's how we do it!* Later, she could have me breathe into my lower body or whatever, have me focus on feeling my feet, or scream some form of *hallelujah* while standing before the ocean. But now I just wanted to chew and check out, slurp and turn up the radio, call the restaurant, and then crash. I needed my binge to work to my benefit, to manhandle my fear, anxiety, and fire; otherwise, I was wasting my strange, precious high.

Sofi, as I had feared she'd do, asked me to breathe into my body, to feel my hips, stomach and feet. She was fully wasting the aggro *check out 'n' go-go-go* fuel I'd just injected. When it appeared, I'd pulled off *feeling into my senses* as requested. Sofi continued, *Okay, Giana, take a bite.* I took a bite, and she made sure I chewed, that I thought about chewing. *Chewing? Truly, Sofi? Anyone visiting Bingetown doesn't think of chewing!* By now, any thrill I'd summoned readying for our little trip to *Bingetown* was already dissipating. Sofi also asked me to take notice of what I was tasting. What part of my tongue sensed the buttery flavor of the croissant—which part, the warm richness of white flour? When I was on the very last bite, Sofi had me pause for a few minutes and look in various directions. She was aiming to deescalate the amount of attention I'd fixed on the food in my hand, hoping I find my environment as appetizing as the last bit of croissant I had between my thumb and forefinger. Her technique was effective; after breathing deeply (on cue) and letting my gaze travel from the car stereo to console, to the trees lining the sidewalk and then back to my food, I noticed that the croissant had become a bit less appealing. It didn't really steal the show as it had done before. In fact, it wasn't the center of the entire universe. There was something else to be present to, and I could *feel* it.

Regardless of how I'd achieved a greater so-called sense of presence, I was more than ready to get out of the car, hit our next targeted mark, the farmers' market. Sofi, of course, wouldn't let us off the hook so easily. Instead, she had me focus again on the last piece of my croissant, now resting on my lap. Contemplating this cooled-off remaining bit, I let Sofi know that part of me felt like I wanted to eat the last bite just to quickly finish this exercise and get on with our day. Sofi smiled, asking me if I'd be willing to yell about it. *Sofi*, I explained, *I just spent nearly an hour speaking with my inner twelve-year-old at your recommendation. If I can handle that, I'm pretty sure I can deal with yelling about a piece of food.* Soon, I was screaming to Sofi, as prompted (good thing Audis come with high-quality acoustic glass windows). *I want to finish it!* She requested I repeat this at full volume, adding *F-off* to the end, continuing on in an extended period of aggressive call-and-response. Our next fifteen minutes in the car were filled with an array of pejoratives and a verbal stream of expressed irritations I'd evidently piled up for some time, and not just about my poor remaining bite of croissant. *Good, clean, therapeutic fun.*

In truth, I was discovering something there. Allowed to eat foods on my forbidden list sitting next to Sofi, while she worked in full-throttle to support my ability to remain, at least, semi-aware during the process, was a doorway in the right direction toward something *like* food freedom, or at least, *food recognition* mid-*wolfing*. If I could locate the following: console, tree-lined street, pink lip-gloss, passenger seat and the bag of pretzels on my lap, perhaps I might eventually take in my own body, as well, while emptying the bag's contents. It seems to me that those seeking support for emotional eating could be most benefitted by being chaperoned on their wild, scary gorging sessions. In this way, a client invests in a therapist who literally has her put her money where her mouth is.

CHAPTER 23

*Wa*king from the Food Coma:
Cognizance after Carbonara and Campari

Now don't get me wrong: my one-on-one work with Sofi was essential. However, the real kicker came when she brought in a second pair of hands. Evidently, bringing Giana back to home base was a lot of wrangling for one cowgirl alone, so Sofi called on LiYana Silver, a therapist she'd brought up previously in our conversations. Though Sofi hadn't met LiYana in person, she was a fan of her book, *Feminine Genius*, and the two had developed a cordial email relationship. LiYana is an impactful author as well as a nourishing healer, helping women to connect to their inner wisdom, what she called our individual *oracle*, or our actual female genitalia. Our creativity, in terms of traditional schools of energy medicine, comes from the same center as our reproductive organs, the *second chakra*. Wouldn't it make sense then that if we women are driven toward securing a more impactful seat at the world's roundtables, we'd prioritize connecting to the *oracular* bodily seat that supports us? When we learn to read our own physiology, learn to track our oracular, *generative* sensations, we then remain in deeper relationship with our insightfully rich interiority. Maybe all of the astrological readings we've sought have been, at best, a placebo for the *real-deal* North Star we've had guiding us, but in the opposite direction, *down south*. Maybe we women have always known that despite all of the logical advanced-planning and mid-decision mulling over we might do, it pales in comparison to the moment we end up making a choice by the seat of our pants—literally. However much I've been hesitant to talk about my heart, much less my female anatomy, Sofi resonated with LiYana's resourceful expression. After interviewing dozens of mindful-eating, nutritionally informed, *beyond-diet* embodiment and health coaches, Sofi felt LiYana was the one we should bring aboard our *body–mind–spirit* spacecraft. (In this case, we'd take an odyssey from my life in a spiritual outer space to land, hopefully, on Earth, in my physical body.) Preparing to sink our teeth into the next tier of the multilayered Giana tiramisu, together we'd suit up with the collective intention of taking one step toward an integrated Giana—one giant leap for womankind.

LiYana flew in from the rolling hills of Asheville, North Carolina, on a Friday evening, with the idea of working straight through Saturday and Sunday. It takes quite a bit for me to clear out an entire weekend without work interruptions from the Grill, but I made sure to put my office manager in charge; I made a real effort to prevent distraction. Sofi already complained about the regularity of my having to step away to attend to various fires during her visits. Especially because we'd made the effort to have LiYana travel all the way from North Carolina, I knew it was probably important to make myself generally available. Distraction, I understand now more than ever, has been my best method of avoiding taking up residency in my body, and Sofi really wanted LiYana with us in order to have another strong female voice to advocate on behalf of my choosing feeling over fleeing. Sofi felt confident that LiYana could help us get somewhere, particularly somewhere deeper in the neighborhood of Giana's residential selfhood. My finding peace with food would be supported by this, she insisted. I had to learn how to feel the floor of my body; otherwise, I'd keep stuffing the opening of my mouth to compensate for how closed the rest of me remained.

When Sofi and LiYana arrived on the Friday evening of our weekend retreat, true to my nature, it turned out I had an event until late that night, a benefit dinner I'd forgotten I'd previously tattooed on my calendar. After the banquet, my friends and I went dancing for a while, and by the time I returned to my healing home, it was past midnight. Sofi's and LiYana's bedroom lights were out, and I climbed into bed fully spent. I wasn't asleep for more than a few hours when I was awakened by a middle-of-the-night text from Frankie. (This is classic Giovanni style. Our family remains on high alert, staying energized even when sleeping, always ready for an emergency.) Frankie's text read, *Call me,* and so I did—at 4:00 A.M. My father's brother, his next of kin, had unexpectedly died that morning in Italy. Suddenly, we all needed to board a plane as soon as possible to make it to the funeral. Our conversation was to the point, and we agreed to reconnect in the early morning.

I slept lightly for a few more hours, but awoke with the sun and rang Sofi from my bed. She was only down the hall, but it was early, so it was easier to call. I relayed the latest Giovanni news to her, and she met it with calm amid my storm. Sofi expressed her condolences, and then assessed our trio's previous plan for the weekend, contemplating how we might revise it. *Would it be possible, she asked, for the three of us to spend the day and night together, at least, and maybe you could fly to Italy tomorrow evening instead of tonight?* That sounded theoretically doable to me, but I knew my family. My father would want to head to Italy that evening, and I'd have to help arrange his trip or maybe even go with him on the plane. Between planning and processing, this would potentially be a full-time ordeal. Remember, my family operated as a single unit. For all intents and purposes, we had one passport.

LiYana and I had met online for a couple preliminary sessions in the previous weeks, but we still hadn't met in the flesh. Even though both Sofi and LiYana had not yet exited their individual bedrooms, I could feel the peaceful, compassionate connection between us, available even in the middle of my family earthquake of the moment. After I got out of bed, I prepared breakfast for everyone, and before long, the wafting aroma of my frittata brought both women downstairs. Just as I am coerced by food, I know how to seduce others with the same substance because food equals seduction according to my script: *The Finger-Licking Temptations of Giana*. Once 'round the fire of my front burner, we greeted one another with a group hug. As I spiced our frittata, Sofi and LiYana began to structure our morning hours. We agreed to start right after breakfast in the upstairs room, although I knew I'd have to make a call or two to convene with team Giovanni. Sofi requested we work in the open space of my healing home's top floor. The area is heavily sprinkled with elaborate crystal pieces I've collected from around the world and well stocked with essential oils and holistic medicines. *All my favorite stuff.* The top floor is as lushly comfy as it is airy and light; velvet pillows and Italian merino wool rest under long windows that open to views of the ocean. It's my little paradise.

We ate breakfast downstairs, preparing to ascend after our morning meal. I spoke a bit about how chaotic eating had always been in my Italian family. Obviously, I'd kept my heritage alive, because only moments after I'd commented on the frazzle that would ensue during Giovanni family meals, I was up and multitasking around my kitchen, facilitating chaos between bites. I had to call airlines, speak with Frankie on the phone, and reserve flights, all while dealing with my own fight-or-flight response to the recent death of my uncle. When I came back, commenting on the taste of the food, Sofi shared that she was extremely proud of me. *You actually took a moment to taste your breakfast, Giana*, she declared. One moment of taste bud touchdown, it seemed, was a sure sign of my evolution.

LiYana mentioned that when we eat and we cannot access the *rest and digest* part of our nervous system, our digestion has a hard time firing and effectually absorbing nourishment. *This*, I said, *must contribute to the state of perpetual hunger that I feel. If I can't feel vitamin D hitting my internal organs or benefit from a healthy absorption of its nutrients, then no wonder I crave multiple cartons of milk per day. Maybe this is why I feel food almost bypass me, just going straight to my thighs and my butt.*

After breakfast the three of us headed upstairs. As soon as we hit the top floor, I felt the need to rest. So we made a kind of nest of cushions and blankets to sit comfortably, and then we began our *process*. I knew that before long, I'd have to dive back into my current family drama, to deal with the intensity of the passing of my uncle, my father's closest brother. For now, though, I wanted to deal with my ancestors' effect on my body, to take care of myself before I'd have to take care of my family. The thing is, from spiritual retreats to Dunkin' Donuts dirty dozen, whatever it is I'm seeking might just be a way to give myself a moment to step away from my full-time family affair. I turned my phone on silent, something I rarely did. Preventing any interruptions was really the highest expression of respect to my company that I could express. LiYana set the timer for three hours.

As I opened myself to our experience together, I confirmed the feeling I'd had in our previous phone calls: LiYana was an astute guide. She shared a technique that she described as calling ourselves *home*. We employed the tool of visualization, which happens to be my clearest entry point into the realm of healing. From there, I was able to drop more deeply into breathing and physically access my body as central to our experience, rather than feeling mentally adrift, lost in some other realm. Sometimes, using neurolinguistic programming, LiYana would request that I focus my gaze in a specific direction. In other moments, she'd ask to speak to different developmental parts of me, exploring components that felt stuck in certain ages. This wasn't unlike the work Sofi and I had done, but LiYana had her own distinct medicine and embodiment approach. Working with Sofi and LiYana together felt like having reinforced support for my metamorphosis. Sofi often took notes while LiYana led our session time, or physically put her hands on my body to ground me as I traveled deeper into myself. Some people find accessing their imagination or energetically traveling to a kind of ethereal space a giant challenge. For me, though, I can stay in a space like this indefinitely. Put me in a pink bubble, and leave me to ferment liquor from grapes of wrath, *no problema*.

I struggle more to stay focused on keeping my attention in the here and now of my stomach. You want me to deal with my breath and the sensation of my legs, and put them together with my mind at the same time; then you ask me to run an inventory on my emotions and tell you about it? *Gawsh*, you're then basically asking me to join Cirque du Soleil and ride the tightrope on a unicycle.

There, in our upstairs nest, with still a couple hours before my *Giovanni Family Alert* was set to sound, Sofi and LiYana asked me to name what I wanted to create. I began, of course, with my main mission: I wanted to find a way to *get in my body*. This was a statement I'd been saying quite a bit lately, though I was still not sure what that actually meant. I elaborated as best I could. I wanted to feel aware, connected, centered, and able to assimilate my life, as in, be the opposite of *hyper-anxious*. One of us mentioned the word *sensual* in this process of cultivating a relationship to the body. LiYana asked me if feeling sensual was something I could relate to, something I wished to activate. Until then, I'd mostly associated the word sensual with an idea of romantic love, and so I answered that, yes, for the right relationship, I believed I could feel sensuality.

Giana, Sofi interjected, *is this what sensuality fully means for you? What about the idea that the right relationship might start with yourself? Is it possible that sensuality could also be a state or sensation you might feel on your own, without a companion, without a man or anything else? If yes, what might this feel like?*

Ummmm, I replied, *that's a good question. What does sensuality mean to me?* I threw out a couple of words and finally landed on one that had come to my lips lately in recent weeks, when I described the season to a friend: the mid-late autumn—its colors and the cozy feeling in my house. The sweet flowers being dried post-harvest, the teas I was brewing, these things feel *luscious*, I determined. *Sensuality feels like a lusciousness that is deep, that comes from your soul.* I'd hit on something that I knew inherently but was now experiencing in more of a *somatic* way, inside my body.

296

LiYana expounded on our subject. *Sensuality*, she shared, *is literally of the senses, right? It is an ability to take in information from our five senses (and even the sixth!). It's the confirmation of how we're taking in what we smell. It's being present with what we taste or the richness of sound, etcetera, that actually changes our body, and then we relate to other people from that place.* LiYana inhaled deeply as a kind of affirmative punctuation, as though she was drinking in fragrant perfume. She was in the presence of her own senses!

We drew a parallel about how we could know our boundaries in relationships and partnerships, recognizing how our senses are essential guides for us in this process, helping us to navigate and choose. Our senses help us to live safely and with healthy boundaries in place. Senses, Sofi and LiYana confirmed, can help me identify what I want from an integrated place. This would require something different than my typical from-the-head-up approach, a body-centric kind of perceptivity. Why, when senses provide so much, had I refused heightening them or trusting them? Why did I feel as though they led me astray, made me hungry for this, unable to resist that, let down here, personally injured over there?

When it came to supporting clients' intuitions, I was an ace. In fact, I helped nearly all of my clients crank their best destinies to full volume—but was I doing this for myself? We women are, more than ever, discovering how to power up from our own inner realm, how to physically feel our *Yes* and *No* and even *Maybe*, how to take action from a place of self-connection. We are realizing it is less selfish if we prioritize filling our own cup first, so then we actually have something substantial to offer. What a contrast this is from what we did for, like, the last five thousand years! Even the basic flight attendant spiel goes something like, *Please administer the oxygen mask to the whole back half of the plane, buckle everyone's life vests, and make sure to collect any used airsickness bags. Since you're already up, why not buy the whole cabin mixed drinks mid-turbulence, plus any other item from the snack menu or the crappy duty-free brochure. Despite the plane's erratic altitude levels, walk steady with a heavy stack of in-flight mags on your head. While you're at it, beyond considering just the needs of these travelers, you should secure the whole world's comfort before you even consider putting on your own mask. If you do all of that, then we'll let you sit back down, but only in the non-reclining emergency row.*

There I was, symbolically living on *airplane peanuts*, starving my sensual self, even if, ironically, my healing home was filled with fluffy invitations—massage tables, a home sauna, libraries of health-promoting handbooks. I have bubble baths and organic remedies handmade by homeopaths. There's enough stored olive oil under my own roof to keep a shop well stocked for a year. *Yep*—as appreciative as I am to have delectable treats galore and this incredible space to call home, I am ashamed to admit that I still feel like a blind bull in my own Italian china shop, *hangry* to find an exit to freedom.

As bullishly strong as I believe I am, as nearly built with wrecking balls for appendages, I've hired others to muscle through, to help me break down my own barriers. I'd have other people to confirm my own experience, to recognize my walls, and still others to help me tell my story so that I can release the narrative and free myself. In the process of examining my many walls of self-protection, I've finally had to look at the importance of creating *healthy boundaries*. If I'm going to learn how to stay present within my body, I need to feel myself as a safe physical container. And I don't want to teeter like Humpty Dumpty, perched on the edge of precarious self-esteem, as I'd frequently described feeling. I had a call to find deep-rooted peace in my personhood, beyond walls—a next-level, all-embracing kind of self-love. *I want to actually taste life. If I'm eating my words, I want to linger on phrases flavored with strong sentiments of appreciation and compassion. I want to stop starving.*

CHAPTER 24

Spoon-Feeding the Italian Senses: Minestrone Soup for the Soul

When Sofi and I practiced eating in front of the mirror, we discovered how deeply all of our senses are nourished when we eat with appreciative presence, giving our mindful attention to what we're doing. It's as though eating, itself, is a meditation, an obvious place to psycho-spiritually *fill one's cup*. Meanwhile, statistics show that more than 90 percent of us spend mealtime viewing digital or television screens. Doesn't it make sense that by coupling our consumptive experience with dizzying stimuli and distracting preoccupations, we are robbing ourselves of essential nutrients? One of the few darn things humans seem to agree on is that eating food is a fundamental requirement for all human functioning, right along with breathing and sleeping. Imagine multitasking our slumber! Just like the ill effects produced by a series of poor nights of rest, even if we had Gwyneth Paltrow's personal chef preparing the perfect paleo picture of health on a colorful plate for our every meal, eating in a distracted state takes its toll on much more than just our waistlines and blood sugar levels. What if eating, the act of fueling ourselves, is nature's invitation for us to connect with the web of life through our bodies, a built-in app-like reminder to pause, to ceremonially honor bounty, to remember what *matters*? What if a successful meal is less about how well we count our calories and more about how heartily we count our blessings? What if eating is how we refill, reaffirm, and recommit to our sense of being valuable, part of a giant ecosystem, macro-to-micro finessing our feelings of loving kindness and ability to access our best-lived life? Imagine that!

Even when sharing meals with the most enlightened people I've known, I find we often remain preoccupied with conversation throughout our eating experience, usually discussing something entirely unrelated to the moment. There we are, talking about our personal lives and philosophies, or even meditation and mindfulness, while altogether missing how our cells are replenishing right there in the moment, failing to notice that we are taking in life energy. I wonder, how much do I do unto food that has been done unto me? *If I've felt unacknowledged, how have I taken that out on food by bingeing on it without recognizing its flavor, its medicinal potency, its pure nourishment? Have I reached for synthetic, processed Ho Hos as a way to devalue my own organic, unrefined nature?*

In our room, Sofi and LiYana called me back, waking me from wherever I'd gone. I did my best to describe how I often experienced Giana only through the eyes of others. I did not have an independent sense of myself. LiYana imparted her wisdom then, and, fortunately, Sofi wrote it down, because, honestly, I blanked again halfway through her share.

Well, Giana, I think that girls and women are overtly and covertly groomed to adjust every aspect of our body, our presentation, our speech, and our energy to be presentable, to be acceptable or desirable to the male gaze, to the patriarch of the family, or to the potential partner. And we don't even necessarily see it until we start to see it, and this takes all of our authentic being-ness out. You're already sloughing some of this off, but we'll acknowledge that we've all been groomed, groomed, groomed. This thing you've learned to do—seeing yourself through someone else's eyes, asking yourself, "How do they need me to be?" and then being that—is partly your makeup and partly what has been instilled in you over a lifetime of being a woman.

We basked in LiYana's juicy revelation, relishing the passing calm that seemed to naturally move through the late-morning atmosphere;

the room felt nice. Between waves of conversation, we took moments of comfortable pause for our own silent rumination. I turned my upper body toward the light pouring through the window. The sun was now rising higher over the back garden, over the firepit and the river that separated my backyard from the property behind me, and then the rolling blue ocean. Sofi opened an essential oil and took a sniff. LiYana stretched out her legs, the active practice of embodying the senses.

Sofi spoke gently into our quiet, contemplative space: *Giana. The beautiful thing is that you have your own answers, but something I've learned about mindfulness is that we go moment by moment. We make new habits one day at a time, one blink at a time. It's like a mantra we recite, asking ourselves often, "Am I feeling my senses right now?" Listening to our senses—gauging what we need or figuring out what our senses infer—is not something we do once, like going in for an annual checkup. We must incorporate a practice of nourishing self-inquiry into our actual lives. It's central to our homeostasis and optimal functioning. Asking ourselves questions like, "What am I feeling?" becomes a part of how we respond to our regular calls of nature. Especially in a modern world that doesn't even ask before it takes our attention, it is valuable to incorporate this internal investigation. This way, after we take a breath, take a step, or say something, we can check in again: "What do my senses tell me now?" or "How might I get more into the power of my senses?" We stay curious. In fact, that's how we enter the world; we are born curious, before any fear sets in. So embodiment must have something to do with curiosity itself.*

What might my life's flow be like if I checked in with myself on a more regular basis? If I eventually became more present than absent? Or if, rather than punishing myself mentally, I actually engaged my inner self and lovingly checked in the way a mother would attend to her child? What if I regularly self-soothed, as often as the scheduled alarms on my calendar app? What if my alerts barked, GG, *soothe yourself. Check in with yourself!* Why can't I simply trust that I can nourish myself, model *the healer* archetype for my own inner child?

If you ever saw me, you might think I am the happiest person on earth and I think I am too. Until I'm not. I'll feel some sort of dismay or sorrow and maybe let it linger for a second or two, but pretty immediately, I'll turn it into my ole standby: some form of *anxiety*. Then, I'll take action to *exterminate* that sensation, drown it out, shut it up. Since I was young, whenever anyone has asked me, *How are you?* my answer has always been, *I'm good*. What else could it have been? I mean, actually figuring out how the heck I'm really *dealing with feelings* and bravely sharing that information on the fly? Impossible. That's like asking me to tell you the square root of one-point-five trillion divided by a dozen donuts multiplied by the number of times I've skipped church on the holy days of the Catholic calendar plus three—and all in the conversational window of a sentence or two. Nope. For me to drum up a real answer would cost whoever is taking the risk of asking me at least a handful of therapy sessions. And to turn my assessment into a one-line answer, I'd likely need to hire top greeting card writers. How am I? I could maybe offer up a Hallmark sentiment: *I'm sorry I am at a loss in knowing how to answer that. Please accept my sincere attempt to process my condolences.*

Since I never metabolized any of my actual feelings when I was young, it's as though I'm now cleaning out a giant garage, doing all of this personal growth and development work to figure out how to get in my body. That's why I can't divide my present from my past. It's like I've got to go deep into storage every time I think, into this packed underground garage filled with thousands of pounds of unopened mail. I want to respond to your query, RSVP to your beautiful invitation to the moment, but there I am, looking for the return envelope and drowning in a tangled mess of Valentine's Day cards from 1973 and comic book subscriptions from 1968. I can't even find where to start experiencing the moment because I'm still indexing what I felt in second grade, fifth grade, freshman year of college, and so on. But it's not a hopeless den of immotile bricks and cobwebs in this garage of mine. I am somehow figuring out how to clear out what I've held onto in storage, to make room and build some kind of healthier foundation. I'm learning that every time I allow myself to register joy and self-compassion, I help myself to transcend outworn patterns. Somehow this lighting up of joy supports the lightening of my load. I'm starting to grasp the idea that pleasure might be the best general medicine we've got.

On LiYana's cue, in the upstairs room, I again focused on little Giana. I visualized her until I could feel her and even put my arms around her. In my arms, six-year-old Giana could experience a version of loving kindness she couldn't find years ago. She felt safe in the strong embrace of a grown-up. Sitting with me, no one asked her to change. No one called her crazy. She was allowed to just feel sad for as long as she wanted to. It felt fantastic actually, to connect with little Giana in this intimate space. I felt *whole*. Little GG didn't want anything other than to stay in my arms. She didn't need the Wawa, the Cumberland Farms, hypnosis, neuro-transformation, acupuncture, restaurant drama, family chaos, exotic trips, dozens of employees. Little GG wanted me to hold her—and that was simply perfect and complete. That was enough, pure satiety—just me holding my inner kid. Might *internal connection* be a path to satiety? No salami grinder involved? *It wasn't a normal feeling for me; let's just say that.* In fact, when I scoured my mind, I found that even my Eating Words had fallen silent. *Whoa. I think I really just got something. Can feeling self-connection actually quiet my raging internal dialogue?*

The feeling of my experience was palpable. My transformation permeated the room. Even Sofi and LiYana could feel within their own bodies the level of emotionality. We felt we were working within our own trio, but we agreed that it seemed we were doing something positive on a larger scale for the collective psyche of womankind, considering we're all interconnected. *Here's something to consider: when women come together with intention, the healing effect is exponential.*

While the rest of our weekend would continue to be quite profound for me, that specific morning held its own weight. At noon,

I excused myself and headed to my family's emergency meeting, Giovanni style: on the fly. The plan was to decide how my parents would get to Italy as soon as possible and when the rest of us would fly to the funeral. We needed to be with our extended family to mourn and express our condolences. Giovannis always come together for the essentials. Because we are Italian, family comes first, no matter how pissed off we might be at one another. We are well versed in areas of basic survival: eating, dying, baptism, and first communion, all of the good old-fashioned Italian customs and unspoken values. We'll put everything else aside and just show up when the going gets tough, or when we're expected. Of course, our style of family commitment does not include room for having truly vulnerable conversation. *Let's just say that.* To be clear, however, as guarded as we are, we are not fake, not with anyone. We simply spare all long-windedness and indulgent sharing of personal sensitivity. We use the vernacular of restaurant shorthand when we speak. We're straight to the point, hard-boiled, hot from the oven.

The next few hours were a whirlwind. I burned rubber to my parents' house a couple towns over and before long I'd been there for hours. There was no way I could let my family know that Sofi and LiYana were waiting for me back at my house. I imagined trying to explain: *Oh, yeah...I'm sorry I can't stop everything right now for you all because I'm working on liberating my inner-child all day upstairs in my house while crying on the floor.* That would go over about as well as suggesting we psychically teleport my father to Italy. When I finally got back to my house, of course, it had been much longer than my projected *short break* away. Now I was in typical Giana mode: the little girl I'd accessed earlier that morning was way off in another dimension, and I had a ballpoint pen behind my ear, which, for me, means business. When Sofi and LiYana met me in my kitchen (*which also doubles as my office, and, in general, the epicenter of the world*) my laptop was open and I was on one call with another on hold. My phone's alerts and notifications were also going off, as per the norm, and I was pacing from room to room, picking up things, sticking food in the steamer, taking stuff out of the oven, unpacking new Tupperware, and stuffing containers of cooked vegetables into the fridge, all at once. But if you'd asked me, I was home. I was present. I was ready to work. Obviously, this was my own delusion, as both Sofi and LiYana were entirely unable to step into the heart of my cyclonic flux, while I "dealt with" my chaos. In fact, it's pretty amazing—no one can get near me when I create my tornadoes. *Go figure.*

I'd become fully consumed by the family affair, and the day was now slipping away. The truth is, Sofi and LiYana had devoted hours in advance, had planned for weeks to create our time together, and here I was cutting it short as well as spinning out in multiple directions. Eventually, I was able to put my family tumult on the back burner long enough to focus again on my scheduled time with Sofi and LiYana. Somehow it was already 5:30 P.M. and most of our day together was gone.

Back in our little nest on the third floor, with its cushions, blankets, and crystals, LiYana was still getting to know me in person, but Sofi felt comfortable enough to call me out: *Giana, I think we should analyze what has transpired today. Let's consider how you can use this situation as a launch pad to explore how mindful communication might help you create synthesis between your needs and how you acknowledge others' needs.*

We spent nearly the entire evening focusing on ways I could step up to make sure I am able to take care of my own needs while dealing with my family dynamic, how I might responsibly learn to practice language to clearly communicate with dignity. *Dignity* is a word that came to me while we sat calmly and self-connected earlier that morning. Sofi shared that the word *dignity* comes from the Latin word *dignitatem,* meaning *worthiness. Sounds about right,* I thought. *I'm ready to communicate from a place of worthiness, from wholeness.* The next afternoon, LiYana and Sofi headed to the city, and I prepared to leave for Italy the following morning.

When I boarded the plane with my family, in addition to my three pairs of shoes for our six days of travel, I brought with me some new tools and distinct communication strategies. Over the next several days, I did my very best to support my family's collective experience, but by day six, I had slipped a little from my state of communicative enlightenment. All in all, though, I did a pretty *darn-good* job of remaining polite, clear, dignified, and heart-centric throughout our time together, and let's just say, when it comes to long-held family dynamics, employing full-time mindful communication is a work in progress. I value my family more than anything else in my life, and yet, I am most apt to slip from my highest intended state of grace when in their company. The spiritual teacher Ram Dass once said "Think you're enlightened? Go spend a week with your family." I'm not sure, however, I'm soothed by the fact that maintaining our best character around our closest kin seems a universal challenge. I still beat myself up for failing to retain my most heartfelt poise in my family's presence.

As the months continue, I still check in and out. Sometimes I really want to be all of the things I've ambitiously declared: connected, embodied, and present. At other times, I can't seem to muster the energy to retire the checked-out part of myself. *Checked-out Giana* leaves her inner little girl at the Wawa alone, staring at the tuna sandwiches, planning her self-sabotage style of revenge. At the start of my self-exploration, I already knew my journey wasn't about finding a single solution. Stories are not always destined to be a *how-to*. My *happily ever after* isn't about fitting into the size-6 sequined top in my closet. But it is about looking at that top differently, admiring what I love about it, the sparkle, the invitation to dance that it inspires. I realize that there is something inside of me that feels glittery, that feels golden. This might sound silly, definitely not something Gino could hear without laughing at me or looking away. It's nothing I'd ever tell him. Still, I can say it just for me. I can edge closer every day to feeling more and more like myself, and experience how feelings are, in fact, gifts. Yes, emotions are energy charges unto themselves; when they pass through, they shine light and offer lessons. I'm starting to grasp how holding on to these emotions or stuffing them down inside leads to unhealthy patterns, whether one experiences them as numbing behavior or writhing pain. I remember saying to LiYana and Sofi in the middle of our first session, partially because I was mourning the loss in my family, *You guys, we just don't know how long any of us will be here.* Mystery underscores life. In fact, it triumphs over all other intelligence. We don't know how long we'll be here or, frankly, even *why* we are here. No wonder it's so crazy having such a darn-close family, strongly bonded on a physical plane in the midst of all this powerfully fragile unknown.

On a December evening, Sofi stood in my kitchen, holding a bottle of sparkling water. It was the night before Christmas Eve, and Sofi had taken the train in from Manhattan to attend my holiday party. She was smiling, practically staring into me with a look I can only call *stunned wonderment.* Normally, I wouldn't let anyone check me out for more than maybe two seconds without anxiously doing something to break their stare. But I let Sofi look at me and shake her head in awe.

I can't believe you made, like, thirty dishes, Giana, Sofi said, bouncing lightly to the festive music.

Actually, there are fifty-two different dishes out tonight, I replied, multitasking by talking to her while playing hostess to about everyone I've ever known in life.

Whaaaat?! Sofi exclaimed, grinning as she rolled her eyes. *You are seriously a dynamo, Giana. Most people don't have a giant holiday party like this, but even if they do, I'm pretty sure they don't personally oversee the preparation of this many dishes!* She gestured toward the full tables.

I watched her making sense of the scene: the seventy-plus bodies dancing, talking, and eating. Almost everyone I knew and loved was standing in my living room; even my DJ and bartender were old friends of mine. The kitchen staff I hired to support me in the last few days were nearly my closest people there outside of my family members. My friends and coworkers played and mingled with my entire extended family, who'd come from Italy and various New England towns. Members of my holistic spiritual groups were there too, nestled together on cushioned chairs, discussing various oracular visions. My personal trainer was talking to my acupuncturist, and around the room, conversations were intersecting. A psychic friend insightfully predicted future market trends for a property manager friend of mine who had just informed my web designer about places for sale on the Connecticut coast. My web designer had just booked a session with my massage therapist, and my massage therapist had spent the last half-hour taking notes from my mom about how to make a proper eggplant *caponata*. Josie, my best friend from college, plucked a stuffed mushroom off a traveling tray mid-conversation with my siblings, laughing over one of Gino Jr.'s lighthearted jokes. I wondered, *If the members of this diverse group of people can integrate in celebration, might this reflect the eventual integration of all of my parts, my pieces?*

My friends had arrived from far and wide for overnight stays. Many were dressed up finely (per my request, mostly because I didn't want to stand out in my sparkling dress). My outfit was comparable to my mannequin's tiny halter top in its sparkle, but it fit more comfortably to celebrate where I was at the moment, both my body shape and mindset. I felt great just where I was that night. The DJ was playing my all-time favorite soul music and dance tracks. My holiday party is the one occasion of the year I look forward to the most. We'd been going in high gear for six hours, all around the nucleus of my kitchen (probably the only location I can remain committed to staying put for so long). My guests delighted over lobster ravioli and butter-leaf salad with chunks of fresh Italian farmland *Parmigiano*, a cheese that is my favorite and practically my namesake, *Parmi-Giana*. I had just received a mammoth hunk of it from Italy, the conquest of my first cousin's latest trip to the Adriatic. The fragrant block of golden, aged *formaggio* sat across from sautéed greens, which I made in my steamer and brought into a near confit, green and alive with vitality! Pacific Northwest salmon, flown fresh to my house the day before, rolled in lemon, garlic, sea salt, and oil, slightly crispy on the outside and medium pink within. We had multiple kinds of soufflés and Italian breads. *Focaccia, rosetta, ciabatta, y friselle, va bene.* Polenta with marinated vegetables, from mushrooms to asparagus. All of these delights were on offer to my beloved guests, who lined up at my buffet.

Until recently, I mostly associated eating buffet style with the anxious feeling of not knowing how to set limits and fearing the familiar sense that I'd never have enough. Inevitably, I'd leave the buffet overstuffed, feeling like a failure. Here I was though, having created a buffet in my home with my favorite foods. While my food was so beautiful and truly loved (even devoured!) by all, for me, the foods at the buffet weren't the highlight of my night. The people filling my home, these were the relationships that fed me, really: my family, my friends, my staff, and my coworkers. But my primary relationship was the one I was cultivating with myself. This was a different kind of take on the buffet. Rather than feeling out of control as the consumer of the buffet, or the consumer of life, I stood in my experience as the creator. I didn't have to feel forced or threatened by what was in front of me at any metaphorical buffet because I could trust myself on a basic level. I didn't have to be the best ever; I just had to be enough. From here, I could figure out how to eat, simply, *enough.* I could find satiety because I could create my own safety. Both literally and metaphorically speaking, I don't have to eat at any buffet if it doesn't suit my palate. Or, if I want seconds, fine. *Don't mind if I do.*

The DJ started playing "I'm Coming Out" by Diana Ross, and everyone got up and started moving, from my sister to my extended Italian family to my spiritual friends. It seemed we all understood the song's message on a basic level, we all agreed: how we choose to show up in the world, how we stand inside of ourselves, this is what makes or breaks our destiny. I could make a solid argument about how I don't know how to be in the moment, but Sofi told me later, as she

"giANA DANciNg"

saw me that night—not just with her eyes, but also with her *senses*—that I could've fooled her! There I was, having provided for everyone, typical of Giana, but also, Sofi reflected, I'd provided for myself. I'd created an evening we could love together, and yes, I was eating, but I was also celebrating, dancing, and staying connected to myself. Just to be clear, I'm not fixed, not solved; I mean, I had a *wolfification* episode only a few days ago. And as much as I might seem like someone who connects to others seamlessly, I still often wonder how to feel, how to receive, how to really know I'm connecting. Maybe all of us, even Gino senior, have felt the struggle to connect, to be appreciated, to freaking just trust someone, or to simply trust ourselves. Perhaps this is a facet of our human condition: learning throughout a lifetime how to love each other the best we can and how to love ourselves.

That night, after spending the evening with my friends and my family, dancing to the DJ, and indulging in the food and the drinks, I reflected on the year. Just one year ago, as crazy as it seems, I was barely able to share with anyone the issues I had related to eating. I didn't mention it, and no one brought it up. Despite all of the self-help workshops I'd attended, before this last year, I'd never explored ways to appreciate my body's physical cues. At best, I'd attempted to force myself into a size 6 under hypnotic submission, and that was it. Now, here I was, eating a late-night bite of tiramisu, contrary to my restriction diet, but totally in line with my *sense-rehabilitation* diet. And I tasted not only the tiramisu, but also, beyond the creamy mascarpone, some of the fruits of my labor. I had begun to step in the direction of valuing my body as a safe space, as an entity, a living, mutable container. I was starting to grasp how it might feel to allow myself to be as I am from a body-feeling place rather than to reinforce my sense of self through aggressive walls, restrictions, and forceful drives. Even better than that, I could be a charismatic container—flexible, full-spectrum, and multicolored. With that kind of versatility, I could stay in my body and let my heart grow bigger. I didn't have to forego my spirituality to actually be here, on Earth. In fact, I was *getting* the lessons, finally figuring out that physical embodiment might be the actual door to living from within a holy, spiritual center. I didn't have to go out to space and into past centuries to find something I could call *mystical*. Just having a navel—no joke—well, that's pretty darn mystical on its own, and with just a few more years of hard labor, I might even brave gazing at it like Galileo checking out the largest moon of Jupiter. *It's all possible!*

In the annual tradition of my holiday party, at the end of the night, my closest girlfriends and I anchored ourselves around the kitchen island, laughing and sharing. Some of us sipped tea or sparkling water, while others nursed glasses of wine or chocolate liqueur. Just to sit with my friends, to know that the next stop was the comfort of the amazing grace of my bed, I felt appreciative and richly alive. This, this is what little Lia, my mother, wanted from the start. It was also what Gino probably felt driven to build for us, and really, what *all* humans should have the right to experience. This feeling of *enoughness* I'd just tapped into, it was palpable. I could nearly taste it. *I am enough.* Yes, Giana, you are enough. These words felt both spirited and grounding, and they were kind. We could eat these words.

CHAPTER 25

*M*etaphysical Nutrients Are Richer Than Tuscan Truffles over Tagliatelle

A s I gather my pieces, these parts of myself, and cultivate the healing power of my breath—as I reclaim my basic resources and grow self-worth, I maintain my *accountability posse*. These are the people who are helping me learn to live from a place inside of myself, to see life through my own eyes and senses. I manage my restaurants on my own, *but look*, when it comes to gaining greater residency inside myself, I'll employ all of the help I can get. This is how I'm learning to drink from my own comforting cup of *tè alla camomilla*, Giana style. LiYana and I meet regularly in virtual meetings. She is securely nestled into her mountain home in North Carolina while I'm on my cell phone in Connecticut, usually running between my car and my kitchen, the family office, or a restaurant. She knows me well enough to politely request we take moments to pause, to lengthen our inhale and exhale.

LiYana requires I show up, and to tell you the truth, sometimes I think I need to be paying someone by the minute just to practice *staying present*. If it's not costing me anything to talk to someone, I might just turn them into channel fuzz. It has been a month since Sofi, LiYana, and I worked together on the top floor of my home. I've gone to Italy and back to bury one relative, and now I'm preparing for the upcoming funeral of my mother's sister. Weekend *Giana Gemma* work travels have come and gone. The new year is already in full swing despite the fact that I still have holiday party leftovers, with salmon in my downstairs freezer and jars of persimmon jam and cocktail mix still lining the floor of my storage area. I'll usually squeeze LiYana in on Tuesday mornings between my Italian lesson and my piano lesson. Then I'll head into the one battle I'll always wage well on my own, like a good Giovanni daughter: the ten solid hours of work in the world of the American Grill. When I return home, I'll set up for my livestream interviews; for example, this week I conducted a scintillating convo with an expert clinician who uses flower remedies to help people overcome severe illness. During my week, I try my best not to stop at Cumberland Farms, and instead, eat something like a Cobb salad. Sometimes I'll slip, believing I'm aiming for the treadmill, but end up treading tire, instead, to the Chinese take-out place on my way home.

In my LiYana sessions, we are combining body-awareness exploration and trauma release, with some active takeaway practices: healthy, habit-forming homework. LiYana is easy to talk with; she allows space for me to reflect and experience. This morning, she warmly greeted me, *Hi, Giana! How are you feeling?* I immediately felt safe, and I dove in for a while. *I'm good*, I told her (yes, it's my typical reply, but this morning, I actually was feeling quite good). LiYana asked me what I've noticed over these past weeks of working together toward my *embodiment* process. *Honestly*, I replied, *when I started this work, I was sort of internally rolling my eyes. I knew I had to do it, but in some ways, I just didn't want to take myself seriously. I didn't think I was ready, but since then, I've realized that there is no real starting point. We start where we are, right?* I let her know that since I'd previously believed I had to go to distant places, like to islands with shamans singing in languages I couldn't understand, perhaps *pausing to breathe* might be too elementary. I'd breathed, like, a million times. What more could I get out of it? How *embodying* could it be? It makes sense though, particularly in relationship to ThetaHealing®, that breath is the doorway to slowing down, shape-shifting, finding connection between all of these pieces of myself.

I told LiYana, *I'm feeling better just being myself.* LiYana asked me to explain.

Well, I said, *I recognize I am more comfortable when I'm conducting interviews. I'm not berating myself on the way in or out. I also feel more comfortable in my skin, and that I have something to say.*

LiYana confirmed this as an accomplishment, and let me know so in her nourishing, stable way: *That's huge, Giana. What it sounds like you did—which is amazing—is that you added in a nutrient. It wasn't a physical nutrient, but the metaphysical nutrient of connection. You added in the element of connection, and your system was able to then receive a nutrient it really needed. The net result was the experience of feeling more comfortable in your own skin. Your interviews felt more connected, and so did your relationships. You felt more in flow because you got something you needed. Well done.*

In the end, now that I've really unpacked the picnic basket, the whole kit and caboodle, I see that it's almost like emotional eaters aren't eating. We are not absorbing *food's* nutrients, much less any *metaphysical* nutrients. Most emotional eaters are probably barely breathing, so we're likely stunting our physical sensations and our general feelings. Maybe the whole act should be called something more appropriate, like *emotional beating.* Demolishing the party-sized bag of processed faux-flavor cheesy saltiness does the trick; we've consumed as a way of successfully compartmentalizing and quelling the inner cacophony that results from refusing our sensorial openings.

Meanwhile, am I closer to eliminating this behavior?

It's hard to say, but I do see that I am closer to absorbing my largest missing nutrient, *vitamin self-compassion*, and I've a hunch it's the antidote for metaphysical *starvation*. Every day I'm discovering more and more how the real staple ingredient in anything—whether we're talking about Italian hot sauce or a hot romance—is how well we love ourselves and nourish our senses.

If you know me, you know that I don't typically come off as an introvert. I'm happy to talk to people I've never met before, striking up conversations with perfect strangers. Still, really letting anyone in, revealing weaknesses or concerns, is not Giovanni style. No one in my family ever modeled being an *open book*. In a way, the idea of coming clean, of being boldly honest, of risking being perceived as overly revealing is the biggest *no* I've ever faced. Good Italian girls are supposed to cook well. They follow the directions of the male family leader. They honor their extended family. They've lived a successful life if, after they die, their grandkids remember them for their *meatball-making magic*. And, heck, before a good Italian woman takes care of herself, she'll make sure her twice-removed great-aunt's second cousin is set up in comfort. And let's not forget, the perfect Italian girl is a good Catholic. She finds her spirituality solely in the church, needs to share neither her epiphanies nor her emotions outside of the choir, and most definitely does not need to climb onto some mystical massage table surrounded by charged crystals. These notions have been handed down for so long, they're heavier and yeastier than the oldest-existing bread starter in some southern Italian farmland kitchen. How would I tell people, as strongly spirited as I am, how I've been struggling my entire life with a giant challenge around eating, something that should be a *piece of cake* (no pun intended)? Well, frankly, that's just way too much exposure, way too big of an admission for my self-protective, good-Italian-girl roots.

We Italian immigrants—the historic farmland workers—we don't spend time sharing our stories because, for generations now, we've been focused full-time on basic survival. We'll continue to sell our vintage wines from heirloom vineyards and allow ourselves a bit of nostalgia (strictly through our taste buds), but we won't dare share the complexity of our lives—not if we can help it. Secrets are the closest things we have to jewels, so we guard them well. That's what makes Italy so darn delicious. Can you imagine the number of *nonnas* who've gone to the grave having never given out the secret to their spaghetti sauce? But here I am, part rebel, part confessor, part woman, just wanting to raise a point, bringing these deep aspects of myself to the surface, both on the page and from my soul.

Through my sharing, maybe I'm looking not only for myself, but also for members of my *global community*. I'm looking for the ones who know this journey of taking the risk of living beyond their parents' limitations while still honoring the essence of their family's heritage. I'm seeking the *sisters* who don't need to live by rules within the structure of what has existed until now, but who are cultivating a new kind of container, a limitless vessel to hold the riches, the treasures that have been here for us all along in the wealth of our bodies.

My biggest takeaway here, in retrospectively unpacking my history and inviting a deepening of feeling into my form and flesh, is that having examined my entire life, I wouldn't go back in time to choose another family. *Nope.* And I wouldn't change the legacy of my family's lineage, alter a single thing. Despite the obstacles we've had to surmount, whether as obvious as war or as secretive as struggling with ourselves to find internal worth, I wouldn't have it any other way.

How does this realization relate to the very essence of my exploration, as I attempt to understand my relationship with my Eating Words? Truth is, I just chose food as my battleground. All along, I was never *just eating*, but also dealing with every conflict, my loose ends, my lost parts, my obsessive and rebellious and shameful pieces. I chose food, like some choose drugs or other escapes, to be a transference place where I cope with my life. Like many, I found a substance to control anything that felt unknown and unmanageable. What does a manager do with the randomness of life and fate, with feelings that are too active, too challenging, too mentally swarming, or physically flooding? Addiction is a container of its own, a place to put the stuff that has no distinction, that doesn't take sides, the things made up of contradiction, the amalgamation of sensations equal parts numb and painful.

When we have trauma at any point in our life (which, *let's get real*, we all do, to one extent or another), we need tools to overcome it. We need some kind of outer encouragement or an inner guidance. We need calm, nourishing places in which to find resources to help us overcome distress and find success despite what we've experienced. If we haven't been taught how to deal with inflicted trauma, if we've been left on our own to compensate for our injuries, it's far more likely we'll create the same self-abusive relationship again and again in all areas of our lives.

Epilogue

ven though food has been my biggest challenge, it's also
been my biggest opportunity, an invitation for me to begin to
understand how my whole physiological being works. But then what?
How am I going to *get better*? How am I going to recover? What can I *do*
about this? Don't problems need solutions, and don't solutions require
external action? External action has been my modus operandi, my
method of finding salvation and feeling accepted. Just *do* something,
Giana. (My version of Nike's *Just Do It* slogan, by the way, has been
more like, *Do IT. IT,* as in *Italy. Do*, as in *Do eat most of the pasta in
the southern region of the country any time you're there.*) But the most
wise-woman part of Giana is less concerned about coming up with the
million-dollar answer to what I can *do* about...anything, really, and
more interested in gaining greater awareness, gaining sensation, and
leading with love. She wants to remind herself—and, *heck*, why not,
even remind *you* too *right now* to take a deeper breath.

I'm sure some of you might want to know if I've gotten closer
to *curing* myself, or if my BMI falls within the normal range. While
obtaining a *normal*-range BMI admittedly sounds great, frankly, I'm
attempting to approach transformation from a more internally focused
starting point. I'm considering how essential it might be to know
how to truly give myself my own nourishing medicine, especially in
relationship to developing trust, both with myself and others. Yes, I'm
learning about trust and what that internalized language might sound
like. This feels essential to *all* of my work in the world. Through this

self-explorative process, I've only become more certain about how we grow together as a global culture: we gain insight, and we share our insight. And this is how healing happens, through shared insight. Transformation.

After decades of revved-up phrases, like *Eat it all! I don't care! You're going to do it anyway!* playing on repeat in my head like a malfunctioning audiobook app, I believe it's high time I discover words that feel supportive and true to who I am now and what I want to feel! I have lived with words that don't really sound to me like *mine*, words that haven't been *my allies*, and now I need to find my authentic words. This is why I've explored my story. I know that whether I've ordered a *house salad, hold the dressing*, or *all of the house specials plus extra sauce,* I'm eating my words as much as I'm eating the whole basket of garlic bread before the rest of my dinner arrives. For this reason, I want to discover the words that will feed me well despite whatever else is on my plate (or scattered across my passenger seat and dashboard).

And, of course, I have thoughts like, *Let's get real, Giana. Are you ever going to know what you're talking about?* I might pause and give my best classic-pink lip gloss, half here-half there contemplative *Hmmmm*. Well, I guess if my hopeful realizations are ultimately a bunch of cannoli cream fluff, I'd rather have hopeful words than aggressive ones running through my brain. Yep, these days, I'm pretty sure I'd rather be flooded with faith in myself than starve my entire system through self-denial. So, there's that.

Acknowledgments

In these last seasons, I largely kept my book-writing process undisclosed, mostly because I was incubating Giana's tale, but also because I was so darn nervous about actually sharing such a raw story about food and feelings. Still, I couldn't imagine having the confidence to take on this project without the people I most love in my life, my family, friends, and coworkers. I also can't imagine having approached a book about eating without having spent years deeply immersed in the world of culinary arts, nor written about healing without having been both a practitioner and eternal student of holistic therapies. For my mentors and clients, I am filled with eternal gratitude. I surely could not have gotten this story together, nor out into the world, without my writing coach. Oh, and, of course, I am thankful for my own family's Italian heritage, and their brave sojourn to Middletown, Connecticut in the last century, which helped me to describe the Giovanni's migration so distinctly.

About Isabel Chiara

Isabel Chiara, creator of "The Life Actualization Process," has been a guide, mentor, and leader throughout her entire life. Over the last thirty years, she has been both studying and working in transformational energy modalities, serving others, whether through entrepreneurial work, culinary prowess, or her professional intuitive guidance. With dedication, Isabel activates unlimited potential and empowerment for her clients, helping them to ignite their full passion and align with their most authentic life path, masterfully supporting the liberation of constricting beliefs, definitions, and self-limitations. As a result, her clients are able to access a deeper wisdom and joy within their lives and experience a world of prosperity, miracles, and magic. Isabel spends her time exploring her backyards in Connecticut and New York City in addition to connecting to her deep roots in Italy. She can often be found traveling the globe, whether leading a retreat or on a personal pilgrimage. When at home, Isabel is busy with her career as the owner of multiple businesses. For the full breadth of Isabel's extensive certifications and modes of therapy and information about sessions, see her website below!

Links and Resources

Isabel Chiara, author and international abundance coach:
https://isabel-chiara.com/

Learn about the amazing LiYana Silver's work here:
https://liyanasilver.com/

Honorable mention to renowned teachers, the late, great Shakti Gawain and Dick Sutphen:
http://www.shaktigawain.com/
https://www.dicksutphen.com/

CPSIA information can be obtained
at www.ICGtesting.com
Printed in the USA
FSHW011134080421
80224FS